JOB EVALUATION
METHODS

By

CHARLES WALTER LYTLE, M.E.

PROFESSOR OF INDUSTRIAL ENGINEERING, NEW YORK UNIVERSITY

SECOND EDITION

THE RONALD PRESS COMPANY ⟩ NEW YORK

Library of Congress Catalog Card Number: 54-7648

PRINTED IN THE UNITED STATES OF AMERICA

PREFACE

Everyone in industry today, from top management down through the rank and file, needs to know about job evaluation. The methods and the results of job evaluation significantly affect policy making, public relations, collective bargaining, the day-to-day operations of business concerns, and, of course, all phases of industrial relations on all levels before and after hiring.

This volume—like the first edition of 1946—presents its subject analytically according to the functional steps that comprise the evaluation procedure. Each chapter is confined to a single phase of the whole procedure. Thus successive phases such as policies, methods, measuring scales, etc., are treated one at a time so that each can be investigated thoroughly, comparatively, and impartially. The analytic approach followed in this volume has several important advantages. It gives a sound, logical, and easily understood presentation. It makes possible the comparison and selection of appropriate measures to fit any particular set of conditions. And finally, this approach fully stands the test of practical use in devising job evaluation plans and in making or modifying installations.

Since the first edition of this book, job evaluation has become far more widespread and experience with its methods has matured. This Second Edition takes into account all the new applications and successful procedures. For example, job evaluation has been applied to many jobs previously "exempt," such as supervisory, technical, and high-level executive positions, and many of the recent, well-known cases are described and compared step by step. Much material has been added to the treatment of rate structures for solving the problems peculiar to this field; and numerous combinations are worked out both in table and chart form to show the effects of assignable variables. The discussion of merit rating (which may or may not supplement job evaluation plans in actual practice) now includes the findings of psychologists who worked during World War II to establish more reliable man-rating. A wholly new chapter which high-spots the principles of wage incentive methods has also been added. Many other changes have been made throughout the text to insure accuracy and a detailed, up-to-date exposition.

iii

The job evaluation manuals of various companies and the numerous journal articles have unquestioned value, but these are almost entirely confined to single installations or to case history and explanations of particular plans. While such material should be carefully studied, case studies alone are not sufficient for the requirements of the serious student. Something more is needed—namely, a comprehensive and systematic survey of the subject—and this the author has undertaken to provide. He has written the book for the reader who wants to explore the field thoroughly by first learning the principles and fundamentals before proceeding in more detail to the exact ways in which plans are devised, set up, and made to operate smoothly. Thus, the analytic approach and the thorough presentation make this book readily adaptable for use in senior or graduate courses in colleges of engineering and commerce.

A few words should be said about the nature of job evaluation as it is understood in this book. Care, judgment, flexibility, and imagination, rather than an exhaustive technical knowledge or training, are the prime requisites in undertaking job evaluation. Obviously a plan will follow previous patterns and practices as to fundamental provisions, but each installation should be hand-cut as to details to fit the special conditions and needs of the individual company. This point is constantly stressed throughout the book. There is such a thing as going too far in copying existing installations because there are limitations in all such plans, working conditions vary in different companies, and no two groups of management and worker representatives see exactly alike on all points. Even after installation, plans usually need modification or additions from time to time. Employer's and employee's interests must be kept equally in mind at all times, and hence the author advocates a reasonable degree of participation on the part of unions in setting up and operating a job evaluation plan.

While the principles for an analytic approach to job evaluation do come from the study of previous experience, any temptation to present the material as an exact science or as a collection of standardized patterns has been steadfastly resisted by the author as not in keeping with the true nature of the subject. However, liberal use of forms, tabulations, charts presenting graphically the setup of rating curves, and illustrative case material from well-conceived and successfully operating installations help the reader to grasp and visualize the subject in its entirety.

Acknowledgment and thanks are due the managements of our progressive companies, large and small, whose manuals and example have provided much valuable information; to the consultants specializing in this field; and to the associations which have given special attention to job evaluation, particularly the American Management Association, the National Electrical Manufacturers Association, the National Metal Trades Association, and the National Industrial Conference Board. To each of these the causes of better job evaluation and better labor relations, as well as this book, are much indebted.

Finally, special appreciation is expressed to members of the author's advanced classes of graduate engineers who have not only stimulated his observation but also rendered timesaving assistance in sifting the best material out of a very ample unbound literature.

CHARLES W. LYTLE

Philipse Manor
April, 1954

CONTENTS

Job Evaluation Methods

1

A MINOR FUNCTION BECOMES
A MAJOR ONE

> Questions relating to the amount of work which labor should
> accomplish and the amount of wages which labor should receive
> are at the bottom of most grievances.
>
> —JOHN W. NICKERSON

Job Requirements Are Not Simple. What the employer requires
of the employee in work and what the employee requires of the
employer in wages have always been delicate questions. Either
party has often got the better of the other party. Collective bargaining is democratic and helpful but by itself does not assure correct answers. This fact is evident from the frequent demands for
rebargaining. In fact, we can hardly expect correct answers from
unaided bargaining if we consider how many variables are involved.
Bargaining done in ignorance on both sides is always a needlessly
slow, costly process, and when the conditions of the bargain keep
changing, so that it must be done over every year or every six
months, it may give little improvement over old-time unilateral
guesswork.

We do not find it necessary any longer to haggle for hours over
the price of an automobile. Why should we find it necessary to
haggle over the most vitally important commodity of all—a human
service? The answer is that it is not necessary to bargain on each
individual job. Job evaluation is merely a convenient name for systematic preparation for pricing in the labor market, closely comparable to modern pricing of merchandise. The latter is made
possible by adequate cost analysis, the former by adequate job
analysis.

Job evaluation, then, is neither more nor less than an effort to
apply sound principles of measurement to determine what each job
in an organization is really worth. That is not what the management
thinks it ought to pay, nor what the worker, or his union, thinks he

3

ought to get, but the fair share, to which a satisfactory performance of a job should entitle the man who performs it, of the profitable result to which his performance contributes. To make job analysis adequate for job evaluation it is necessary to think beyond the concept "amount of work" because that implies only the quantitative part of the employee's contribution. That part is tangible and can be positively checked by comparing the units produced per period of time with set tasks as is done for incentive payment. Less tangible, and hence more difficult, is the qualitative part which involves skill, effort, responsibility, and working conditions, not to mention the many possible subordinate considerations that are covered by these four major considerations.

This qualitative part of the employee's contribution is a matter of guessing in old-fashioned "rate setting" and is but incidentally considered in that part of job study known as "motion and time study." Hence a separate and different kind of job study must be made with the specific purpose of measuring the qualitative contribution. Such further study begins with job review or "job analysis," carries through "job description-specification," "job classification," and ends with "evaluation." This foundation should underlie every job rate whether for time payment or for incentive payment. Despite the fact that a wage rate is important to the employee as the limit of his "take home," to the employer as an influence on costs, and to both as a basis of harmony, job rating has been the last management problem in this field to get professional attention. Modern job analysis and its recent extension, job evaluation, are now solving this long neglected problem impersonally and objectively. These terms may be defined as follows:

Job analysis is the review study of definite jobs to ascertain what kind and what degree of man-qualities are necessary to make man-job units operate satisfactorily.

Job evaluation is the extension of job analysis to ascertain reliably the relative worth of jobs, to transform these appraisals into a structure of adequate rates, and to provide standard procedures for all additions to, and adjustments in, the rate structure.

Job Evaluation, One of a Group of Controls. Labor efficiency or man-productivity is the variable effect of, or response to, plant conditions and practices which are variable causes. The latter variables can largely be controlled, for better or for worse, by the policies, plans, and activities of management which create the jobs, or more accurately, the *man-job units*. Graphically we can picture man-job unit productivity as the resultant of five or six *job-control com-*

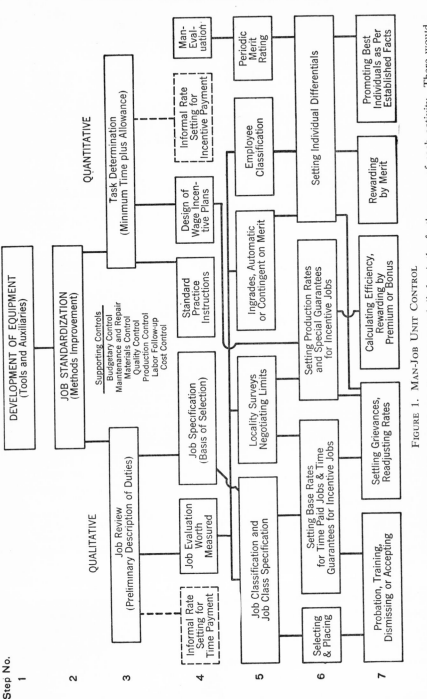

FIGURE 1. MAN-JOB UNIT CONTROL

Vertical connections between the boxes indicate (above) the sources and (below) the further uses of each activity. There would also be lateral relationships on each level. Steps 1 and 2 construct the man-job unit. Steps 3 and 4 derive and record pictures of the job and its hypothetical holder. Steps 5 and 6 build the economic structure and locate the man-job units therein. Step 7 puts the whole into operation. There are, of course, other steps both for line execution and for staff facilitation, but the ones here charted are particularly fundamental to the development and operation of the man-job units.

ponents.[1] Obviously, if we wish to change the direction or increase the magnitude of the man-job productivity resultant we must begin by installing, building up, or correcting the job-control components, not just one or two of them, but all of them.

Let us suppose, for instance, that two like-sized factories, A and B, make identical improvements in one component, say wage incentives. That would be building up one of the job controls and each factory might achieve the same man-job unit productivity gain in percentage. But if A, because of the weakness of other job controls, had been below B in productivity before the change, it would continue to be below B after the change. The weakness of A's other controls would not be corrected by the addition or strengthening of the single component and the resultant productivity would not be as much improved as it could have been if all components had been re-aligned. From the fact of equal percentage gain A would seem to be improving as much as B. Actually A might still be far below its rightful potential.

Of the five or six components constituting job control the most fundamental are the standardization of conditions and the standardization of operations (see Figure 1). The former—development of equipment, that is, the design or selection of the most expedient equipment, jigs, tools, gauges, and the like—establishes the physical potential for quality of product. The latter—job standardization, that is, motion and time study [2]—establishes the physical potential for efficient operating. The first can largely be purchased from without while the second must be developed almost entirely from within. When these two components of job control have been fully developed the factory will have attained improved, standardized jobs. The tasks or amounts of work per hour which derive therefrom can be used as bases for much of the planning and controlling, for efficiency measurement, for extra-financial incentives, and the like. But all this, as already explained, does not bring parity of wage rates; by itself it increases disparity of rates!

Prerequisites of Job Evaluation. Concurrent with the adoption of extra-financial incentives, or even in lieu of them for many jobs, should come the components of job review-analysis and job evalua-

[1] C. W. Lytle, "Job Evaluation—A Phase of Job Control," *Personnel*, XVI, No. 4. Also Roland Benjamin, Jr., "The Dynamics of Job Evaluation," *The Management Review*, XLII, No. 4.

[2] Developed directly from the works of Taylor and Gilbreth with the objective of determining the least costly methods of utilizing the physical assets. References recommended: Ralph M. Barnes, *Motion and Time Study* (New York: John Wiley & Sons, 1948); *Production Handbook* (New York: The Ronald Press Co., 1953).

tion. Like the arrangement of an incentive these components should follow, never precede, job standardization, because they presuppose the existence of definite and reasonably stable jobs. If jobs are definite and stable, because of automatic machinery, then perhaps further job standardization may be omitted, but we can scarcely imagine any kind of practical work which cannot be improved by an appropriate application of motion and time study. Extra-financial incentives are positively dangerous if not preceded by these and other preparatory controls. Job review-analysis and evaluation can be used more peremptorily but usually should not be. Certainly management must have gained labor's confidence in its general competence and fairness before attempting to build the component review-analysis and evaluation. When management has achieved the prerequisites it can gain a more complete confidence by creating a systematic and analytic job evaluation.

Primary Purposes of Job Evaluation. In brief we may state the primary purposes of job evaluation as follows:

1. To establish a general wage level for a given plant which will have parity, or an otherwise desired relativity, with those of neighbor plants, hence with the average level of the locality.
2. To establish correct differentials for all jobs within the given plant.
3. To bring new jobs into their proper relativity with jobs previously established.
4. To accomplish the foregoing by means of facts and principles which can be readily explained to, and accepted by, all concerned.

Job evaluating can become a control of importance because:

1. By reducing all essential job facts to convenient form it enables a management to implement policies of fairness.
2. By adopting sound principles and impartial techniques it trains the supervisory force to be more nearly objective.
3. By clarifying lines of authority and responsibility it obviates misunderstanding.
4. By substantiating confidence it lessens grievances and simplifies wage negotiations.

Conformity to sound principles makes possible consistency in job rating and the latter is the cornerstone of mutual fairness. If man-merit rating can be added as a top layer to all base rates, then payment by time can have a limited but important incentive effect (see

Chapter 13). If any manager, not yet using job evaluation, thinks that rates set otherwise are already consistent let him examine the statistical picture shown in Figure 2. This figure may show a worse case than his own but it represents about the usual situation before completing job evaluation.

Secondary Purposes of Job Evaluation. In this text we will not dwell on the use of job analysis as an aid to hiring, the sole aim of many managements in adopting job analysis between 1914 and 1937. All such assistance and more can come from extending job analysis on through job evaluation. Certainly a unified rate structure embracing all jobs is important to any employment department. We will say here that, either for hiring or for transferring and promoting, even for demoting and discharging, a set of job description-specifications is considerably more valuable when consistent base rates or rate ranges are affixed to them.

The secondary purposes are well indicated by the following outline of a job evaluation program.

1. To determine qualities necessary for a job when hiring new employees.
2. To determine qualities necessary for a job when making promotions.
3. To determine if the system of advancement in a particular plant is from the job of lowest order toward the job of highest order.
4. To determine qualities necessary when bringing back men who have been laid off or have been on leave for war service. During the interval there may have been changes in job content.
5. To support explanations to employees as to why a particular man would not be suitable for a given opening. Many seniority clauses give preference to length of service only after the requirements of the job in the way of experience, etc., are satisfied. If the job rating has been made up by an independent agency and the entire plant has been rated there is likely to be less stress on mere seniority.
6. To determine if men now occupying various jobs have qualifications required by the specifications.
7. To determine if all men are placed to best advantage in respective jobs available, also to guide the revamping of jobs for skill conservation.
8. To analyze hourly rates and to determine if they are in line with rating given.
9. To compare periodically wage rates with those for similar occupations at other local plants.
10. To point out where greatest opportunities lie for development of automatic equipment and improvement of working conditions, removal of hazards, etc. Any plant where job ratings are very high, indicating a predominance of highly skilled labor, usually is a plant where there are very few automatic operations. High ratings indicate places where it is most likely that improvements in equipment can be justified.

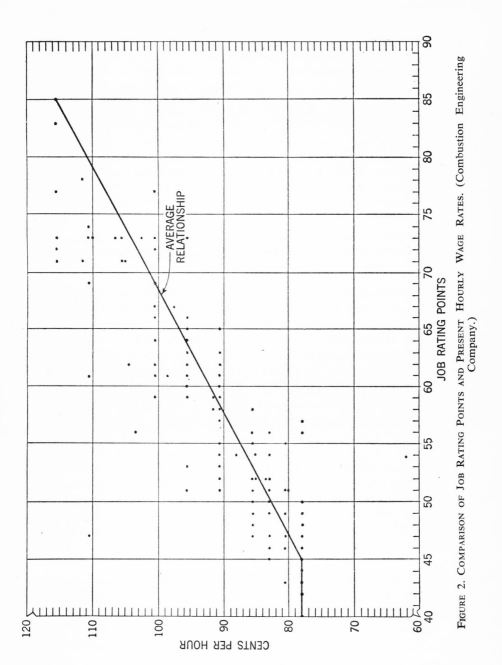

FIGURE 2. COMPARISON OF JOB RATING POINTS AND PRESENT HOURLY WAGE RATES. (Combustion Engineering Company.)

Primarily job evaluation is not concerned with improvements in tools and methods but such possibilities are sometimes brought to light during the analyst's review studies, in which case a report should be made to the industrial engineering department.

11. To train new supervisors. Specifications outlining duties of each man are useful in starting a new foreman on the job. Even an old foreman may have a wrong conception of job content and worth.

12. To facilitate explanations to an employee of the fact that any improvement in working conditions theoretically should mean a reduction in his wage rate. For example, if a worker is located in a poorly heated building and better heating is installed, the installation of heating equipment, an improvement in working conditions, lowers his job classification. Theoretically the base rate for the job should be lowered accordingly. Actually, poor working conditions rarely carry high ratings.

It is not advocated that better working conditions be provided for the express purpose of lowering workers' rates. However, if an employee is shown that he is paid a higher rate because his working conditions are not the best, he will probably be better satisfied with his job.[3]

Collectively job evaluation facilitates the making of safe plans for the rearrangement or replacement of large numbers of workers. Only by such means is it possible to enter bargaining negotiations without fear or fumbling. Without it decisions are often influenced (1) by the favoritism of a supervisor, (2) by the advertising ability of an employee, (3) by bad guesses regarding the ratio of demand to supply, or (4) by precedents previously influenced by any of the foregoing. Job evaluation can eliminate all these extraneous influences. The first two are precluded and the third, that of demand-to-supply ratio, can be kept from being confused with the relative worth of jobs by measuring the relative worth in terms of abstract points regardless of money rates. The supply-demand influence should be left to bargaining. In short, job evaluation completes the phases of job study and makes possible a rate structure which is independent of off-side, disrupting influences. Naturally this condition allows a management to proceed with confidence and should do much to gain and keep the complete confidence of workers. This advantage alone will usually justify whatever costs are involved. It was, in fact, the exposure of this need that plunged management into the movement during the latter half of the prolonged depression, 1935–1940.

Transformation of "Rate Setting." The original purpose of job analysis was to classify jobs in order to correct the setting of job rates. Various attempts at job classification were made by Civil

[3] Eugene Caldwell, "Job Rating," *The Iron Age*, CXLIV, No. 10.

Service reformers, beginning with the Civil Service Commission of 1871. But modern job analysis was started in 1909 by a requirement of the Civil Service Commission of Chicago and the subsequent work of the Commonwealth Edison Company of that city. No doubt inspiration for this step came from Taylor's practices: his further specialization of jobs, his "science of work" studies, his more careful selection and placement of operatives, and his examples of increasing unit labor cost to reduce unit total cost. Apparently Taylor and other engineers were too busy with the improvement of methods [4] to go far into this, the last step of job study. In fact, these pioneers, in developing better shop management, were putting most jobs on incentive payment and were content to work backward from total earnings to derive the base rates. Time-paid workers were left to supervision and "functionalized foremanship" was supposed to solve supervision. Furthermore, Taylor had little union contact until after 1912. Thus the personnel men developed job analysis, as they named it, and for several years it remained mostly in large offices (see Chapter 7).

World War I gave impetus to this personnel function. From that time on its use spread wherever there was a functionalized personnel staff. It seems, however, that the rate-setting function in factories was held jealously by line executives and they paid little attention to the new personnel files of job description-specifications. In fact, the techniques of job analysis were only then emerging from the experimental stage. Foreman-made descriptions were tried. Then the personnel staffs made their own. Ranking or grading whole jobs was the usual method of determining their relative worth. A few industrial engineers were beginning to analyze work on basic "characteristics" but even in such experiments no one attempted to use weighted points to measure the relative worths. In 1924, Merrill R. Lott tried out the first thorough-going plan for weighting separate work characteristics. His fifteen characteristics included three that are now considered extraneous and others that were not well related but he, and those who followed, did get the pioneering done in time for a more urgent need.

Pressing Need Had Developed by 1937. Meanwhile, jobs had been getting more specialized and more individualized. This outcome was the natural consequence of the many choices in equipment brought into being for various scales of operation and of many special solutions to "the one best way" which motion study was be-

---

[4] By this procedure he reduced unit labor cost without reducing employee earnings.

ginning to effect. No longer was it safe to assume that jobs bearing the same titles in different factories were identically the same jobs. Employers could use only the relatively few key jobs for rate comparisons, and even these needed to be checked by personal inspection. Thus the "going rate" for any class of jobs in a community became less evident, and more undependable, as a basis for informal rate setting. This lack of reference points meant that the management of each plant had to work out its rate structure more independently of interplant comparisons.

By 1937 another force, that of the unions, was pressing to the same storm center. Organized labor had long advocated "standard rates" and numerous states had passed minimum wage laws. The National Industrial Recovery Act of 1933–35 put the latter on a federal scale and the National Labor Relations Act of 1935 intensified the activity of the unions. After the Supreme Court sustained that law in 1937 the two-year-old CIO was able to increase its membership by large numbers of unskilled and semiskilled workers and to exert a power never before wielded by American employees. Wage rates for large groups were set by collective bargaining and pushed upward frequently. Hours came down and, in not a few cases, efficiency per man-hour fell off alarmingly. In short, bargaining became as unbalanced in favor of employees as it had ever been unbalanced in favor of employers. Many a manager found it difficult to defend his base rates. Where that occurred the higher-ups in management became interested and demanded some kind of "job-pictures" to help them get a grasp of the whole situation. Thus the few companies which had learned how to build a stormproof rate structure were stormed by their less farsighted neighbors asking for help. Soon the National Electrical Manufacturers Association, the National Metal Trades Association, and other employer associations were deep in the new business of job evaluation.[5]

Peace-to-War, War-to-Peace Conversion Benefited. It may not have been appreciated at the time but it can be seen now that it was fortunate to have thoroughly reliable methods of rate setting pushed into being before the war expansion began in 1941. As the American machine tool industry benefited from its depression-completed redesigning and tooling, so American management benefited from its depression-completed development of job evaluation. The rate structure of many a plant was more free from "out-of-line rates" than ever before. New jobs could be fitted quickly into the structure. New thousands of employees could quickly be assigned high but

[5] In 1938, of 63 companies questioned, 32 were found to be doing job evaluation.

consistent rates. New demand-supply requirements could be adjusted without upsetting any of the weighted values. Hence these prepared companies were better able to meet the demands of war without undue rate confusion and without loss of confidence on the part of unions.

Many managements that were not prepared in this respect at the time of conversion lost no time in getting prepared for the reconversion. They realized that when wage and salary controls were eased or relinquished there would be a great commotion wherever management failed to develop a program of job analysis and job evaluation. Much confusion, distress on the part of top management, and in many cases actual strikes were avoided where this preparation took place. A mature program of job control perhaps does not insure perfect calm, but it can do a great deal to smooth out the agitation. Job evaluation and all it connotes provide a factual basis for decision and for negotiation. It implements policy and wins confidence, and these advantages are always helpful when management is confronted with difficult problems.

Here are only a few of the job evaluation problems which needed attention during post-war years. Some jobs had been split to make one skilled job for a woman and one heavy job for a man, neither of which rated as high as the original job. As women withdrew from industry or as the scale of operations shrank, it became necessary to recombine some of these narrowed jobs and put the more general job into a higher classification. Other jobs were upgraded on responsibility resulting from certain war conditions. Such jobs needed to be re-evaluated and reclassified downward. Many jobs were hastily put on incentives, without an evaluated base. In fact, the extension of evaluated bases for incentive jobs had barely begun at the end of the war and that had to be undertaken without delay in plants where it had thus far been neglected. We assure top management that it will now save itself much trouble by installing job evaluation where no steps have been taken in that direction. In fact, it will also save itself much time for other matters.

Surveys Indicating Present Use. A survey made by the National Industrial Conference Board in 1948, covering 3,498 companies, showed that 59 per cent of them had job evaluation applied to nearly all hourly paid jobs. Over half of these companies applied job evaluation to salaried jobs, one third to supervisory jobs, and one eighth to executive jobs. About the same time the Bureau of Labor Statistics reported that unions were participating in these plans at 50 per cent of the plants making metal parts, assemblies made of metal, and the like.

A later NICB survey reported that 70 per cent of the plans in use were point systems, 10 per cent factor comparison systems, 14 per cent combinations of the foregoing, 4 per cent mere classification, and 2 per cent other unnamed systems.

Recently The Dartnell Corporation of Chicago surveyed 96 companies [6] regarding their use of job evaluation. All but 8 of the companies had installed their plans since 1940. Of these plans, 74 used weighted points, 8 comparison of characteristics, 8 characteristics comparison combined with weighted points, and 6 ranking. Only 38 companies brought in consultants for installation. Only 12 companies were nonunion, but 41 did not include the matter in their union contracts; 43 did. Fourteen companies did not apply it to the office force; 82 did. Only 12 companies had training programs for preparing their supervisors, but 85 held meetings with their supervisors. All but 16 companies held meetings with their employees and most of them used the employee magazine plus bulletins to explain what was coming.

[6] See *Report No. 605* (Chicago: Dartnell Personnel Administration Service).

2

POLICY AND ORGANIZATION

> Sound personnel administration means so organizing and treating
> people at work that they will utilize their maximum individual
> capacities, thereby attaining maximum personal and group satis-
> faction and rendering their maximum service to the enterprise
> of which they are a part.
>
> —THOMAS G. SPATES

What Labor Wants. Elmo Roper, conductor of *Fortune's* poll,
has stated labor's real wants or basic needs as:

1. Full employment at reasonably high wages
2. A chance to advance
3. Just to be treated like people
4. A feeling of dignity and responsibility

Other pollsters have reported much the same basic wants but
have added: "a feeling of belonging—of being on the team,"
"a greater guarantee of security," and the like. These writers
believe that the other wants—seniority rights, compulsory union
membership, and the like—are devices for getting the real
wants. Regardless of how these basic needs may be expressed,
management should sincerely try to meet all of them and the best
way to meet them is to anticipate them through its policies, which
should stem from primary long-term determinations made by the
most able and responsible officers, that is, by top management. In
such planning evaluation can contribute much toward the fulfill-
ment of the real wants of labor. And what are the wants of management? Primarily the same, because these basic needs of labor
have become the prerequisites of sound personnel relations; when
sound relations are achieved management's greatest need—full
cooperation—can be expected to follow.

First in importance both to employee and to employer are, therefore, the achievement of steady work and just individual remunera-

tion. Regularization of employment is beyond the scope of this text, if not beyond the reach of any text, but there is hope because employers are now thinking in terms of "finding work for men" along with "finding men for work." Just remuneration is within our scope and is always possible if a management will approach the problem intelligently and fairly. Not only must the management believe that it is being fair, but the rank and file of employees must believe it, and to that end they should be informed on the policies that concern them.[1] Furthermore, the policies must be implemented by standardized procedure and by adequately trained staffs, supervisors, facilitating services, and any other help necessary. The standard procedures must also be open to scrutiny.

Wage Determination in General. In a free society there are many influences that affect wages. Reynolds of Yale University expresses the employer limits [2] as "maximum shutdown point," that wage level above which a company could not go for lack of ability to pay, and "minimum shutdown point," that wage level below which a company would fail to attract labor. Actually "ability to pay" does not often enter the discussion, probably because profits have been badly cramped by taxes. Willingness to pay is very much an issue. The "wage pattern," or the precedents set by "wage leaders," has undoubtedly had influence, but in the opinion of Ernest Dale it has been exaggerated. There are certainly such trends as the willingness to take fringe benefits in lieu of unattainable wage increases. The most interesting of these modern concessions has been the granting of "productivity increases." Unlike the cost-of-living adjustments, they are one-way movements, and hold out the expectation of continued gains. Labor is resistant to downward adjustments even if real wages remain constant and in fact is fearful of any arrangement that might tend to freeze the present standard of living.[3] Most important of all the economic considerations is that of the prevailing or "going wage rate." This is fortunate because both management and labor can get facts on prevailing prices provided the jobs to be priced are known definitely as to content and relative worth.

[1] Many American companies have published their personnel policies. Excellent examples of these may be obtained from The American Rolling Mill Company, The American Smelting and Refining Company, Dennison Manufacturing Company, General Electric Company, General Motors Corporation, Procter & Gamble Company, Socony-Vacuum Oil Company, and others.

[2] L. G. Reynolds, *Labor Economics and Labor Relations* (New York: Prentice-Hall, Inc., 1949).

[3] See *Management News*, October, 1952.

Practical Objectives. If the whole management is just and reasonable, free from discrimination or favoritism, and withal faithfully consistent and patient, employees are bound to return confidence. To retain confidence indefinitely there must be adherence to full, incontestable facts, and to sound principles for their use. Job evaluation is the means of establishing the incontestable facts on relative job worth and that is the part we are concerned with. The following discussion is therefore focused on describing, rating, and pricing jobs. Within this boundary several questions must be answered at the very beginning. Is the general objective to rearrange the money rates in better relation without altering the existing average wage? Is it to elevate the whole rate structure to the prevailing general wage level? Under government regulations, is it to achieve as many increases as are permitted? Or is it only to eliminate existing violations of regulations? When the general objective is settled the more specific questions can be considered.

Specific Considerations. The practical considerations regarding base rates emanate from management aims, which usually are:

1. Adoption of wage and salary levels which will meet competitive costs and assure stability.
2. Establishment of correct differentials between jobs.
3. Establishment of proper hours of work.
4. Anticipation of requirements for overtime and shift work.
5. Cooperation with employees as to grievances and adjustments.
6. Measurement and recognition of individual merit.

1. Within the so-called general wage level there are numerous wage and salary levels in each plant. A just level means, therefore, the one prevailing in the community for similar work, that is, for work requiring the same kind and degree of work characteristics. Facts of this sort must be gathered through locality surveys and analyzed for numerical distribution, not merely averaged. It is impossible to ascertain these levels correctly without the use of accurate job description-specifications. In peace times it is common for the more prosperous companies to exceed these levels, but in any case the actual going rates must be known and checked periodically (see Chapter 10). The practice of putting women on lower wage levels than men has been under attack from many directions. Considerations of justice are overwhelmingly against it and yet it continues to a surprising degree. The pros and cons of this complex question are of considerable importance; they are treated briefly later in this chapter.

2. A differential means the difference in rate, or in rate range, midpoint to midpoint, also floor to floor and ceiling to ceiling, between successive job or occupational classes. Under good job evaluation these differentials are freed from chance and favoritism. They are worked out as parts of a whole rate structure according to policy. Enlightened employees want this practice followed as much as their employers do and one of the main sources of dissatisfaction is removed when it is done on an impersonal and orderly basis. Union objections to systematic derivation of differentials invariably mean a lack of confidence in the management, not a preference for opportunism.

During World War II, P. F. Brissenden, Vice Chairman of the Second Region, National War Labor Board, made a vivid picture of this opportunism or lack of policy and system.

These intermediate minimums are likely to resemble the chaotic hodge-podge of wage rates which is characteristic of factories in which the management has allowed its wage structure to develop by chance and as the uneven impact of various pressures may have dictated. It is necessary, therefore, to build up, not a hodge-podge of bracket minimums but a balanced, symmetrical pattern of such minimums. For this purpose it has been possible, fortunately, to capitalize upon the experience of employers who, by careful evaluation and classification, have substituted order and design for chaos and disorder in their wage structure.

Putting the matter positively, the policy and its implementing procedures should have as their objective the derivation of differentials which can be shaped into an orderly and stable rate structure (see Chapter 11).

3. Both the amount of work per hour or task and the number of hours are related to the amount of pay. Hence these quantities are coming increasingly into the scope of bargaining. Tasks are derived, however, through technical studies and, if carried out according to acceptable policies, are usually left to management except for the right of appeal through grievance procedure (see Chapter 12). Hours may also be left mainly to management but certain ramifications of the hours question, particularly those affecting the number of employees, are sure to be drawn into bargaining. For instance, in states where an unemployment compensation law provides a "merit rating," a choice arises between the use of overtime during seasonal peaks and the hiring of extra employees. In such cases a general policy can dispel fear but this plan may not be practicable. If a temporary policy is developed it should be explained as such. Whenever shorter hours are in prospect the man-

agement should give the employees enough of the facts for them to gain a true view of the situation.

4. The payment for overtime, in excess of 40 hours per week, was fixed at time and one half by the Fair Labor Standards Act of 1938 and the Wage-Hour Act of 1940. Since these laws apply only to manufacturers or others engaged in interstate commerce, those employers who believe they are exempt from these provisions of law, because they engage only in intrastate commerce, should obtain a ruling from the Wage-Hour administrator in their district before adopting any basic work week in excess of 40 hours. This procedure is recommended to reduce the possibility in borderline cases of having the courts rule and order back pay plus penalties. There remain the questions of extra pay for Sundays and holidays, and also for extra shifts. These matters are always covered by bargaining if there is a union but there is a choice of policy as to method of compensation. For extra shifts an hourly differential may be established, such as 6 cents for the second shift and 9 cents for the third, or a percentage, usually between 5 per cent and 12½ per cent, may be added to regular earnings. It is best to apply the percentage after base earnings are calculated rather than to change the piece rate or base hourly rate to include such "bonus." This method minimizes the possibility of complaints that wages have been reduced, when the extra amount is removed, in cases where employees are transferred from a night shift to the regular day shift.

5. With the extension of staff services and union in-shop activities, practices pertaining to adjustments and operation have become so varied as to discourage any general comment. Always management must be prepared for adjustments and can obviate inconsistent practices by formulating a blanket policy and a set of standard practice procedures. As an end procedure there is usually what is called the machinery for settlement of grievances. This "machinery" is arranged jointly with the union and provides for bilateral informal hearings at several levels. If a grievance passes up through the highest level without reaching a mutually satisfactory settlement it must be mediated or arbitrated. For this purpose the bargaining agreement may provide an impartial chairman, on a temporary or a yearly basis. This step may be accomplished directly by the joint selection of a disinterested outsider or indirectly by calling in the State Mediation Board, American Arbitration Association, or other similar group. Both parties agree to continue work during the hearings and to abide by whatever decision is handed down. There is no doubt that these practices have prevented strikes and lockouts. On the other hand, there has been a tendency to over-

work the idea. Employee expression need not run wild. Union leaders should discourage all unnecessary resort to this outside settlement. A little two-way conciliation at the source will save both sides money and unnecessary irritation. If, for instance, an employee has devised some improvement which substantially reduces the time required for his operation, the management should recognize this development as ingenuity and pay that employee a lump sum amounting to the net saving for six months. The operation can then be studied and a higher task set for all doing the operation. The latter without the former is likely to create a grievance.

6. If in the bargained agreement [4] arrangements for seniority have not precluded recognition of merit by means of rate increases, it is highly desirable to develop a policy which will give substantial rewards to the variegated and ever changing abilities and performances of individual employees. This recognition is important as a matter of justice and as a matter of human satisfaction, both of which underlie morale. The procedure must provide for systematic measurement of merit, for payment of individual differentials on top of base rates, and for promotion when opportunity arises, all based on facts and sound principles. Management is grossly derelict in its responsibility if it has no policy here.

Unions Also Have Policies. Not later than at step No. 9 (see steps at end of this chapter), preferably at step No. 3, discuss the plan with responsible union representatives and *put all cards on the table.*[5]

Toward job evaluation, as toward most management tools, there is no single union attitude. Partly because union officials must be politic and partly because they deal with different kinds of management, the attitudes of two locals of the same union may be widely different and the attitude of any one local may be different tomorrow from today. This is opportunism rather than inconsistency. Top union policy is more constant over a period of time. The variation there is largely a matter of general strategy. There seem to be three of these strategies [6] as follows:

[4] See Personnel Policy Board, Department of Defense, Report of Subcommittee: "Development and Recommendation of a Department of Defense Wage Policy," Oct. 1, 1949; National Industrial Conference Board, Studies in Personnel Policy 94, Union Contracts Since the Taft-Hartley Act; American Management Association, Personnel Series 136, "Wage Policy and Problems in a Preparedness Economy"; General Electric Corporation, "Supervisors' Guide to General Electric Job Information."

[5] E. N. Hay, "How We Established Written Employee Policies," *Personnel,* XVIII, No. 2.

[6] C. W. Lytle, *The Setting for Job Evaluation* (Controllers Institute of America, Current Compensation Problems, 1947).

1. Complete opposition. Job evaluation has evolved as a management tool and management is always out to get the better of a union. Furthermore job evaluation is likely to be a rigid system and can fortify whatever worths emerge from the system. This is likely to lessen the scope of bargaining if it does not actually freeze the status quo. Therefore we will have a better chance to win our demands if no such system is in existence.

2. Toleration plus veto. Although it is a management tool, this particular management has been honest and we may gain by the objective treatment. All we fear is some specific case in which we may want to fight for more than the system allows. We will not therefore oppose this plan but will accept no share of responsibility in its creation or in any advance determination. We can then oppose any particular result and correct it at the time of negotiating or by registering a grievance.

3. Limited approval through participation. The rate of pay is legally within our bargaining rights. Job evaluation is the constructive way to derive relative worths. Therefore we insist that participation equivalent to bargaining be allowed us from the start. In this way our experience enters into the pooled judgment and we will be more sure to get justice all along the line. Final bargaining is available anyway for the translation into money rates and we can resort to grievance machinery—arbitration—whenever we are not satisfied.

Under the first strategy it may be inexpedient for management to attempt any kind of job evaluation or at best to confine the attempt to a crude form of job classification.

Under the second strategy the union may seem acquiescent at first and make a lot of trouble later or it may order its locals to take no step toward acceptance until the top union officials are in possession of all facts as to proposed characteristics, job descriptions, measurement scales, and the like. This means delay and revision, but if both parties are willing to compromise there may be a very satisfactory outcome.

Under the third strategy there will be need for many exchanges of views from the beginning and a heavy expenditure of time for committee work, but the results are likely to be excellent and of a lasting nature. We think this possibility is particularly hopeful in the newer industries where there are no historical precedents and where job contents are not as well stabilized as in older plants.

The Question of Rates for Women's Jobs. Job evaluation deals with jobs impersonally and is not concerned with the race, creed, color, age, or sex of the employee. Equal pay for equal work is the very essence of job evaluation. Nevertheless many companies continue to retain differentials between comparable jobs on the basis of sex only. Also, many companies pay lower hiring rates to women than to men. Doubtless the custom of having different job classifications for male and female arose from the fact that male and female operators did not often work on identical jobs. In both World Wars women did take many kinds of jobs and after each war a large number of women remained on men's jobs, often doing as well as, or better than, the men. In fact a study reported by our Department of Commerce indicated that 23,350,000 women had work experience in 1950. Of these 36.8 per cent held year-round, full-time jobs while 17.9 per cent held part-year, full-time jobs and 45.3 per cent held intermittent or part-time jobs. The permanent role of women in our labor force is indicated by the increasing proportions of married women and of older women holding or seeking jobs. About 51 per cent of these women are married, 33 per cent are single, and 16 per cent are widowed or divorced. About 25 per cent of our women job holders have children under 18 years of age.

Claims for Equal Pay. The women's arguments for equal pay are many and are addressed in every direction.

To working women: Equal pay is a matter of simple justice. It insures women's receiving what they are entitled to for the work they do. It will help the women meet the present high cost of living by removing any wage disparities. The great majority of women have to work to support themselves and one or more dependents and are not working for "pin money."

To housewives: Wage differentials based on sex are unfair to men (husbands) also because they sometimes drag down men's wage standards. Equal pay means more economic security for housewives and their children, for it protects the wages of male heads of families.

To working men: Equal pay affords men greater wage and job security. It discourages employers from hiring women for less money, or as sometimes happens, from replacing men with women at lower rates.

To the industry: Equal pay protects fair employers from the unfair competition of those who attempt to use women as undercutters of men's wages.

The equal pay policy reduces friction over rates. It improves employee morale. The women's attitude toward their work improves and their efficiency increases. An equal pay system is easier to administer than a dual rate structure based on sex.

Other claims for "equal pay" are: The practice of equal pay for women is essential to a healthy economy because by protecting wage levels of all workers it sustains consumer purchasing power. This fact is better understood after consideration of the results of wage discrimination against women—that is, unequal pay—a situation that bears a close analogy to the principle of Gresham's Law, that bad money drives out good. It is an axiom of wage theory that when large numbers of workers can be hired at lower rates of pay than those prevailing at any given time, the competition of such persons for jobs results either in the displacement of the higher paid workers or in the acceptance by them of lower rates.

That the practice of wage discrimination against women on any large scale in the United States can very seriously affect the wage structure is evident from a consideration of the importance of the woman labor force in the country's economy. At the time of writing twelve of our more highly industrialized states have already passed "equal pay" laws.

Policy Determination. We might summarize the matters needing policy determination as follows:

1. Accessions and Separations
    Hiring from within and from without
    Minimum and maximum age requirements
    Restrictions on employment of women
    Restrictions on employment of relatives
    Restrictions on absence, conditions of reinstatement
    Conditions of simultaneous outside employment
    Order of layoff, effect on service record, seniority
    Terms of dismissal and severance compensation
    Causes for discharge
2. Payment
    Allowances for sickness absences
    Vacations with pay and pay in lieu of vacations
    Terms of payment for holidays
    Arrangements for bonuses or premiums
    Time and method of paying wages earned
3. Standard Practice as to Rates
    Hiring rates
    Learnees' rates
    Level for base rates, trend, and limit lines

Number and width of job classes
Range of rates per job class
Classification and reclassification of employees
Conditions of transfer and promotion
Conditions of guarantees
Conditions of change from incentive work to time-paid work
Determination of earnings when two time rates are involved

4. Hours

Normal hours of work day and week, lunch period, etc.
Rules for registering in and out
Rules regarding tardiness
Rewards for attendance
Rules for eating, smoking, rest periods, etc.

5. Work Beyond Regular Shift

Conditions of overtime payment
Choice between overtime and further hiring
Terms for shift work

6. Grievance and Adjustment

Procedures for change of rates (or tasks)
Breakage of tools, spoilage of material, etc.
Furnishing of work clothes, etc.
Progressive steps for settlement of grievances

7. Promotion

Use of systematic merit rating
Follow-up of personnel staff
Preplanned paths of promotion
Training in preparation for promotion
Medals and nonfinancial recognition

EXAMPLE OF WAGE AND SALARY POLICY

THE SMITH MANUFACTURING COMPANY, INC.[7]

ACTION TO BE TAKEN

1. Have Executive Committee review and approve.
2. File such forms with Treasury as may be required to authorize any parts of the policy statement.
3. Make such modifications as are required by Treasury rulings on specific applications.
4. Present to Executive Committee in final form for adoption.
5. Establish a stated schedule of review periods at which this policy is to be carefully reviewed and revisions drawn up for Executive Committee's approval.

[7] Courtesy of a clock manufacturer in Connecticut.

6. Appoint an officer to assume the responsibility for review, revision, and submission to Executive Committee at proper date.

STATEMENT OF WAGE POLICY

THE SMITH MANUFACTURING COMPANY, INC.

1. In order to clarify our thinking and to stabilize and standardize our methods of paying salaries and wages, and in order to insure compliance with Law, Rulings, Executive Orders, General Orders, etc., we are reciting herein our wage and salary policy.

2. This is a statement of policy, written for the purposes mentioned. It is not to be construed as an employer-employee agreement. It is not a plan for increases and advancement. It is not to be submitted to any group outside our company for approval.

3. It is subject to acceptance by the Executive Committee. It is subject to revision and amendment as new regulations or the needs of the company may dictate, provided that all such changes be approved by the Executive Committee.

4. The company will compensate some of its employees on a wage basis, some on a salary basis, and it will pay rates as good as, or better than, the weighted average prevailing in the locality for classes of labor for which there is a supply and demand in the local market.

5. WAGES means compensation for personal services, which is computed on an hourly or daily basis, a piecework basis, or any other comparable basis.

6. SALARY means compensation computed on a weekly, monthly, annual, or comparable basis.

7. For compensation purposes, the company classifies all personnel into the following groups:

   a) Officers
   b) Executive employees
   c) Administrative employees
   d) Operators
   e) Shop clerical employees
   f) Office employees

8. Officers are the corporate officers, as shown in the company's corporate statement. These officers are paid a salary on an annual basis. Some of these are paid a salary in two parts—one part is drawn each week and the other part is drawn each quarter. Others draw their salary every month.

9. The Board of Directors has delegated to the Executive Committee sole jurisdiction over officers' salaries. Therefore, any change in an officer's compensation must be authorized by the Executive Committee before submission to the Treasury Department for approval.

10. In the case of the Smith Manufacturing Company, Inc., the salary of any officer should not be increased or decreased without approval of the Treasury Department.

11. In the case of the Smith Manufacturing Company, Inc., it is advisable to obtain Treasury approval of any reclassification of an officer to another office if any salary change is involved.

12. Officers shall not be required to observe specific working hours nor any fixed vacation period. They are selected for their special value to the company and should be free to deliver the best at their command and not be circumscribed by narrow limitations. Vacations should be arranged by agreement among the officers themselves. During the present emergency, it is suggested that officers limit their vacations to two weeks in each calendar year.

13. Executive Employees are those who qualify as Executive Employees under Treasury Department regulations and the Wage-Hour Act. They shall be paid a salary on a weekly basis. Some of these may draw their salary on a weekly drawing while others may draw part of their salary weekly and part of it quarterly.

14. In the case of the Smith Manufacturing Company, Inc., any change in an Executive Employee's salary for any reason should be submitted to the Treasury Department for approval.

15. While the emergency lasts, the vacations of all employees under the rank of officer will be limited to one week. All Executive, Administrative and Office Employees who are in the employ of the company on June 1st and who have been in the company's employ for a period of one year previous to June 1st shall be allowed one week's vacation with pay during the vacation period starting June 1st. All such employees who on June 1st have been in our employ less than one year shall be allowed 2 per cent of all the take-home earned by them in the period from June 1st to May 31st.

16. For all employees whose wages are computed on the basis of 1/10 hour and who are in the company's employ on June 1st, vacation pay shall be figured as 2 per cent of all the take-home earned during the immediately preceding period from June 1st to May 31st.

17. If an employee, whose wages are computed on the basis of 1/10 hour, is in our employ on June 1st of any year and has not *due to layoff* been absent more than a total of six months during the period from June 1st to May 31st, that employee shall not lose vacation credit for the time the employee was laid off. In the case of such employees, the average take-home for all full weeks worked shall be computed and that average shall be allowed for every week the employee was laid off. The value of the weeks laid off, thus computed, shall be added to the value of the weeks actually worked in computing the vacation pay on the basis of 2 per cent of a 52-week period.

18. The company reserves the right to make exceptions to strict interpretation of its vacation policy in the case of old and faithful employees and in the case of employees who have rendered exceptional or unusual service. Old and faithful employees shall be those who have served satisfactorily for a total of 15 years or more. In the case of "exceptional or unusual service," exceptions will be made where the employee's extra efforts and consequent fatigue have caused absences which ordinarily would count against vacation credits. Such absences will not be counted. Also, the company reserves the

right to order an employee to take a rest at full pay for any length of time that the company feels will help that employee to recover from unusual fatigue and permit that employee to resume and continue his usefulness to himself, the community, and the company.

19. Any employee, absent without leave, shall be deemed to have resigned as of the date or time at which he first did not report for work as expected. Such employees may be reinstated on the company's payroll, at management's option, contingent upon satisfactory explanation of the absence. Employees who are not reinstated shall be subject to rehiring if they wish to resume work with the company. Reinstated employees shall not lose vacation credits. Rehired employees shall have all vacation credit prior to the absence canceled. Their credit shall start again as of the rehiring date. It is understood that the company may accept the resignation implied or refuse to accept it, may reinstate or not reinstate, may rehire or not rehire, entirely at the company's option. Employees whom the company has decided to dismiss for any reason, or whom the company refuses to rehire, shall be given a release. Any employee who refuses to accept rehiring without credits as a basis for returning to work shall be deemed to have voluntarily resigned. In such cases, a release will not be issued.

20. All vacation credits must be used up in the period in which they apply. They do not accumulate.

21. Executive Employees and Administrative Employees shall be allowed during each year, starting June 1st and ending May 31st, one week's sick leave with pay. In the office such employees will be charged 1/11 of a week's salary for each half day of absence. In the shop, such employees will be charged 1/12 of a week's salary for each half day of absence. It is understood, of course, that no matter how charges are deducted, these employees must be paid for an entire week if they work any part of a work-week.

22. The work-week shall be a period beginning at 12:01 A.M. Monday and ending at midnight on Sunday.

23. In the office, the first half day begins at 12:01 A.M. and ends at 11:55 A.M. The second half day begins at 12:48 P.M. and ends at midnight.

In the shop, the first half day begins at 12:01 A.M. and ends at 11:12 A.M. The second half day begins at 11:30 A.M. and ends at midnight.

24. Operators are all those who perform manual work in the shop or who spend in the shop more than 20 per cent of their time during a normal work-week at work other than clerical which cannot be described as executive, administrative, or professional. Operators shall be paid wages which shall be computed on the basis of 1/10 hour.

25. All adjustments in the base rates of Operators must be made in accordance with the provisions of the government or any amendment or substitute thereof or by virtue of the approval by the W.S.B. of an application for wage adjustment on suitable form.

Any employee shall have access to his own rating file in the personnel office. All the employee need do is to speak to his foreman who will make an appointment for the employee. Foremen are instructed to make these appointments at the earliest opportunity.

Rating files will be continuously reviewed and worthy cases will be further studied and ranked according to relative merit.

These ranked cases will be placed in two separate files: (1) those eligible for reclassification, and (2) those deemed worthy of wage increases. Employees whose rating papers are placed in these files will be known as Eligibles.

As opportunities for advancement or increases arise, rewards will be distributed to those Eligibles. Those whose qualifications make them best fitted for available better jobs will be reclassified. Those most deserving of wage increases will be given increases. Advances and increases will be effected in accordance with government regulations. This process will continue down the list until available benefits are exhausted or until all Eligibles are rewarded.

In cases where two or more employees are equally deserving, they shall be rewarded in accordance with their length of service—the longest in service shall be the first considered.

To safeguard the interests of all employees, the cases of those who do not "make" the Eligible Files will be given careful study. Every effort will be made to help build their effectiveness to the point where they can make progress in the company's service.

26. Employees whose wages are computed on the basis of 1/10 hour may spend a week away from the shop on vacation or remain at work by arrangement with management. If they spend a week away from the shop, they will not be paid any wages during their absence. They will in any case receive their vacation pay as above.

27. There shall be no sick-leave allowance for Operators.

28. Shop Clerical Employees are those who work in the shop and whose work is largely mental in its aspects, even though a certain amount of manual activity may be involved, and who spend more than 20 per cent of their time during a normal work-week at work which cannot be described as executive, administrative, or professional. Shop Clerical Employees shall be paid wages computed on the basis of 1/10 hour.

29. Adjustments in the wages of Shop Clerical Employees must be made in accordance with the provisions of the government.

30. There shall be no sick-leave allowance for Shop Clerical Employees.

31. Office Employees are those who work primarily in the office, whose work is largely mental in its aspects even though a certain amount of manual effort or activity may be involved, and who spend more than 20 per cent of their time during a normal work-week at work which cannot be described as executive, administrative, or professional. Office Employees shall be paid wages computed on the basis of one half day.

32. Adjustments in earnings of Office Employees must be made in accordance with the provisions of the government, or any amendment or substitute thereof, or by virtue of approval of an application for wage adjustment on suitable form.

33. Office Employees shall be allowed vacation with pay, as stated above in paragraph 15.

34. Office Employees shall be allowed one week's sick leave with pay. Against this credit of one week's (11 half days) pay during each year, beginning June 1st and ending May 31st, they shall be charged one half day's pay for each half day's absence because of illness.

35. The following days shall be observed as holidays:

New Year's Day
Good Friday
Memorial Day
Fourth of July
Labor Day
Thanksgiving Day
Christmas Day

36. If any of these days falls on a Sunday, the holiday will be observed the following Monday.

37. Officers, whose salary is on an annual basis, are not affected by the holiday schedule. They may work or they may not work on the holiday and their compensation will remain unchanged.

38. Executive and Administrative Employees, if they work on a holiday, shall be entitled to extra compensation as follows:

In the case of Executive or Administrative Employees who work in the office, the extra compensation shall amount to $2/11$ of their weekly salary for each holiday worked which does not fall on Saturday and $1/11$ of their weekly salary for each Saturday holiday.

In the case of Executive or Administrative Employees who work in the shop, the extra compensation shall amount to $2/12$ of their weekly salary for each holiday worked.

39. Operators who work on holidays shall be entitled to time and one half for all hours worked. If the holiday occurs after 40 hours have been worked in any work-week, the operator will still be paid time and one half for all hours worked and no greater amount by virtue of the fact that he is already entitled to time and one half on the basis of hours worked. Premium time cannot be pyramided; it can be collected on one basis only.

40. Care should be exercised in figuring holiday time credits where the end of the 40-hour period falls sometime during the holiday. In this case, the effect of the holiday is to entitle the Operator to time and one half for all hours on the holiday worked before the 40-hour period expired. He gets time and one half for all hours over 40 anyway.

41. Shop Clerical Employees shall benefit by holidays in same manner as Operators. See paragraphs 39 and 40.

———

Other matters pertaining to policy are discussed in Chapters 5, 11, and 12.

Sequential Steps in Organizing. We define organizing as:

1. Determining and relating purposeful functions.
2. Breaking the functions into duties; allocating these to specific jobs. (Size of plant affects this.)
3. Delegating adequate responsibility and authority for each job.
4. Selecting and training personnel to do each job.

These respective steps are discussed in detail in the following paragraphs.

Determination of Purposeful Functions. Obviously two kinds of functions are involved at the time of starting any new program, namely, research functions and operating functions. If the program is somewhat technical and in need of constant upkeep the research functions must be continued with the operating but usually on a reduced scale. In the case of job evaluation,

Research functions include:

1. Design and standardization of methods, techniques, and procedures.
2. Harmonization with practice of other functions.
3. Classification of jobs and job titles, to build and maintain a rate structure.
4. Arrangement of intercompany surveys.
5. Preparation of data for policy appraisal.

Operating functions include:

1. Interpretation and enforcement of policy.
2. Maintenance of records.
3. Recommendations for or against rate changes.
4. Cooperation with work of other staff services.
5. Cooperation with work of dispute committees.
6. Facilitation service to line officers, foremen, etc.

Organizing a Wage and Salary Division. With the foregoing determination of functions (see also Chapter 1, Figure 1) in mind it is now possible to define the duties involved, group them into jobs, write descriptions and specifications for each job, evaluate these jobs as to responsibility, select the man to head the division and perhaps help him to select his assistants—in short, to organize the nucleus of a new wage and salary division.

The size of a company, of course, must be considered in grouping the duties into jobs. In very small companies an assistant to one of the line officers might have to take on the whole set of duties or, in case there is already a personnel functionary, he would take charge, hiring a suitable assistant to relieve himself of subordinate duties in this or in other functions. All these staff functions are difficult for small companies to undertake but the amount of such indirect work that can be justified is often considerable. Companies having as many as five hundred productive employees can go into most of these functions if they avoid unnecessary detail and companies having a thousand or more productive employees can usually afford specialists for all genuine services. Although the work of wage and salary administration must be constantly coordinated with the work of a methods department, it is unusual to find these functions combined. In practice they have developed separately. Usually it is best to keep them separate provided each group is trained to cooperate as needed. In very large companies this cooperation may be accomplished through special liaison assistants.

Another consideration which affects the organization is the extent of application of job evaluation. The nature of incentive work provides a reverse process for deriving base rates and, while that is certainly not the ideal way of fixing rates, at least many managements have seen fit to leave well enough alone, that is, they have at first chosen to apply job evaluation only to time-paid work. Furthermore, most companies have been content to stop below or just above the supervision level. Even so, it is well to consider at the beginning whether or not the plan to be adopted can later be extended without radical change. Thus the question of what plan to follow must be decided very early in the development. This question is often answered by the higher management after seeking advice from a trade association or from a consultant.

In any case someone already in the organization must be selected to father the project. Usually the chief personnel officer gets this assignment but sometimes another officer may volunteer or be drafted because he has acquired a longer and more intimate familiarity with a larger number of the jobs. In two such cases the treasurer was in charge of the new division until the creative work was completed. Two other large companies put the function directly under their general managers. Because no one executive is likely to be familiar with all jobs, it is customary to use the committee form of organization. A top steering committee might be composed of an assistant personnel director, to serve as chief wage and salary administrator, and the superintendents of the departments concerned, not more than six. All should have analytical ability and be capable of maintaining a high degree of objectivity. This wage (and/or salary) administrative committee will then transfer or employ a man as "chief rate analyst" to do much of the detail work between committee meetings. Eventually this specialist may be promoted to the position of Chief Wage and Salary Administrator. One of his important duties is to train an assistant analyst for each plant. This training is done by such means, among others, as conferences, rotation of assignments, and periodic visits. The aim is to achieve uniform practice.

The Procter & Gamble Company uses a combination of permanent and temporary committee membership. For a department the superintendent is a permanent member and serves as chairman. In the factory an industrial engineer makes a second permanent member while in the office the office manager makes the second permanent member. These permanent members rate all jobs but are aided by three others who rotate, namely, the foreman or supervisor of each group being studied and two others who have had recent experience with or know the particular jobs. The Industrial Relations Supervisor acts as secretary and under some agreements a union representative sits as an observer.

Order of Steps to Be Taken. Before completing the new organization it will be helpful to lay out a schedule of steps to be taken. They may be briefly stated as follows:

1. Choose the most suitable method and the main techniques.
2. Choose the major job characteristics, then the minor ones, and apportion limiting values if weighted points are to be used.
3. Start selling the proposition to all concerned; seek suggestions.
4. Build definitions, measuring scales, or comparison techniques, and assign relative values.
5. Design forms or questionnaires and collect preliminary descriptions.
6. Identify and evaluate key jobs, using one characteristic at a time but all of them in succession (keeping within limits of No. 2).
7. Edit preliminary descriptions and establish grades.
8. Evaluate remaining jobs on all characteristics (keeping proper relationship to key jobs), harmonize job titles, and grade.
9. Now, if not sooner, be sure union representatives concur in job descriptions and weightings.
10. Make intercompany survey on key jobs only, but try to find at least one per class or labor grade.
11. Design a whole rate structure as a guide, using existing wage scale tentatively.

12. Bargain as to new money scale (pricing). Fix new trend line and revise ranges.
13. Readjust all rates relative to line; standardize and put into working form; finally fix all operating procedures.

The order of these steps is logical but not sacred. Some steps may be taken simultaneously, some omitted according to which plan is adopted, but as a general treatment the succeeding chapters will adhere to this order.

Should a Consultant Be Engaged? As this work has been developed successfully with and without the aid of consultants it is evident that there are pro and con conclusions on the subject. Furthermore it is possible to use a consultant at the very start of the project and then apply it without a consultant. Perhaps the determining considerations are the size of the company and the resourcefulness of the local management. Certainly a consultant experienced in job evaluation can get right to work without any experimenting. He will usually have a plan which he knows thoroughly and will bring a staff, picked and trained for this particular kind of analytical ability. If the local company can match the consultant in such specialized ability and experience there is little need to bring in the outside service and none of the initial experience will be lost. This factor suggests a combination of consultant and company-employed staff, the former to direct and the latter to carry out the directions. The techniques can be acquired rapidly if the right personnel are assigned to the work, but progress will not be rapid unless the local men are relieved of other duties. Some think that the consultant will have superior prestige. This is often true but the local management must eventually carry on by itself and must sooner or later win employee confidence on its own account. If speed of installation is important perhaps a consultant should be asked to do the whole work of installation; otherwise, we advise a large company to do everything itself and a small company to do all it can under the temporary guidance of a consultant. The matter of tailor-fitting is best served by those who have long known the company ways. Incidentally, the by-product of managerial training which accompanies this kind of work is sufficient reason for a company to do as much as it can itself even if the time of completion is a little later.

A recent NICB survey reports that 50 per cent of all companies employ a consultant, 20 per cent follow their trade association plan, 6 per cent adapt known plans, and 24 per cent develop their own plans unaided.

Description of Analyst's Own Job. When a new program as far-reaching as that of modern wage and salary administration is to be installed it is necessary for top management to write and coordinate the new duties that each official must add to his existing duties. This will not mean much additional work for some officials who are to be involved, but each should know exactly what is expected of him and how far his authority and responsibility will be extended. The head of the new division will, however, have a job that must be set up correctly both as to his place in the chain and as to his relationships with other executives. The Dartnell Corporation in its "Personnel Administration Service Report 65" reprints a job description for a head analyst as follows:

The position of job analyst has been established and is under the direct supervision of the personnel manager. The analyst will act as a technical coordinating head for the company-wide evaluation program. The responsibility of the job analyst will include the following:

1. Instructing and directing in the correct procedure all representatives of management who are called upon to prepare job descriptions.

2. Supervising the development of job descriptions by department superintendents.

3. Reviewing all job descriptions.

4. Evaluating the description of each applicable occupation within the company in accordance with accepted company policy and procedures.

5. Reviewing and securing approval of all evaluations from the department superintendent of jobs within his line of authority.

6. Contacting each department superintendent at regular intervals for the purpose of reviewing each job under his jurisdiction to determine and record any and all changes in job content that may have occurred since the preceding review. Any corresponding changes in evaluation which are required are to be made concurrently.[8]

Cost of Doing Job Evaluation. As the writing of job descriptions is the determinant of the time needed to install job evaluation, so the number of distinct jobs, not the number of employees, is the main determinant of money needed to install it. There are, of course, other influences, such as (1) history of the case, (2) degree of confidence—attitude of union leaders, (3) number and size of plants, (4) extent of application, and (5) thoroughness of the descriptions and specifications. Type of plan seems to make very little difference.

The rate of progress runs at three to four jobs per day but may be slower if long preparation must be included. Thus the installation time will take from three months to six months, usually between

---

[8] See also last paragraph in Chapter 5.

three and four. At the Sperry Gyroscope Company, where a high degree of union participation was welcomed, 23,000 employees on 426 jobs required 64 separate three-hour meetings; these extended over four and a half months. For 7,000 employees S. L. H. Burk found it necessary to employ permanently about eight analysts. Another company reports six analysts to maintain the work for 4,000 employees, 1,000 different jobs evaluated. Still another reports a staff of 25 for 20,000 employees, 400 jobs.

Installation costs are reported in various terms. Those who report it on a man-hour basis say it costs 3.5 cents to 5.3 cents per man-hour. On payroll basis 0.5 per cent of annual payroll has been reported repeatedly. On a job basis $50 has been reported, but some consultants say from $65 to $100. Naturally it costs more to hurry it through by means of consultant services. Certainly it will cost more proportionately for a small company or for one that extends it to supervisory, office, and professional jobs.

The cost of rectifying inequities must also be considered and that is a matter that is likely to be large in some plants and small in others. A survey of representative New England companies indicated that from 21 per cent to 82 per cent of employees were relatively underpaid and it required from 1.8 per cent to 13.5 per cent increases in payroll to eliminate these inequities.

There is better agreement on the cost of operating a program. Most reports say 0.1 per cent of the annual payroll.

3

METHODS AND TECHNIQUES

It is necessary that the plan of job evaluation be so simple and so readily understood that an employee, after being given proper instructions, can evaluate his own job.

—D. W. WEED

Comparison of Methods. The first activity of the newly selected analyst will be to study the plans which seem most suitable, ascertain what companies similar to his own have done, estimate time, cost, and other factors, all of which he will report to the steering committee for decisions. The first decision should be on the extent of application and the second one on choice of method. We classify all methods into five types as follows:

1. Ranking or Grading, sometimes called Labor Classification.
2. Straight Point.
3. Weighted-in-Money, advertised as "*the* Factor Comparison Plan."
4. Weighted-in-Points, *without* separate treatment of universal requirements.
5. Weighted-in-Points, *with* separate treatment of universal requirements.

Two Techniques of Measurement. The only techniques so far developed of measuring the characteristics are:

A. Direct Comparison of Characteristics (outgrowth of Method 1).
B. Indirect Comparison of Characteristics Against Predetermined Degree Definitions, with point allotments (outgrowth of Method 2).

Either one is to be applied successively to each characteristic of a given job. Advocates of A claim that:

1. It holds the analyst's attention to the true objective, that is, the worth of the characteristic required by a job in question relative to the worth of the same characteristic in other jobs.

36

2. It involves no fixed ceiling in point value.
3. It insures against the danger of human let-down which is likely to accompany the use of many long and perhaps vague word measures.

Advocates of B claim that:

1. It forces the analyst to measure all the variables.
2. It can provide much more definite gauging.
3. It sets the gauges once for all and thereby insures against the danger of let-down in standards.

In general, Technique A, Direct Comparison of Characteristics, may be likened to the hand fitting of parts as they are put into an assembly, while Technique B, Indirect Comparison of Characteristics Against Predetermined Degree Definitions, may be likened to the machining of parts within tolerance to fit a set of gauges, in consequence of which the parts are guaranteed to fit into the assembly without hand fitting.

We reserve the term *plan* for a particular application of methods and technique, i.e., the Weed Plan originated at the General Electric Company, which combines Method 5 and Technique A, or the Kress Plan first applied by the National Electrical Manufacturers Association, which combines Method 4 and Technique B. Either of the techniques can be used in connection with Methods 2, 3, 4, and 5. It is true that Technique B has not been used in connection with Method 3, but it is also true that Technique A is frequently used in connection with Method 4 for assembling new jobs into a rate structure originally constructed by Technique B.

The use of *specific examples* for measurement, as in Benge's ladder scale or in Jones's picture illustrations, might be added as a hybrid technique, but it is more in the nature of an ideal to be kept in mind when setting up any kind of job measure.

1. The Ranking or Grading Method. Under this method simple essay descriptions of jobs are made and sorted in the sequential order of their worth *as whole jobs*. The jobs most common to various plants are then checked as to the going rates in the community and the other jobs are rated by interpolation.

Disadvantages:

No one committee member is likely to be familiar with all the jobs.

Appraising each job as a whole does not allow any analysis and cannot be expected to give accurate measures of worth.

The ranking is likely to be influenced by the magnitude of existing rates.

Equal differentials are sometimes assumed between adjacent ranks and that assumption is frequently incorrect.

Very liberal range limits must be provided to correct bad guesses.

Advantages:

It is the simplest of all procedures and therefore takes little time or paper work; direct cost of the application is negligible.

It can eliminate personalities and thereby be superior to old-fashioned rate setting.

If checked with outside standard job descriptions, it can give a practical but rough job classification. If that is the main objective, this is the quickest way to establish it.

It is practical although crude and avoids any hypocrisy of seeming to be scientific.

Some unions prefer it because it leaves more room for bargaining.

DISCUSSION OF GRADING OR RANKING.[1] A majority of the companies which use the grading or ranking method have a job analyst or a member of the personnel department interview each employee, and from that interview make a detailed description of each job or position on a job description form especially prepared for that purpose. Figure 3 is a guide or set of instructions used for this purpose by the American Rolling Mill Company.

In ranking jobs the usual procedure is to select two key jobs because of their extreme difference in value and then to rank the jobs in each department between them. Some companies have a list of characteristics which they consider in making this ranking, such as the following list used by the Socony-Vacuum Oil Company:

1. Difficulty of work.
2. Volume of work.
3. Responsibility involved.
4. Supervision required.
5. Supervision of others.
6. Knowledge, training, experience necessary.
7. Conditions under which work is done.

These are considered not specifically but generally, and the different characteristics are not weighted or given any point value. In some companies this ranking is done by a job analyst especially selected and trained for that work; in others, by a committee, and in still others, by a member of the personnel department. The ranking is then reviewed by the superintendent or foreman of the depart-

[1] Selected from article by J. E. Walters in *Mechanical Engineering*, LX, No. 12.

RECOMMENDATION FOR
OCCUPATIONAL CLASSIFICATION OR RECLASSIFICATION

Occupation Name—Present_____Recommended_____

Section_____Department_____Division_____

Present Zone_____Recommended Zone_____Date_____

Statement of Duties and Responsibilities. (See Reverse Side)

INSTRUCTIONS

Statement of Duties and Responsibilities

1. Describe the kind of work performed; state in some detail the method, process, routine, or manner in or by which work is accomplished. Where work is of a general nature, illustrate with typical tasks. Utilize Bedaux S.P.B.'s where available.
2. State the kind of supervision received and from whom.
3. State the kind of supervision exercised, if any, and over whom.
4. Describe the nature of responsibilities other than supervisory. Consider the extent to which work affects quality of product; the probability of causing delays or damage to equipment; the accountability for conservation of materials such as fuel, steam, air, water, acid, etc.; the possibility of injuring fellow workmen; and related factors.

Statement of Minimum Qualifications

1. Formal education (the amount of schooling or equivalent education).
2. Previous mill or trade experience required; what occupations; length of such experience.
3. Knowledge of equipment design, construction, and operation necessary for assignment to occupation.
4. Knowledge of methods, practice, principles, processes, product, materials, etc., required for appointment.
5. The required knowledge of technical subjects such as chemistry, metallurgy, combustion, mathematics, mechanical drawing, etc.
6. Personal qualifications such as initiative, tact, resourcefulness, dependability, alertness.
7. Physical qualifications—any unusual requirements as to stature, strength, agility, eyesight, hearing, age, etc.

Nature and Conditions of Work

1. Posture—standing, sitting, stooping, etc.
2. Fatigue—requirements for expenditure of physical or mental effort—the tediousness or monotony of the work.
3. Hazard—possibility of injury to operator and the probable severity of injury.
4. Surroundings—disagreeableness of work resulting from unusual heat, cold, dampness, dust, dirt, smoke, fumes, acid, lack of ventilation or illumination, etc.
5. Requirement for skill, accuracy, and dexterity.

Checked: Approved and Recommended By:

Superintendent_____   Works Manager_____

Ass't. to Wks. Mgr._____

Note: Retain one copy and send original and three copies to Staff Supervisor of Compensation and Production Standards.

FIGURE 3. OCCUPATIONAL CLASSIFICATION OR RECLASSIFICATION RECOMMENDATION FORM. (American Rolling Mill Company.)

ment concerned, and revisions are made in the light of discussions of high and low rankings.

The Kimberly-Clark Corporation since 1933 has used six characteristics similar to those of Socony-Vacuum Oil Company but minus Nos. 2 and 7. Furthermore it ranks the jobs jointly with the representatives of the employees. The company feels that this democratic process shows sincerity and brings a better understanding. During all discussions about the job rankings, changes may be made until a final ranking of jobs is agreed upon and approved by the management.

Usually, after the jobs are ranked by departments, a comparison of rankings in each department is made with those of similar departments. Where differences of opinion are shown by this ranking in the different departments, adjustments are usually made after a discussion between the job analyst and the superintendents, foremen, or department heads, resulting in the ranking of jobs in the company as a whole.

2. The Straight Point Method. Under this method work characteristics are selected and written down at the left of each job description card. Across the top five or six degrees are indicated and assigned points in unity increments from zero to four or five. The job is then appraised as to each characteristic and the resulting degree marked. These chosen degree points, zero to four or five for each characteristic, are all added to measure the total worth (see Figure 4). This method made history in two respects: it took the first step toward analysis and it showed the possibilities of prearranged degrees, Technique B.

Disadvantages:

The allotment of unweighted points to the characteristics ignores the fact that some characteristics are much more important than others, hence these are undervalued and the others are overvalued.

Stress is likely to be placed upon the disparate characteristics of a job rather than upon the comparable characteristics in all jobs.

Like the ranking or grading plan, it places too much dependence on the arbitrary judgment of individuals, hence the classification based upon it is still unreliable.

Advantages:

Some analysis is possible and something better than over-all appraisal is likely. The first disadvantage can be obviated by making several subdivisions of "skill." General Foods did just that and continued to use this plan until recently. Procter & Gamble Company is still using such a plan. If a com-

SKILL	KIND	NONE	SLIGHT	AVERAGE	MORE THAN ORD.	EXCEPT.
	MANUAL	●				
	NUMERICAL	●				
	VERBAL					●

INTELLIGENCE	KIND	NONE	ROU-TINE	TRADE JUDG.	SUP. JUDG.	MGR. JUDG.
	TECHNICAL				●	
	PRACTICAL				●	

PERSONALITY	KIND	NONE	LITTLE	ORD.	MORE THAN ORD.	EXCEPT.
	APPLICATION - RELIABILITY - COMPANY INTEREST				●	
	TACT				●	
	FORCE				●	
	ABILITY TO TEACH OR SUPERVISE				●	

TRAINING	KIND	NONE	LIMITED	GOOD	MORE THAN ORD.	EXCEPT.
	TRADE TRAINING				●	
	GEN'L EDUCATION				●	
	EXPERIENCE				●	

REPLACEMENT COST	VALUE	NONE	$10-19	$20-29	$30-39	$40-
	MARKET PRICE				●	
	PRICE PERSON REQUIRED				●	

OPPORTUNITY FOR PROGRESS	POSSIBILITIES	NONE	LIMITED	FAIR	GOOD	EXCEPT.
	WITH COMPANY				●	
	ELSEWHERE				●	
	TRANSFER POSSIBILITIES				●	

COMPANY TRAINING COST	COST	NONE	SMALL	ORD.	MORE THAN ORD.	CONSIDERABLE
	LENGTH OF TIME				●	
	TRAINING LOSS	●				
	POINT VALUE OF RATING	0	1	2	3	4

FIGURE 4. CLERICAL JOB RATING BY THE STRAIGHT POINT METHOD. Department— General Correspondence; Position—Section Chief, Adjustment Section; Job Rating Score—51 points.

pany today does not feel ready for either of the weighted point methods this one may still be used as a makeshift for the transition period.

3. The Weighted-in-Money Method. Under this method the characteristics are selected as in the foregoing and are then directly weighted in money. The weighting is done by ranking a series of jobs on one characteristic at a time, applying a penny value [2] to that phase of each job, and then repeating successively on each other

[2] Promoters of this method soon renamed it "Factor Comparison," which shifts emphasis to the technique.

characteristic. No range of limits need be set for any characteristic and no predetermined degrees need be defined. When the last characteristic is assigned its money weight for the given job, it is necessary only to add the amounts for all characteristics and the sum becomes the money rate for the job.

Disadvantages:

As wage levels change in a community the evaluated rates must be changed by use of a multiplier. If any occupational group develops an exceptional demand-supply ratio, then an extra multiplier must be used, that is, such rates must be doctored differently from those of other groups. In time of rapid change, such as that of 1941–43, the carefully derived relativity of the various worths is likely to be obscured because that relativity is recorded only in terms of money rates which, as job rates, are no longer applicable. Pennies as points lack the detachment of abstract points and using them to measure characteristics is likely to be influenced by constant thought of the total existing rate. It has been claimed that this method avoids the fixing of maximum values for the characteristics. There are no predetermined limits as such but the very absence of predetermined weight ranges necessitates reference to the past rates, that is, what share of the whole job rate should be allotted to a characteristic. When these rates are determined for key jobs, the key jobs become limits for in-between jobs. Finally, any hope of simplicity resulting from bypassing intermediate weights is offset by the necessity of repeated juggling.

Advantages:

It allows unlimited room at the top for any exceptional worth.
It obviates the step of translating from points to money.
In normal times when the relative worth of occupational groups does not change unevenly a single multiplier can be used to keep the whole structure up to date.
Solely because of the Characteristic Comparison, Technique A, it shortcuts all the drudgery of Predetermined Degree Definitions, Technique B, and their repeated use; also it insures close adherence to the relative worth of each characteristic through a whole series of jobs, hence makes possible a direct and reliable classification. The latter is its surest virtue.

4. The Weighted-in-Points Method—Without Separate Treatment of Universal Requirements.

Under this method work characteristics are selected and each is assigned its proportionate share of a potential maximum, i.e., some assumed point value for the highest theoretical job. This value is arbitrarily set at 100, 500, 1,000 points, or higher, as preferred. The Rubberset Company has used 3,500 points. Each characteristic has a weighted maximum value of its own. In turn each characteristic is analyzed in terms of progressive "degrees"; most of them have five. The degrees are carefully defined to match the gradations as variously required by a whole series of jobs from sweeper to toolmaker or perhaps to supervisor. Each degree is then assigned its proportionate share of the maximum points for the particular characteristic (see Figure 5). Each job is studied relative to these predetermined degree definitions, each characteristic is thereby measured in points, and the latter are added to derive the total point worth for each job.

Characteristics	1st Degree	2d Degree	3d Degree	4th Degree	5th Degree
SKILL:					
1. Education	14	28	42	56	70
2. Experience	22	44	66	88	110
3. Initiative and ingenuity	14	28	42	56	70
EFFORT:					
4. Physical demand	10	20	30	40	50
5. Mental or visual demand ...	5	10	15	20	25
RESPONSIBILITY:					
6. Equipment or process	5	10	15	20	25
7. Material or product	5	10	15	20	25
8. Safety of others	5	10	15	20	25
9. Work of others	5	..	15	..	25
JOB CONDITIONS:					
10. Working conditions	10	20	30	40	50
11. Unavoidable hazards	5	10	15	20	25
Total points	100	......	......	......	500

FIGURE 5. POINTS ASSIGNED TO CHARACTERISTICS AND DEGREES. (National Electrical Manufacturers Association Bulletin 43.)

Disadvantages:

This is the most preplanned of all the methods and is at best slow. In fact, it can be overdone, getting into more detail than is justified. In that case it assumes an appearance of being more exact than it is. Analysts do not agree on the relative values.

If the predetermined degrees are not precisely defined and the definitions not conscientiously kept in mind, the results may stray from the correct values. Classification is automatic.

Advantages:

With a limited number of subcharacteristics this method need not be excessive in detail or, if great detail is wanted, the job descriptions can be measured automatically at the source, thereby minimizing the judgment of the analysts (see "Questionnaire Method of Job Description" in Chapter 7).

If the definitions are well made and adhered to, this plan can be operated to attain a high degree of precision. It is by its nature the most analytical and can be the most objective of all the methods. Analysts should vary the values under different circumstances.

As the resulting classification is almost independent of guessing it is favored by many for the original setup of extensive rate structures.

After a "structure" is once built, the correct niche for any new job can readily be found by the characteristic comparison technique, thus short-cutting the original technique of using abstract measures. In fact, job-to-job comparison can always be applied as a final check on automatic classification.

By way of summary we quote A. W. Bass, Jr.: [3]

In the first place, the mere ranking of jobs under each factor contains no significance until these rankings are in some way measured and some abstract measure is obtained which will express the value of jobs in their mutual relationship. The obvious advantage of a detailed analysis is lost if there be no method of measuring the results obtained.

Second, all the factors selected are not of equal importance in contributing to job value. However, by careful weighting, it is possible to represent these varying values, and reflect them in the final point value of the job.

Third, in using points, there always remains a concrete measurable record of the analysis made and, should the rating subsequently be questioned, the actual evaluation always remains and can readily be rechecked.

5. The Weighted-in-Points Method—With Separate Treatment of Universal Requirements. This method recognizes that every job holder must have such underlying assets as a mature and healthy body, a sane and well-disposed mind, and ability to communicate. No job requirements fall below this universal plateau. Therefore, if the point credits for the job at absolute bottom worth are taken as this constant basic worth of all jobs, the variable worth of other jobs need only be measured from that and the difference in points added to the universal point worth to derive the total point worth (see Figure 6). The Characteristic Comparison technique is used with six characteristics. These are given point ranges but there are no subdivisions into degrees. The total of characteristics taken for universal credit is set slightly below the total amount of the characteristics required by the job of least worth. This lifts the zero points to a fixed level for all further measurement. Precedents for this practice have been established in merit rating.

[3] "Evaluating Shop Jobs by the Point System," *The Iron Age*, CXXXVIII, No. 11.

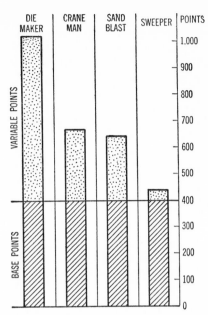

FIGURE 6. UNIVERSAL AND EXTRA POINTS FOR FOUR JOBS. (*American Machinist,*
LXXXIII, No. 9.)

Disadvantages:

Since it is difficult to discern demarcations between the top of the universal
credits and the bottom of the variable credits, except in terms of the job of
least worth, use of Technique of Measurement B is usually not attempted.[4]
Whatever superiority in accuracy that technique might provide is therefore
sacrificed (see Technique of Measurement B).

Advantages:

The method combines the advantages of weighted points, cited under
Method 4, with the advantages of Characteristic Comparison, cited as Technique of Measurement A, and at the same time narrows the range of variability which is to be measured by direct comparison. The concept of this
narrower variability is true to life and the resulting appraisals should give
true if not precise reflections of the existing facts. Additional points may
easily be put on at the top. It is also the simplest of the weighted point plans.

The Procter & Gamble Company of Cincinnati combines a 500-
point "basic allowance" with its straight point plan. Each of the
ten variable characteristics carries 100 points, five of which are
subdivisions of skill.

---

[4] A Cleveland consultant has used this "base factor" and predetermined degree
measurement.

Point Systems in General. In the opinion of W. H. Frater, "Point value systems have an advantage over ranking systems—but a point value system hasn't departed so far from a ranking system, it simply puts the jobs in rank by the technique of taking little pieces, so that the errors are compensating. The result is a more homogeneous and accurate whole." Similar testimony is given by S. P. Farwell: "We have found the point system extremely valuable.

Characteristics	Benge	Kress, National Electrical Manufacturers Association, National Metal Trades Association	Weed
SKILL	1. Mental requirements 2. Skill requirements	1. Education 2. Experience 3. Initiative and ingenuity	1. Mentality 2. Skill
EFFORT	3. Physical requirements	4. Physical demand 5. Mental or visual demand	3. Mental application 4. Physical application
RESPONSIBILITY	4. Responsibility	6. Equipment or process 7. Material and product 8. Safety of others 9. Work of others	5. Responsibility
JOB CONDITIONS	5. Working conditions	10. Working conditions 11. Unavoidable hazards	6. Working conditions

FIGURE 7. COMPARISON OF CHARACTERISTICS IN THREE PLANS

We do not consider that it supplants judgment, but it gives the basis upon which judgment is exercised."

Synopsis of Three Specific Weighted Plans. Methods designated as Nos. 3, 4, and 5 in the foregoing outline are most widely used in American industry and consequently deserve more specific study at this stage of our exposition. The Benge plan illustrates Method 3, the Kress plan Method 4, and the Weed plan Method 5. All three plans may be said to conform to the standard four major characteristics which are subdivided in the plans as indicated in Figure 7.

No. 3—The Benge Plan.[5] This plan was originated about 1928 by Eugene J. Benge, working under "Mitten Management" at the Philadelphia Rapid Transit Co. Some of the principles Mr. Benge followed in preparing his plan are:

1. The evaluation scale should be expressed in cents per hour, not in points.
2. The number of factors on which job judgment should be based should not exceed seven.
3. Job specifications should be subdivided into the same categories as the evaluation scale.
4. There should be no upper limit to the amount allowable for a given factor, thus providing a scale sufficiently flexible to take care of new jobs and of the importance of a single factor (such as the hazard of the overhead lineman's job).
5. There should be some means of comparing each factor of a particular job against that factor in comparable jobs, rather than against a predetermined scale for that factor. After all, the primary object of the whole study is to determine the proper relative standing of all jobs in the company, and it is felt that this end can best be accomplished by making job-to-job comparison, according to a single factor at a time.
6. Repeated judgments of a group of competent persons using the job specifications, and spread over a considerable period of time, should be pooled to yield the final figures.

Mr. Benge says, "by outlining a monetary unit the factor comparison method gets away from an arbitrarily established and undefined unit like that used in the point system." His method, therefore, remains as originated, namely, a "Direct-to-Money Method."

The following are definitions of factors used in the Benge job comparison "scale."

1. Mental Requirements—the possession of and/or the active application of the following:
    a) (inherent) Mental traits, such as intelligence, memory, reasoning, facility in verbal expression, ability to get along with people, and imagination.
    b) (acquired) General education, such as grammar and arithmetic; or general information as to sports, etc.

[5] Eugene J. Benge, "Gauging the Job's Worth," *Industrial Relations,* III, Nos. 2, 3, and 4, and E. J. Benge, "Job Evaluation and Merit Rating," (*Manual of Procedures,* National Foremen's Institute, 1944).

    c) (acquired) Specialized knowledge, such as chemistry, engineering, accounting, advertising, etc.

2. Skill:

    a) (acquired) Specific job knowledge necessary to the muscular coordination only; acquired by performance of the work and not to be confused with general education or specialized knowledge. It is very largely training in the interpretation of sensory impressions.

3. Physical Requirements:

    a) Physical effort, such as sitting, standing, walking, etc.; both the amount of exercise and the degree of continuity should be taken into account.

    b) Physical status, such as age, height, weight, sex, etc.

4. Responsibility:

    a) For raw materials, processed materials, tools, etc.

    b) For money or negotiable securities.

    c) For profits or loss, savings, or methods improvement.

    d) For public contact.

    e) For records.

    f) For supervision, which includes the complexity of supervision given to subordinates and the degree of supervision received.

5. Working Conditions:

    a) Environmental influences, such as atmosphere, ventilation, illumination, noise, congestion, etc.

    b) Hazards—from work or its surroundings.

    c) Hours.

In order to narrow the task for a committee the foregoing general definitions were made in advance. Mr. Benge describes these definitions as "only an outline from which the committee may adopt or may make departures."

Benge Procedure on Key Jobs. The procedure set up by Benge starts with the Job Analysis Record. This is a printed form, on one side of which are listed job details, including descriptions of duties and opportunities. On the reverse side the nature and conditions of work are shown, with their many subdivisions, preceded by boxes for the interviewer to mark.

As a further help to procedure, "Items appearing on Job Specifications" are classified according to Benge's five major characteristics. From these two forms a job specification is prepared, a copy of which goes to each member of the committee. Then each job is treated on a job comparison sheet, by making, first, job-to-job comparisons separately for each of the five major characteristics. This job comparison is made at the start only for key jobs. Approximately twenty-four key jobs are selected, which are ranked according to their mental requirements. The same procedure is followed for skill, physical requirements, and so on. Once these key jobs are arranged according to their values in their various characteristics, the data are entered on a new "Data Sheet for Recording Ranking," and the total of each job is calculated. The findings of the investigation of the four or five members of the committee are collected in a new chart showing the ranks assigned for each job in each of the five characteristics. The findings are totaled and the averages are calculated.

The next step is to distribute the ratings of the tentative key jobs over the five columns. For example, if a job is paid X cents per hour each member of the committee has to ask himself how much of that X cents is being paid for the job's mental requirements, how much for skill, and so on. The total distributed must equal the actual hourly rate. After each member of the committee has recorded his opinion as to the distribution of the rate for each tentative key job, results are summarized, scrutinized, and criticized. The results thus found are entered in a new form, "Allocation of Present Hourly Rates of Tentative Key Jobs." Again the total of the findings of the members of the committee are averaged and put on a new form showing the present rate, the ranks, and the appropriate cent percentage of each total job rate (see Figures 19 to 22).

By comparing the ranks resulting from ranking and from distributing hourly rates the discrepancies which might still exist are ironed out and any odd figures eliminated. Benge claims that the order in which the jobs appear in this last form has been properly determined by the ranking process since the gaps in cents-per-hour between jobs were determined by the allocation of money. "In other words the rankings in each factor have been correctly priced." The votes of a job evaluation committee cited in his writings vary from 82 to 93, that is, 11 cents. For checking purposes Benge uses a scatter diagram showing on the ordinate the present hourly rates and on the abscissa the evaluated rates for jobs. A line representing the consensus of points is taken as the trend line against which subsequent rating is to be checked.

Benge Procedure on Supplementary Key Jobs. In handling supplementary key jobs the ranking technique is omitted. Using the "factor scales" prepared from the original key jobs as reference, each member of the committee and each analyst immediately evaluates each supplementary key job by distributing the average wage being paid to it among the five characteristics in accordance with its estimated importance. If in the opinions of those doing the evaluating the maximum and minimum values assigned to any characteristic of a supplementary key job vary by more than 10 per cent then a discussion is held to reconcile the disparity. After the discussion, the members of the executive committee and the analysts are privileged to change their original estimates and a second evaluation is undertaken. Should the disparity persist after the second evaluation then the supplementary key job is discarded— for developing the scales. Moreover, should this wider comparison seriously challenge the validity of the original key jobs, then they too may be discarded.

The ladder-like scales derived from the original and supplementary key jobs should now progress in fairly even steps. For the higher grade jobs, however, the steps of the scale tend to group together at constantly widening intervals. This phenomenon is attributed to the fact that for the higher grade jobs the differences in each characteristic increase geometrically rather than arithmetically. It is the concerted opinion of Benge, Burk, and Hay that this geometric increase best approximates the geometric series of preferred numbers. Accordingly, for the sake of convenience in evaluating other jobs, they choose to set up standard step values within the scales by superimposing upon them a formula for preferred numbers (see Chapter 11). The ultimate value for "N," namely the number of steps, is determined by trial and error; that is, the value of "N" finally accepted is the one which necessitates the fewest changes from the original data.

No. 4.—The Kress Plan. This plan was developed by the late L. B. Michael and by L. V. Fisher, Western Electric Company, and adapted about 1935 by A. L. Kress, who had had experience in job analysis. His was made the official plan of the National Electrical Manufacturers Association, further developed by the National Metal Trades Association, and copied from all directions ever since. There are eleven characteristics and five degrees for each as shown in Figure 5. In the choice of 500 points for the potential maximum the plan lies midway between the extremes. Of course the fifth degree is never reached for all characteristics in any job. Where the worth of skill is high, the worth of effort is usually low and vice versa; where the worth of responsibility is high, the worth of working conditions is usually low. Thus the highest weight for a job is rarely above 380.

ᵃᵇᵃᵇᵃᵇᵃᵇᵃᵇᵃᵇᵃᵇᵃᵇᵃᵇᵃᵇ

Mr. Kress has written and spoken frequently on all phases of the wages question. We select his early list of principles as printed in 1937.[6]

JOB RATING SHEET

JOB NAME AUTOMATIC SCREW MACHINE OPERATOR DEPT. SCREW MACHINE JOB NO._____

GENERAL JOB DESCRIPTION

Set up and operate automatic screw machines, such as #00, #0 and #2 Brown & Sharpe Single Spindle or 9/16" and 1" Acme Multi-Spindle.

JOB REQUIREMENTS

MAN WOMAN BOY SPEC. AGE REQ. 30-45 years

HRS. OF WK. (IF NOT REG.) Regular

REQUIRED EXPER. PREV. JOBS TIME

APPRENTICESHIP Yes 3 to 5 years on same or similar types of machines

DAY WORK RATE		AVE. HOURLY EARNINGS	OCCUPATIONAL WAGE
START	MAXIMUM		
.85		$1.05	$1.02

JOB ATTRIBUTES	OBSERVERS EVALUATION					
	1ST DEG.	2ND DEG.	3RD DEG.	4TH DEG.	5TH DEG.	POINTS ASGN'D
SKILL						
EDUCATION			✓			42
EXPERIENCE				✓		88
INITIATIVE & INGEN.				✓	ᴬ	56
EFFORT						
PHYSICAL DEMAND		✓				20
MENTAL OR VIS. DEMAND				✓		20
RESPONSIBILITY						
EQUIPMENT OR PROCESS			✓			15
MATERIAL OR PRODUCT		✓				10
SAFETY OF OTHERS			✓			15
WORK OF OTHERS			✓			15
JOB CONDITIONS						
WORKING CONDITIONS				✓		40
UNAVOIDABLE HAZARDS		✓				15

TOTAL POINTS_____ 336

LABOR GRADE____ 3

DETAILED DUTIES

1. Get necessary cams, chucks, tools, etc. from tool crib according to job layout.
2. Set up and adjust machine.
3. Grind and sharpen cutting tools and blades.
4. Operate group 2 to 5 machines depending on work requirements.
5. Determine proper feeds and speeds, where not specified.
6. Maintain tool set-up.

SPECIAL QUALIFICATIONS

1. Work from prints and job layouts.
2. Able to select proper cams, tools, chucks, cutters, blades, etc. if not specified on layout.
3. Work to close tolerances using complicated tool set-ups.
4. Able select proper cutting lubricant.
5. May direct the work of helpers.
6. Education equivalent to grammar school plus 4 years apprenticeship.

SAFETY REGULATIONS AND HAZARDS

Remote possibility of dermatitis from cutting oils and lubricants.

FIGURE 8. AN EARLY NATIONAL ELECTRICAL MANUFACTURERS ASSOCIATION JOB RATING EXAMPLE.[7] (NEMA Industrial Relations Bulletin 43.)

[6] National Electrical Manufacturers Association, *Industrial Relations Bulletin* 43 (1937) and 45 (1938). A Manual and a Guide were published in 1946. The latter was re-edited by this author in 1953.

[7] For characteristics and weightings used by the Wright Aeronautical Corporation, see Figure 24.

Where job rating is used, the following principles should be kept in mind:

1. Rate the job and not the man. The requirements of the job are usually definite and fixed. The man on the job may have plus qualifications or may not quite measure up to the job requirements. A job rating plan should not be confused with any plan to grade employees. The man on the job may be paid more or less than the job itself is worth, in relation to other jobs. Each element should therefore be rated on the basis of what the job itself requires.

2. The elements selected for rating purposes should be easily explainable in terms that will avoid any overlapping which might lead to rating the same qualifications under several headings. The elements should be as few in numbers as will cover the necessary requisites for every job.

3. Success with job rating is absolutely dependent on a uniformity of understanding with regard to the definitions of the elements and on consistency in the selection of the degrees of those elements.

4. Any job rating plan must be sold to foremen and employees. Success in selling it will depend on a clean-cut explanation and illustration of the plan.

5. Foremen should participate in the rating of jobs in their own departments.

6. The greatest degree of cooperation from employees, in job rating, will be achieved where they themselves have an opportunity to discuss the ratings.

7. In talking to foremen and employees avoid discussion of money values. Talk point values and degrees of each element. Discussion of money values will lead to juggling.

8. Too many occupational wages (or rate ranges for given labor grades) should not be established. It would be unwise to adopt an occupational wage for each total of point values.

As we expect to allude to the Kress plan in some of the subsequent chapters, we will represent it here with an early example of results only (Figure 8).

No. 5.—The Weed Plan. This plan was developed by the late D. W. Weed at the General Electric Company. It has been kept simple to a remarkable degree. There are six characteristics, which are not subdivided.[8] Each is defined but there are no predetermined degrees. The Characteristic Comparison technique is used and even that is narrowed to the variations that occur above the amounts of each characteristic which are common to all jobs. The latter amount, or universal credit, is set at four hundred points. The six characteristics and their weight ranges above base are shown in Figures 9 and 10.

[8] They are subdivided for salaried jobs. See Chapter 14.

Characteristic	Relative Weights		
	Low	High	Per Cent
Mentality	0	100	8⅓
Skill	0	400	33⅓
Responsibility	0	100	8⅓
Mental application	0	50	4⅙
Physical application.................	0	50	4⅙
Working conditions	0	100	8⅓
Total		800	66⅔
Universal credit		+400	33⅓

FIGURE 9. POINTS AND PERCENTAGES ASSIGNED TO CHARACTERISTICS, WEED PLAN

Definitions of Characteristics.[9]

MENTALITY. By mentality is meant schooling, acquired either in a formal or an informal way, that an individual must have before he can qualify to learn the job in question.

SKILL. Skill is defined as learning time. By this is meant the total time spent in various assignments that is necessary before an individual is qualified for the job in question, plus the normal amount of time required on the job so that he is competent to do the job in an expeditious manner.

RESPONSIBILITY. Responsibility is measured by the chance of error and its probable cost either in materials or machinery.

APPLICATION. Application, either mental or physical, is the degree and continuity of attention on the job.

WORKING CONDITIONS. Working conditions refer to conditions surrounding a job which make it less desirable than the ordinary job from the point of view of the type of operator required.

The Weed procedure is to begin with a few key jobs that are best known to all raters. Assort these according to the highest and lowest rating in each characteristic. Jobs in between these are selected until a list of some 50 key jobs is developed. Mr. Weed stresses the point that in selecting additional jobs it is essential *that only one characteristic should be considered at a time,* and the rating for these characteristics should be on the basis of one known job. Once the key list has been established and agreed upon, the evaluation then becomes simple and any new job is evaluated in each separate characteristic by comparison with a rating of the given jobs in that characteristic. Actually the highest weight given any job is 1,045 points out of a potential of 1,200.

[9] *Job Evaluation*, a General Electric publication of October, 1942. The plan was discontinued by General Electric late in 1945 but continues in use elsewhere.

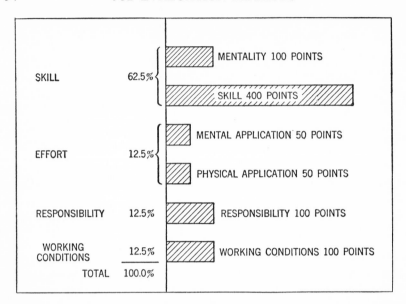

FIGURE 10. THE WEED PLAN FOR HOURLY PAID WORKERS, MAXIMUM VALUES ALLOTTED IN PERCENTAGE FOR MAJOR CHARACTERISTICS, VARIABLE PORTION ONLY. (General Electric Company.)

Example of Choosing a Plan. When the National Metal Trades Association faced the problem of selecting a plan it went through the following experience.

First the association made periodic wage surveys by areas in order to determine if its own wages were higher or lower than others in the same area for comparable jobs. It was found that surveys based on job names alone proved nothing because jobs with the same names, but in different companies, varied widely in character. Next a Job Rating Committee was set up to determine:

1. How companies could appraise their own wage differentials.
2. Whether N.M.T.A. could or should recommend the use of a single job rating plan by all its members.
3. How to improve its wage survey methods so that employers could better appraise their own wage levels.

After due deliberation, the committee decided that valid wage comparisons between plants could be achieved only through the consistent application of a single plan. It was decided that a good plan should possess the following attributes:

Simplicity—simple and easily understood by all involved.
Consistency—in application in each plant and between plants.

Incorporation and weight—of such essential factors as education, experience, and physical effort.[10]

The National Electrical Manufacturers Association had a thoroughly tested plan and the N.M.T.A. decided to adopt it.

[10] *Factory Management and Maintenance*, XCVII, No. 10.

4

CHOOSING JOB CHARACTERISTICS

> When men find themselves confronted with a multitude of problems, such as exist in every trade, and which have a general similarity one to another, it is inevitable that they should try to gather these problems into certain logical groups, and then search for some general laws or rules to guide them in their solution.
>
> —FREDERICK W. TAYLOR

Work Variables That Characterize Jobs. Ever since Taylor pointed out that there is a science of work, even for the simplest work, industrial engineers and personnel staffs have been studying jobs; for a long time, however, no one got around to reducing job requirements to fundamental characteristics. By fundamental characteristics we mean the basic kinds of human abilities and endurances that are required by all jobs but in different qualities and quantities. These requirements have been called man-qualities, job factors, work attributes, etc. We call them *job characteristics* because we think this term connotes that each kind of work composing a job has a composite character of its own. When industrial staffs did arrive at this stage of job study they overdid the matter and included some variables which attached to the plant or the community rather than to the jobs themselves. In any *job rating* program it must be remembered that the job only is being analyzed. *Man rating,* for instance, must come as a separate program (see Chapter 13). Only characteristics which are directly required by a job should be included in a job rating study.

Early Selection of Major Characteristics. One of the first attempts at grouping of characteristics was as follows:

1. Previous training. This division determines the minimum requisite schooling and working experience in order to fit an individual for work in a particular occupation.
2. Inherent demands of an occupation, peculiar to the industry or factory under consideration. This division determines the skill

56

required, accuracy demanded, as well as ingenuity and integrity required.

3. Physical conditions under which the work of an occupation is performed. This division determines health and accident hazards, disagreeable conditions, physical effort, etc.

Obviously there is a serious omission in this selection, namely, the characteristic of responsibility. We are indebted to Samuel L. H. Burk for a much better three. He says,

If you must reduce the number to three, may I suggest that you use the following:

1. Job requirements. This includes the capacities and abilities which the individual must bring to the job and the degree to which the job calls on the use of these capacities and abilities.
2. Responsibility or importance. This includes the 'load' which the company puts upon the individual with the required capacities and abilities and can be measured or weighted from the point of view of the probability of error and improvement and the possible consequences thereof.
3. Working conditions. This includes all the factors which are listed under heading 3 (above), "Physical condition."

Weighting the Characteristics Threw Light on Them. The weighted point system of evaluating the job emerged in 1925. It attempted to overcome or to minimize the disadvantages of the straight point system. Lott,[1] who pioneered in this plan, proposed the following fifteen characteristics:

1. Time usually required to become highly skilled in an occupation.
2. Time usually required for a skilled person in the occupation to become adapted to the employer's needs.
3. Number of men employed in an occupation in the locality—the labor supply.
4. Possibility of an employee locating with another company with a similar earning capacity.
5. Educational requirements of an occupation.
6. Prevailing rate of pay in locality.
7. Degree of skill, manual dexterity, accuracy required.
8. Necessity of constantly facing new problems, variety of work.
9. Money value of parts worked on—possible loss to company through personal errors—unintentional.
10. Dependence that must be placed upon the integrity and honesty of effort of the employee.

[1] Merrill R. Lott, "Wage Scales and Job Evaluation," part of which was published in *Management and Administration*, May, 1925.

11. Cleanliness of working conditions.
12. Exposure to health hazards.
13. Exposure to accident hazards.
14. Physical effort required.
15. Monotony of work.

Eliminating Nos. 3, 4, and 6 as being extraneous [2] to job rating, the remaining characteristics can be grouped under four major headings for comparison with other plans, as follows:

1. Skill—items 1, 2, 5, and 7.
2. Effort—items 8, 14, and 15.
3. Responsibility—items 9 and 10.
4. Working conditions—items 11, 12, and 13.

Eugene Benge's Early Work. Following closely on Lott's work came that of another pioneer, E. J. Benge,[3] who advocated direct weighting into portions of the existing money rate (see Chapter 2). He described his choice of characteristics as follows:

When several hundred job descriptions had been prepared, a list of over 50 items (duties, working conditions, requirements, etc.) was compiled, of which a few are:

1. Education required.
2. Skill—degree and kind.
3. Nature of muscular effort involved.
4. Responsibility for equipment.
5. Hazards.
6. Intelligence level needed.
7. Precision required.
8. Monotony.
9. Time to acquire skill of expert.
10. Age.
11. Physique.
12. Opportunities for savings.
13. Posture.
14. Distractions.

After much thought, it was concluded that all items fell within a classification of five major factors:

[2] Other influences at first included but now left to separate consideration were: prevailing wage, opportunity for advancement, cost of living, and profit of company (see A. S. Knowles and F. C. Means, N.A.C.A. *Bulletin* XX, No. 7). Probably inspired by Weed's universal credit at the bottom, some companies have invented a loosely defined "Job Factor" for the top. It is supposed to compensate increasing difficulty of combining job requirements as job worths ascend. We condemn this as unmeasurable.

[3] *Industrial Relations*, III, No. 2.

1. Mental effort.
2. Skill.
3. Physical effort.
4. Responsibility.
5. Working conditions.

Here we have recognition of five major characteristics which, except for the separation of effort into two characteristics—mental and physical—are in name identical with those soon to be adopted by A. L. Kress.

Breakdown Becoming Crystallized in 1937. A survey [4] made in 1937 of several companies having job analysis programs showed that eleven characteristics were in common use, and these were distributed into the four main groups as follows:

1. Skill
   Scholastic content—7 companies.
   Learning period—13 companies.
2. Effort
   Mental application—2 companies.
   Physical resistance overcome by operator—10 companies.
3. Responsibility
   Seriousness of errors—11 companies.
   Originality of problems—4 companies.
   Degree to which work is supervised—4 companies.
   Teamwork and public contacts required—4 companies.
   Supervision exercised by operator—6 companies.
4. Working conditions
   Hazards and disagreeable conditions—13 companies.
   Expense to operator—2 companies.

Job Characteristics Grouped Under Four Headings. Among the characteristics which have been found to correlate positively with wage rates are: [5]

Scholastic content of the work, length of time typically needed by natively qualified but inexperienced operators to develop proficiency, physical resistance overcome by the operator during the work day, seriousness of possible errors on the job, originality of problems to be solved by the operator, degree to which the work is supervised, teamwork and personal contacts required of the operator, his supervision of others, hazards and disagreeable conditions

[4] J. W. Riegal, *Wage Determination* (Ann Arbor: Bureau of Industrial Relations, University of Michigan, 1937).

[5] J. W. Riegal, Director of Bureau of Industrial Relations, University of Michigan: Bulletin, "Principles and Methods of Wage and Salary Determination," Seventh International Management Congress, 1938.

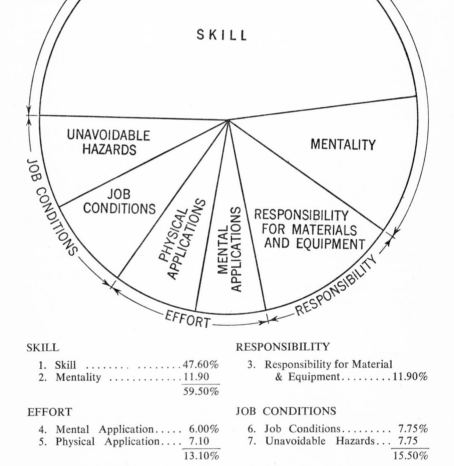

SKILL

1. Skill 47.60%
2. Mentality 11.90
   59.50%

EFFORT

4. Mental Application..... 6.00%
5. Physical Application.... 7.10
   13.10%

RESPONSIBILITY

3. Responsibility for Material
   & Equipment.........11.90%

JOB CONDITIONS

6. Job Conditions......... 7.75%
7. Unavoidable Hazards... 7.75
   15.50%

FIGURE 11. MAJOR AND MINOR CHARACTERISTICS—SOUTHERN CALIFORNIA AIRCRAFT INDUSTRY RESTUDY,[6] EVALUATION PLAN FOR HOURLY PAID JOBS

[6] The original plan of 1942 had the same characteristics but different weights.

which he must withstand at work, and any unavoidable expense caused him by conditions of his employment.

Manual skill has been defined as "the ability to do work marked by precision, speed, and quick, accurate adjustment of motion paths to complex, intricate conditions." If we *stretch this conception to include the knowledge and capability necessary to meet varying conditions together with the capability of improvement* we find that skill so conceived is the most important of the major characteristics in all jobs lying between those classed as unskilled and those classed as supervision. This *broad skill* may be subdivided into mental and physical, into inherent and acquired, etc., but taking it broadly allows us to simplify the breakdown of characteristics, on which the worth of all jobs can be measured. We repeat and delineate these four major job characteristics:

1. Skill—that which must be (with whatever composes it) already possessed by the worker, and additions which must be acquired.
2. Effort—that which the worker must be able to exert in use of both physique and skill.
3. Responsibility—that which the worker must be able to assume.
4. Working conditions—what the worker must hazard and endure.

All these major characteristics are present to some degree in every job, but do not carry equal importance or are not present to the same degree in the various jobs. Basically these characteristics must be treated as potentialities. Willingness to draw on the potentialities comes in response to correct evaluation and incentives.

Critics of job evaluation call attention to the wide variation in point values assigned to the same characteristics. There certainly is a wide variation in point assignments, even when translated into percentages as they should be for comparison. Notice that the revised Southern California Aircraft Industry or SCAI plan, Figure 11, retains several of the point assignments from the Weed plan, but comes out differently percentagewise. The only answer we can make to the critics on this is that conditions vary by industries and localities so that some variance is to be expected. We admit, however, that this can hardly justify the amount of variation between such plans as those of the Southern California Aircraft Industry and the Industrial Management Society as shown in Figure 12, both used more than locally.

Greater Breakdown for Subcharacteristics. If more than a dozen subdivisions seem desirable we recommend that they be made after the first breakdown rather than in advance. This keeps them

SKILL 40%

Points

12 Knowledge of equipment and tools
12 Knowledge of methods
12 Knowledge of materials
19 Length of schooling
10 Judgment—decisions
 6 Initiative ⎫
10 Ingenuity ⎬ Mental capability
 5 Versatility ⎭
 7 Dexterity ⎫
 7 Precision ⎬ Physical skill
———
100

(Adaptation period seems to have been dropped)

EFFORT, PHYSICAL 6.8%

 7 Endurance—exertion
10 Strength, pounds of force applied without mechanical aid
——
17

(Acuteness of senses seems to have been dropped)

RESPONSIBILITY FOR 19.2%

 6 Supervision received
 5 Assigning work (seems to have been added)
16 Safety of others
13 Equipment
 8 Materials
——
48

WORKING CONDITIONS 34%

50 Accident hazards
16 Health hazards
15 Discomfort
 4 Clothing spoilage
——
85
———   ———
250   100%

FIGURE 12. THE INDUSTRIAL MANAGEMENT SOCIETY PLAN (Outline)

in order (see Figure 12) and should show whether or not each item
of the final breakdown is really necessary. McKinsey & Company,
management consultants, have carried this still further and use three
terms to indicate the three gradations, namely, characteristics, components, and factors (Figure 13).

Minor Characteristics Vary from Three to Thirty. While the
"breakdown" into four major characteristics has become almost
universal, there is great discrepancy as to further procedure. For
thorough analysis our pioneers thought that the four major job

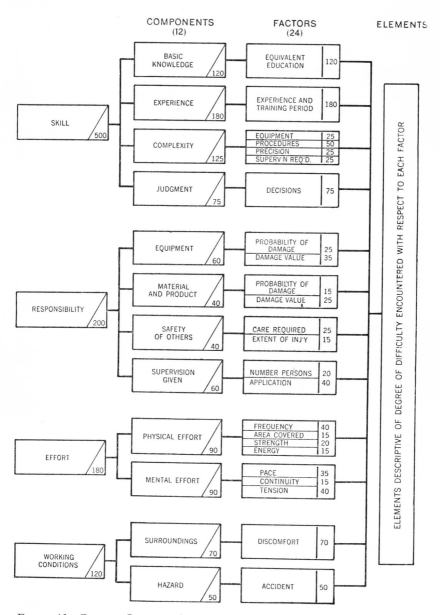

FIGURE 13. GRAPHIC CHART OF JOB GRADATION PLAN. (McKinsey & Company.)

characteristics were too broad and must be subdivided in order to provide a safer method of evaluation. Near the extremes [7] the Weed plan has only six major characteristics (Figure 10) without any subdivisions, while the Industrial Management Society plan has eleven major "attributes" subdivided to make twenty-one in all (Figure 12). In 1940, average practice was found to be nine minor characteristics; but the Kress plan, which uses eleven minor characteristics, has been widely adopted since then so that average practice is probably ten or eleven today.

The Industrial Management Society Plan. This plan, much used in the Chicago area, has eleven major characteristics which are further subdivided to make twenty-one. We have regrouped these for the sake of comparison as shown in Figure 12.

Allotment of Weights in Percentage. The National Industrial Conference Board Bulletin for September, 1940, reported a rather extensive survey made of industries using job evaluation. As this omitted the Kress plan, we present that separately to show the subdivision of the four major characteristics into eleven minor characteristics and how the latter are weighted in percentage (Figure 14). Thus the major characteristics used in 1940 by most industries fell within the following ranges:

1. Skill	27.8%–80.2%
2. Effort	4.7%–22.2%
3. Responsibility	4.4%–35.0%
4. Working conditions	.0%–20.0%

These ranges of importance were unduly influenced by the inclusion of a few exceptional companies. Eliminating these extreme values from the above data, it can be said that the values assigned by 60 per cent of the companies fell within the following ranges:

Major Characteristic	Range of Importance	Median Importance
1. Skill	40.0%–64.3%	50%
2. Effort	10.0%–21.0%	15%
3. Responsibility	20.0%–27.8%	25%
4. Working conditions	10.0%–20.0%	11%

[7] M. F. Stigers and E. G. Reed, authors of *The Theory and Practice of Job Rating*, describe a plan which has thirty-six characteristics. Except for this note we bypass this plan. In an attempt to develop "a complete system designed to give definite results" they have blended motion-time analysis, job rating, man rating, and extrafinancial incentives! Either Johnny or the whole army of management is out of step.

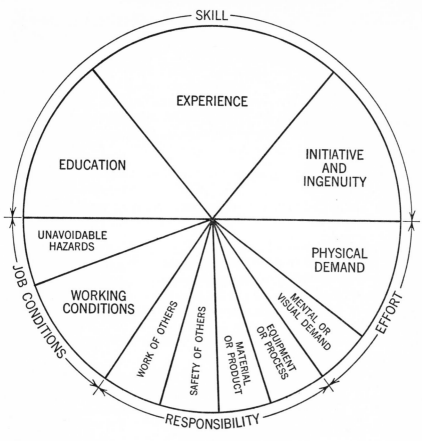

FIGURE 14. MAJOR AND MINOR CHARACTERISTICS—KRESS PLAN, HOURLY PAID JOBS

SKILL

1. Education	....	14%
2. Experience	....	22
3. Initiative	....	14
		50%

EFFORT

4. Physical Demand	......	10%
5. Mental-Visual Demand	...	5
		15%

RESPONSIBILITY

6. Equipment	....	5%
7. Material or Product	.....	5
8. Safety of Others	....	5
9. Work of Others	....	5
		20%

JOB CONDITIONS

10. Working Conditions	.....	10%
11. Unavoidable Hazards	....	5
		15%

The Kress plan allotments, although omitted, come very close to the foregoing median and, if all the companies using this plan were added to the 60 per cent above mentioned, a much larger majority of cases would have approximated the median percentages.

The Standard Pattern. From these studies it seems to be the consensus that all jobs can be measured in terms of the four major job characteristics but that this number is usually not sufficient to measure easily and accurately the small difference between the various job classifications. The use of fifteen or twenty minor characteristics is supposed to give this greater accuracy but entails an extraordinary amount of work when there are hundreds of jobs to be analyzed. Since Benge, Weed, Knowles, and Riegal have all suggested that the number of minor characteristics used should not greatly exceed seven, it might be well to subdivide each of the four major job characteristics into two subcharacteristics, making eight in all. An analysis of various surveys and reports suggests the following subdivisions which appear to be common to most jobs and might therefore be standardized. Standardization of the major characteristics alone brings the advantage of a rough intercompany check on weightings. In suggesting standardization for the minor characteristics we would add a caution against carrying it all the way through point allotment. That at least should be tailor-fitted for each company.

1. Skill
   Mental (intelligence, education, experience, training, reaction time, etc.)
   Physical (manual dexterity, accuracy, etc.)
2. Effort
   Mental
   Physical and/or visual
3. Responsibility
   For people (safety of others, supervision of others)
   For material things (equipment, materials, product)
4. Working conditions
   Hazardous } if either is slight, combine.
   Disagreeable }

For salaried positions the major characteristics may be the same but most of them must be subdivided differently and reweighted.

Where Variations May Be Desirable. In suggesting a standard pattern we have no intention of discouraging variations. In fact, we prefer tailor-fitted programs for all management functions. If a company has ideal working conditions, the characteristics covering that condition might be very little needed. Nevertheless such a job as sandblasting will always need some credit on this characteristic and this job or similar jobs exist in the best-conditioned plants. Then there are extraordinary conditions. The Association of Pulp and

Paper Manufacturers gives 48.8 per cent weighting to responsibility for material and 15.2 per cent to responsibility for equipment while giving only 16.6 per cent to their skill characteristics.

PLANTS A TO I OF ONE COMPANY

	A	B	C	D	E	F	G	H	I
Mentality	100	100	100	100	100	100	100	100	100
Skill	410	345	360	325	360	390	300	350	300
Responsibility	70	50	45	45	60	50	45	55	45
Mental Application	40	40	40	40	40	40	40	40	40
Physical Application....	25	20	15	15	20	20	15	20	15
Working Conditions....	0	0	0	0	0	0	0	0	0

FIGURE 15. VARIATION OF POINT POTENTIALS FOR TOOLROOM JOBS.

Barring extraordinary conditions the need for variation lies mostly in the extension of evaluation from shop to office. Variation may be desired, however, merely to reflect a company's standards as to the class and age of employees which it wants and can get. Even here we believe the main need for variation lies in the apportionment of relative values both as to a characteristic and as to its measures. This need may be expressed as a principle. Keep variations and subdivisions of characteristics to the minimum, alter their definitions to suit plant needs, and let the local management judge the relative values of all minor characteristics, even the degrees. This practice, of course, may be followed within limits set for a whole company. The General Electric Company has found that some of its plants do not run as high on skill as others. The plant where each characteristic runs highest sets the over-all limit (see Figure 15).

The Lockheed Aircraft Corporation has done much to fit plans to its several needs. For hourly paid work it uses the revised Southern California Aircraft plan which was developed to help rapidly expanding aircraft companies at the beginning of World War II. The characteristics and maximum point values are the same as used by the General Electric Company except that the latter's Working Conditions, 100 points, is here divided into Job Conditions, 45 points, and Unavoidable Hazards, 45 points. This change seems to be a Cole influence. Furthermore, the use of predetermined degree definitions is certainly a shift from Weed to Cole technique, but the total potential comes to 790 points. The progressions through the five degrees are by constant multiple except for the two characteristics here mentioned. For them the progression is by a constant addition (see Figure 16a and b).

Characteristics and Degree Values					
CHARACTERISTICS	**1ST**	**2ND**	**3RD**	**4TH**	**5TH**
			DEGREES		
SKILL	See Table on Opposite Page				
MENTALITY . . .	20	40	60	80	100
RESPONSIBILITY FOR MATERIAL & EQUIPMENT .	20	40	60	80	100
MENTAL APPLICATION .	10	20	30	40	50
PHYSICAL APPLICATION .	10	20	30	40	50
JOB CONDITIONS .	5	15	25	35	45
UNAVOIDABLE HAZARDS . . .	5	15	25	35	45

SKILL

SKILL is the technique acquired through training and experience. The amount of skill required for different jobs varies considerably. However, the amount of skill necessary for the satisfactory performance of any job can be measured with reasonable accuracy in terms of the length of time normally required for an average individual of normal mental capacity to acquire the necessary trade knowledge and training.

Training and experience are considered together, and the aggregate item required for both serves as the basis for the assignment of evaluation points. The table below indicates the points allocated to each month and year of experience and training required by the job.

YEARS	POINTS	YEARS	POINTS
Less Than 3 mos.	15	2½	245
3 mos.	55	3	265
6 mos.	95	4	300
9 mos.	125	5	325
1	150	6	345
1½	190	7	365
2	220	8	385
		9	400

MENTALITY

MENTALITY is the prerequisite mental capacity, often measured by extent of education or equivalent, which is initially required of an individual to be capable of learning to perform a given job efficiently.

Depending on the complexity of the job and the degree of mentality required to perform the job efficiently, the following factors are defined:

DEFINITION OF DEGREES

1. Use addition and subtraction; follow written or verbal instructions.

2. Use simple arithmetic such as decimals and fractions; use production illustrations or blueprints for reference or identification of parts.

3. Use algebra and geometry or an elementary science, as applied to simple layouts or standard shop methods; interpret parts blueprints.

4. Use sufficient shop trigonometry or a science to solve problems of moderate complexity; interpret assembly blueprints.

5. Use sufficient shop trigonometry, or a science, to solve complicated problems requiring originality and ingenuity interpret complex blueprints, lofting data, and engineering drawings.

DEGREE	1	2	3	4	5
POINTS	20	40	60	80	100

RESPONSIBILITY FOR MATERIAL AND EQUIPMENT

RESPONSIBILITY for material and equipment is the responsibility required by the job for preventing loss to the Company through damage to equipment, tools, material, or product.

"Equipment and Tools" include stationary and portable machines, material handling equipment, hand tools which are the property of the Company, and all tools, dies, jigs, and fixtures.

"Material and Product" include raw materials, supplies, work in process, and finished parts. Tools, dies, patterns, etc., are considered work in process for the department making them.

EVALUATION PROCEDURE

Estimate the cost to the Company of accidental damage to equipment and tools which could occur in the course of normal performance of the job. Consider only the damage for which the employee would be wholly responsible. Use an average top figure for a single occurrence—not an extreme maximum. Cover the cost of repairs necessary to restore the equipment to first-class operating condition, and estimate the cost of accidental damage to material and product on the same basis.

DEGREE	1	2	3	4	5
DOLLAR RANGE	0 50	51 250	251 500	501 1000	1001 up
POINTS	20	40	60	80	100

FIGURE 16a. SOUTHERN CALIFORNIA AIRCRAFT INDUSTRY PLAN FOR SHOP OCCUPATIONS. (Lockheed Aircraft Corporation.)

MENTAL APPLICATION

MENTAL APPLICATION is expressed as the necessary degree of concentration required by the job. On developmental jobs involving close tolerances and complex mechanisms, mental application would be high, whereas on simple highly repetitive jobs, mental application is reduced to a minimum by the development of a habit cycle of the motion involved.

Depending on the complexity of the job and the degree of mental application required to perform the job efficiently, the following factors are defined:

DEFINITION OF DEGREES

1. Minimum mental application; operations are practically automatic.

2. Light mental application; operations repetitive.

3. Moderate mental application; operations are variable.

4. Very close mental application; highly variable operations involving considerable detail.

5. Intense mental application; extensive detail, requiring utmost care and attention for control.

DEGREE	1	2	3	4	5
POINTS	10	20	30	40	50

PHYSICAL APPLICATION

PHYSICAL APPLICATION is the muscular exertion required by the job, including its degree of continuity and working position.

Depending on the job being performed and the frequency of physical effort required, the following factors are defined:

DEFINITION OF DEGREES

1. Slight physical exertion; intermittent sitting, standing or walking.

2. Continuous handling light weight material; or continuous sitting, standing, or walking.

3. Occasional pushing, pulling, or lifting heavy weight material; or occasional difficult work positions.

4. Frequent pushing, pulling, or lifting heavy weight materials; or frequent difficult work positions.

5. Continuous pushing, pulling, or lifting heavy weight materials; or continuous difficult work positions.

DEGREE	1	2	3	4	5
POINTS	10	20	30	40	50

JOB CONDITIONS

JOB CONDITIONS are the surrounding or physical conditions under which the job must be performed, and which may affect the mental or physical well-being of the employee. These conditions are beyond the employee's control. The following factors are defined:

DEFINITION OF DEGREES

1. Clean working conditions and no disagreeable elements or factors.

2. Slightly dirty working conditions, or general factory noise, but no disagreeable elements or factors.

3. Occasional disagreeable elements or factors, such as heat, cold, dampness, fumes, vibration, irritating noise, etc.; or dirty working conditions.

4. A continuous disagreeable element or factor such as heat, cold, dampness, fumes, vibration, irritating noise, etc.

5. More than one disagreeable element or factor which is continuous, or a combination of such elements or factors as those listed under the above degrees.

DEGREE	1	2	3	4	5
POINTS	5	15	25	35	45

UNAVOIDABLE HAZARDS

UNAVOIDABLE HAZARDS are the accident and health risks involved in the performance of the job. Depending on the possibility of occupational hazards inherent in the job, the following factors are defined:

DEFINITION OF DEGREES

1. Work having very little accident or health hazard.

2. Exposure to very minor accident hazards, such as minor abrasions, minor burns.

3. Exposure to accident hazards such as severe burns and cuts.

4. Exposure to accident hazards such as broken bones, eye injuries, hernia, loss of fingers.

5. Exposure to accident or health hazards involving permanent disability or necessitating removal to another occupation.

DEGREE	1	2	3	4	5
POINTS	5	15	25	35	45

FIGURE 16b. (Concluded.)

Shift from Skill to Other Characteristics. Since 1940 there has been little change in choice of characteristics, but if several recently revised plans indicate anything they indicate that less weight may now be needed for skill and more for responsibility. This seems reasonable because we know that more skill is being transferred to highly specialized machines, and such jobs in turn carry heavier responsibility. See the accompanying tabulation.

Plan	Percentages			
	Skill	Effort	Respon-sibility	Working Conditions
Boeing Aircraft Co........	45.3	16.0	25.2	13.5
Krauter Webber Tool Works	40.0	21.0	29.0	10.0
Western Electric Co.......	39.0	19.5	23.2	18.3
Army Air Force	37.5	25.0	25.0	12.5

In a radio parts factory E. N. Hay found that a reduction of skill items to 30 per cent was necessary to serve the local needs. Messrs. Clerk Kerr and Lloyd H. Fisher have suggested that there may be a shift from skill to the "disutility" factors such as hazard and job conditions.[8]

Weighting Given Skill a Major Influence. As early as 1942 the General Electric Company concluded that skill could be accurately measured by learning time, that is, "the total time spent in various assignments that is necessary before an individual is qualified for the job in question, plus the normal amount of time required on the job so that he is competent to do that job in an expeditious manner." Their manual of that year also tabulated total points and skill points for their jobs. The ratio of these two values was by no means constant, but with numerous exceptions there was a suggestion of parallelism. Other analysts had, of course, realized that, because skill was usually assigned a high proportion of the points, it tended to dominate the total number of points. They made no move, however, to discard other characteristics because they knew that there are always a few jobs which have unusual combinations of requirements. Most analysts would be only too happy to use fewer characteristics if they were sure no injustice would result. In the meantime some psychologists have advocated drastic simplification, in

[8] "Effect of Environment and Administration on Job Evaluation," *Harvard Business Review*, XVIII, No. 3.

fact they have conducted elaborate experiments to prove that three or four characteristics would do as well if not better.

Dr. C. H. Lawshe, Professor of Psychology, Purdue University, began his experiments in 1943. His first observation was that in an unnamed aircraft engine plant there were two clusters of characteristics in use, namely:

1. Education, Learning Period, Initiative and Ingenuity, and Responsibility for Work of Others.
2. Unavoidable Hazards, Responsibility for the Safety of Others, Working Conditions, and Physical Demands.

The rating on any one characteristic in a cluster he suspected would predict the rating of the other ones in the same cluster. The first cluster he has named "Skill Demands Factor" and the second "Job Characteristics." This nomenclature is unfortunate because if those in the first cluster are not also job characteristics they do not belong in a job study. His next observation was that the first cluster contributes 90 per cent of the variance in total points while the second cluster contributes the remaining 10 per cent. This is no surprise for many jobs except in the idea that job values, when averaged, should retain much significance. At least he reports this ratio for six plants separately and they spread from 99 to 77.5. Did individual jobs in a single plant spread as much? It would not take that much spread to invalidate such an idea as a means of deciding the worker's pay.

Lawshe's Abbreviated Formula. Of more moment than the foregoing is Lawshe's use of two characteristics from the skill cluster with one for the conditions cluster and the working out of a multiplier for each of the three, which, multiplied by the respective point value and filled out by a constant, would when totaled proximate the total point value as derived from the full number of characteristics. The formula is as follows:

Abbreviated	Education	Experience	Hazard
Rating $= 2.0$	Rating $+ 1.4$	Rating $+ 5.4$	Rating $+ 30.4$
Illustrations			
of one job $= 2.0 \times 42$	$+ 1.4 \times 66$	$+ 5.4 \times 5$	$+ 30.4 = 233.8$

This job rated by the NEMA plan was third degree for the first two characteristics and first degree for the last. The original point value from totaling eleven characteristic values was 236. Hence Lawshe's abbreviated formula was only 2.2 points short. When the same formula was applied to all 247 jobs in an airframe plant all but seven jobs were within 22 points of the original ratings. NEMA uses 21 points per grade and one point clearance. The present writer applied this formula to 35 jobs that NEMA had used for instruction purposes and found the results disappointing. "Abbreviated ratings" ran from 42 points below the original rating to 46 points above. Twenty-one of the jobs came within ± 10 points of the original values so that they would have a chance of remaining in their proper grades, while 8 other jobs, if not more, of the 24 jobs which were out more than half of a grade range would have to change grade. The good and bad results had less evident relationship to grade than to type of work.

Lawshe's Four-Item System. The four characteristics chosen by Lawshe for his short-cut system [9] are: (1) Learning Period, (2) General Schooling, (3) Working Conditions, (4) Job Hazards. After specifying degrees and points, five analysts rated forty jobs by the simplified system and another five analysts rated the same jobs by the NEMA system. Groups of five ratings were averaged to cancel individual variation. The two sets of average ratings were then compared. On 38 per cent of the jobs there was perfect agreement, but on 88 per cent of the jobs the two systems deviated by one (or less) labor grade, and on 97 per cent of the jobs by two (or less) labor grades. Lawshe then raised the question: "Had the two groups of analysts used a single system, how extensive would the discrepancies have been?" To answer this he made comparisons of rating within each separate system and found that the percentages were similar, although a little less so, within the NEMA results. The most surprising part of the research to this writer is that within each system the analysts made the same grades for only 35 per cent of the jobs by the NEMA system. It was 43 per cent for the simplified system. Properly experienced analysts are expected to make a more trustworthy showing. Lawshe indicates, and we agree in this, that unnecessary characteristics lessen the likelihood of reliable rating. Doubtless our pioneers started us off with too many and we now find it difficult to retract. Along this line Lawshe says, "If the employees, or the organized labor representatives, or the members of management or supervision hold the opinion that certain items ought to be included in a particular scale, this attitude cannot be ignored."

A Proposal for Using Five Characteristics. Instead of trying to compact all characteristics into two clusters and then subdivide them

[9] "Personnel Series N. 119," *Journal of Applied Psychology*, XXVIII, XXIX, XXX; also T. A. Ryan, *Work and Effort* (New York: The Ronald Press Co.. 1947).

into four, we propose that the generally recognized four major characteristics be used, with a subdivision of skill only to make five. We would accept Lawshe's selection of skill subcharacteristics, but rename them:

(1) *Mentality* and (2) *Experience* (i.e., learning period).

We would then add: (3) *Responsibility* and let each plant decide what kind of responsibility is most important for its type of jobs. Then we would insert: (4) *Effort* (i.e., mental and/or physical or visual as each type of work would most need). Finally we would include: (5) *Working Conditions* (i.e., hazard and/or disagreeable unavoidables).

Reversion to the major characteristics would retain the four kinds of needs which all successful analysts have considered to be present to some degree in most jobs. Subdivision of skill, almost always the predominate need, would bring qualitative balance impossible to obtain by weighting any one part of skill.

The specific inclusion of responsibility and effort assures that jobs which run high on those points would not be slighted. The omission of these as independent variables is undoubtedly the reason why Lawshe's experiments fail to show consistent rating for some jobs. Using a single item for working conditions and hazards might require a choice between the latter, but we cannot have our cake and eat it too. If it is worth while to simplify we must do some boiling down and the total weighting for this "cluster" has rarely been given a high rating. We have not even considered the relative weighting that these five characteristics should have, but the allocation of points could be kept close to what has been found satisfactory for the four clusters which they represent. As heretofore we think each plant ought to analyze its own needs and make its own measuring scales to meet those needs (see "The Standard Pattern," page 66).

Some simplification can be gained wherever the number of degrees can be reduced. This should not be done, however, without deliberate consideration. As long as there is any doubt it is safer to set up or retain the larger number of degrees.

5

SELLING THE PROJECT

The selling of job analysis and its administration to foremen and key workers is primarily a problem of insuring their collaboration at all possible points.

—W. R. COLEY

The Idea Must Be Acceptable. Before proceeding any further in planning the project it is advisable to anticipate the various kinds of opposition that might arise from middle management, from the supervisors, or from the labor representatives. This project will materially affect all concerned and it is not wise to complete plans without the support of all such key individuals, first those composing the committees and eventually those less immediately concerned. Of course a sales campaign presupposes something definitely completed to sell but in this case the general policy and broad principles for putting rates in order on a preplanned factual basis, in short a project, must suffice. Besides uncovering all possible objections, and forestalling resistance, it is important to bring out all pertinent suggestions.

Conceivably the proposal to start job evaluation might originate from a staff man, a director, or even a union official. William Gomberg [1] cites the case of the Commercial Telegraphers Union, which asked Western Union to install a job evaluation program in order to resolve the conflicting claims made upon the union leadership by the various craft members, each striving for his advantage in the collective negotiations. In such cases top management itself must be sold on the proposal. Management's interest would include: harmony of industrial relations, initial and operating costs, length of time required to get going, and the prospects for permanency. These men would usually be conversant with the history and success of the project elsewhere. If top management should not be aware of these things the selling party would have a diplomatic job of the

---

[1] William Gomberg, *A Labor Union Manual on Job Evaluation* (Chicago: Labor Education Division, Roosevelt College, 1947).

first magnitude. Suffice it to say that citations from successful installations elsewhere, a scatter diagram of the present job loci, together with cost estimates, representative reactions, and similar data should be enough to sell top management. We are much more concerned with the problem of selling from top on down and across the bargaining table where selling job evaluation is a matter of gaining confidence and imparting instruction. Even here there is likely to be a two-way traffic.

Extension of Committee Organization. Since the committee form of organization is necessary for the initial part of this project, a committee for each major department should be undertaken at this early stage and all such committees used as clearing houses for pro and con opinions. The top "steering" committee can start this move by calling in the department heads to hear the aims and general plan of procedure explained. They should be encouraged to express themselves and their suggestions should be taken into account. Perhaps the attitudes here displayed and the degrees of constructive resourcefulness evinced will be the best guides to deciding which persons should be put on the various departmental committees. Some individuals may honestly doubt the claims for the project; occasionally one will be motivated by jealousy regarding his traditional right to manipulate rates, and some may be apprehensive of union opposition. Some foremen like to increase rates, dislike to reduce them, causing inequities to predominate on the high side. If such is the case show them how systematic evaluation can bring correction.

Selling the Project to Department Heads and Supervisors. Answers to the first objection—that the project may not be all that is claimed—can be in the nature of citations from successful achievements elsewhere or, better yet, the exposure of haphazard rating within their own departments. This is not hard to do. For instance, among reported installations:

An exceptional case resulted in:		A more typical case resulted in:	
Lowering	39.3% of all jobs.	Lowering	20.0% of all jobs.
Raising	43.9% of all jobs.	Raising	30.0% of all jobs.
Total changes	83.2% of all jobs.	Total changes	50.0% of all jobs.

These data mean that in the two cases cited only 17 per cent to 50 per cent of all jobs were already rated correctly and remained unchanged.[2]

[2] One survey found that from 16 per cent to 64 per cent of jobs were within correct limits, 1.7 per cent to 17 per cent above range, and 21 per cent to 82 per cent below range.

If the management has already practiced job analysis, the supervisors will know that the job descriptions and classifications have been valuable as guides to hiring, transfer, and promotion. Evaluation on the same impersonal basis should appeal to them as the next logical step in a more complete plan for job control. The fact that all decisions are the results of collective study should be welcomed as a sharing of responsibility. If the plant has not developed good job analysis, of course, the selling must include that step and may be a large order. Fortunately job analysis is now so generally in use that only certain new or isolated plants are unfamiliar with its advantages.

As to the second objection—loss of freedom in manipulation of rates—the supervisors can be shown that they will participate in the new ratings and that their recommendations will always have consideration, that only guessing and ill-considered requests will be out. Probably they know full well that much of the information must be contributed by them. Acknowledge this and use it as a means of clinching their full cooperation. Explain the operating procedures so they may see that they will no longer be liable to suspicion regarding favoritism. Most foremen will welcome this better way of adjusting rates if the management presents it tactfully and clearly. Two courses may be followed. The policy and procedure may be explained to the foremen at a group meeting, or the essentials may be explained individually to each foreman. Whichever course is followed, the value of the project and the reasons for adopting it should be thoroughly explained.

The third objection—that of union misunderstanding—can best be answered by the management's inviting the union to send a selected representative to sit permanently as a member of each departmental committee. We think that from now on this step will be increasingly important for the solving of all management questions that closely affect labor relations. If management is not ready to share this responsibility it can at least invite union representatives to sit in unofficially. In some situations management cannot expect to sell job evaluation to the employees, but one or more union officials can do so if convinced that the proposal will be beneficial.

Considerations of the Union. The fundamental union principle of "standard rates" has long pointed toward modern job evaluation. In 1921 there was a demand on the Council of the AF of L "to attempt to determine a more sound basis for wage adjustment," and in 1944 it was the United Steelworkers of America, CIO, that demanded similar pay for similar work. That led the National War

Labor Board to order a job evaluation system for the whole steel industry. It does not follow, however, that unions will welcome every job evaluation plan, or the best of such plans, regardless of other questions. Some of the other questions are:

1. Have other management policies been enlightened and considerate?
2. Have these policies been carried out by all representatives of management honestly, faithfully, and with friendliness?
3. Is any conflict likely between this new policy and the union rules for layoff and discharge?
4. Will merit rating supplement the plan and if so will that development lead to transfer and promotion regardless of seniority?
5. Because the job, not the man, is evaluated will the plan lead to introducing high-skilled men on less-skilled jobs, men who can be transferred later to other jobs?
6. Will the plan make more job grades within a family of jobs, thereby degrading all but the top layer and reducing the number of employees per grade?
7. Are there to be separate rates for women? Are men's jobs to be broken in two and both jobs rerated lower as a consequence? Under what conditions will any rate be decreased?
8. Will the union through its official representatives have any voice, other than through grievance procedure, in the establishment and operation of the plan?
9. Will such a factual predetermination of rates curtail collective bargaining, retard, freeze, or accelerate adjustments?
10. Will the plan extend to incentive rates? If so, how will it affect them, particularly the rates on new and untried jobs? How will it affect the guarantees?
11. Will it affect the system of settling grievances? If so, favorably or unfavorably to union interests?

Winning Labor Support. To win wholehearted labor support all these questions must be frankly faced and specifically answered.

Questions 1 and 2 will already have been answered and, if answered negatively, the resulting lack of confidence, or downright suspicion,[3] may take years to overcome, and may prevent any at-

[3] In the opinion of William Gomberg, "the principal barrier is a suspicion of the hocus-pocus of the company-paid technician. If the union gets its own paid technician, not in order to do the whole job, but to work with the management technician, you have 99 per cent of the men's resistance overcome. To allow such an arrangement you have got to overcome the opposition of your own top management first; get it clear as to what constitutes management's prerogative and what constitutes union prerogative."

tempt at job evaluation for the present. Even when the company
record is good, an ambitious union leader may delude himself and
others that before the entrance of the union the management had
been autocratic and mysterious in its dealings with labor but, now
that union protections are in force, unfair tactics will be headed off
as they arise. That kind of leader wants his union members to owe
him for all that is desirable, crediting management not at all. In
this situation a management may not be blocked from its desired
project but it will have to bear with a lot of play-acting until consistent managerial square dealing has extended over sufficient time
to convince the rank and file that there is no cause for distrust.

In short, selling must be a continuous process and every supervisor must be trained and retrained to carry out policy to a perfection that will necessitate very little apology. This training should
be done anyway. Matthew Woll said, early in 1944, that "intelligent
American workers will not be deluded by demagogic slogans."
Fortunately there are many of these intelligent American workers.
There is also evidence that they are gradually improving union
leadership and *good labor leaders* appreciate *good management*.
If they are consulted early in the development of job evaluation
their approval and whole-hearted support can be won. But they too
will want all questions answered, at least in principle, so that they
can in turn win over members of their unions to approve and cooperate.

Conflicts with Union Rules. There is nothing in job evaluation
proper that should affect, under Question 3, either layoff or discharge, except possibly changes in the number of job grades. If
such changes are involved then the governing rules might need to
be recorrelated; in fact, that would be expected. Merit rating, which
is often correlated with rate ranges to determine individual differentials, does directly affect layoff and discharge. Hence if merit rating
is not ruled out by seniority arrangements, the union and management must do some revamping. Whatever way this matter may be
settled it need not upset the essential steps to job evaluation.

Effects on Merit Rating. Certainly merit rating, Question 4, is
needed to determine when, and how much, an individual has improved relative to the qualifications required for base rate. This
step provides an additional layer on top of the derived job rates.
It is by far the fairest guide to promotion and to transfer, and is,
therefore, something of an incentive toward self-improvement of
individual worth (see Chapter 13). Without it the time-paid worker
must fall back on the favor of a foreman or the dropping out of

those ahead of him—seniority. If seniority rules leave no room for consideration of merit, then of course there is little use for merit rating and the consequent top layers of differential. This clash must be settled by bargaining.[4] If seniority is invoked only when merit is equal, then there should be very little trouble because good man-rating can be substantiated. In the former case rate ranges will be much restricted, perhaps disappear altogether, but we have seen job evaluation do surprisingly well on "pin-point" rates, no merit rating. So this problem can be solved to suit the most antimerit unionists without sacrificing the essentials of job evaluation. After all, job evaluation is job rating, not man rating.

High-Skilled Men. As to the introduction of high-skilled men on less-skilled jobs with subsequent transfer to higher-skilled jobs, Question 5, the management should point to the principle of keeping all skill at its highest level. That is, management's aim should coincide with the union's aim, both subject to expediency. Thus the answer to this question, as in the case of Questions 1 and 2, is to correct management policies and convince the union that management is not interested in trickiness, and will not allow any policy, principle, or control to be subverted.

Job Grades Within a Family of Jobs. The number of grades, per family of jobs, Question 6, is likely to be changed in the process of setting up job evaluation since an orderly classification is to take the place of mere traditional classification. When such changes have real significance it should be possible to win union approval by showing those concerned a "picture" of the proposed structure and by giving them all the facts. If there is no ground for suspecting that management is trying to upset seniority, a union is likely to accept this kind of change for the same reason that management wants it, namely, equal pay for equal work. If the effect on seniority is too pronounced to be acceptable, then management will have to compromise or retain the traditional classification. The sacrifice would be annoying but not completely upsetting. Job classification is a superstructure on job values. The substructure need not be disturbed and eventually the superstructure can be harmonized (see Chapter 11).

Rates for Women Workers. The custom of having a separate and lower set of rates for women's jobs, Question 7, is by no means ended by the wartime attempts to include them under "equal pay for equal work." Not only do some regular women's jobs remain as

---

[4] Recently the United States Supreme Court gave unions the right to bargain on merit ratings as well as the use of them.

they were but many jobs formerly held by men have been divided to make more jobs available for women. This practice is necessary in wartime but it must be kept clear of the suspicion that it is done perversely, that is, to put both jobs on lower rates. In other words, such jobs must be treated as new jobs, honestly described and evaluated so that the union representatives can endorse the conclusions. If such division of jobs is temporary, it may be helpful to indicate the change as temporary and retain the descriptions of the original men's jobs to assure the union that the original jobs are to be put back in force when the excessive need for women employees has passed.

Out-of-Line Rates. As to adjustment of out-of-line rates, those which are higher than standard should be left untouched for present recipients, to be corrected as new individuals are brought in. Present recipients are usually trained for upgrading. If not upgraded, such overpaid individuals become ineligible for subsequent general increases. It is customary for transfers to take the downgraded rates but neither transfer nor layoff should ever be used to take advantage of present employees. All these principles must be explained *and followed!*

Union Participation. The extent and nature of union voice, Question 8, is primarily up to management. We have already advocated that some voice be given and given early if the union will accept it. We believe this should be arranged not merely as a negative expedient but as a positive opportunity to get all viewpoints on the development of the plan.[5] The workers often know a lot more about their jobs than will ever be learned by all the office analysts. Suggestion systems, "Nelson committees," and the like, have proved this repeatedly. Furthermore, when a union representative is put to work on a management problem he soon finds that management knows more about its job than has been realized by labor. In short, a worker can contribute real facts, he will gain respect for management, and he will come to believe in the plan he has helped to create—all of which will result in his having the knowledge and the interest to explain, correct, and defend the plan as may be needed.

This aid and support can be a tower of strength in time of trouble. Somewhere along the route someone has to do a lot of explaining to individuals or to small groups as to why one job rate, not another, is

[5] Paquette and Fraser, "Labor Management, Joint Development and Joint Application of Job Evaluation," *Advanced Management*, VIII, No. 3. Also N. L. A. Martucci, "A Case History," *Personnel*, XXIII, No. 2.

to be increased. If the shop stewards are prepared to take on this duty it is likely to be done with a minimum of friction. If management is afraid of losing some of its prerogatives it should realize that the final step of rate setting is definitely included or implied in all definitions of collective bargaining, that an unsatisfactory wage rate must sooner or later come out in the open and hence might better be bargained over as part of an orderly plan, rather than as an isolated grievance regardless of plan. Surely this much participation will not undermine the essential authority of competent management.

One very large union demands that master copies of all job descriptions, values, and rates be handed over as developed and this union prefers to dispute rather than to assume any share in shaping a plan. Another large union has fought for and won a joint union-management arrangement through which extensive researches are undertaken in the interests of better management. In other words the latter union has taken over a share of management prerogatives. Most unions are between these extremes, and will dispute or cooperate as opportunity presents. All unionized shops today have some kind of machinery for settling grievances and about 90 per cent of the grievances involve wages. Thus all unions have some degree of veto in operating any plan for setting or adjusting job rates. Since one of the main objects in job evaluation is to eliminate isolated treatment of individual cases, a new installation of job evaluation should be protected by new rules for grievances arising out of it. These rules must be bargained and new policies should outline clearly just what will be done in all likely situations, that is, the plan itself must provide for adjustments based on facts. The union voice will then be confined to presenting and proving the facts. We believe unions will learn to respect this setup as infinitely more just than depending on pressure regardless of facts.

Influence on Collective Bargaining. The effects of job evaluation on bargaining, Question 9, are considerable in that the rates for specific jobs other than key jobs may eventually be excluded from bargaining altogether.[6] The levels for each occupational grade must usually be left to bargaining as heretofore. Even without job evaluation, union agreements, which terminate on definite dates, have rarely provided completely for wage rate adjustment, that is, in normal times. It is considered sufficient to adjust wage levels at the time a new agreement is bargained, usually once a year. In times of rapid price change or of business uncertainty many agreements do

---

[6] A few union leaders take advantage of a mistakenly high rate by insisting that it is correct and all other rates in the class are wrong. This is as bad trickery as anything to which management has ever stooped.

provide for wage adjustments within the life of the agreement. Such short-time provisions are either permissive or automatic and may authorize increases only or may set a lower limit for decreases.

The *permissive type* usually permits periodic renegotiation every three to six months. In some instances renegotiations are allowed whenever either side can convince the other that a substantial change in prevailing rates, in cost of living, or the like, has taken place. Ten to fifteen days' notice is specified to allow time for bargaining, and arbitration may be specified as the basis of solution. Some agreements call for a periodic review of prevailing rates in the community or among competitors. Frequently the management agrees to maintain wages at an average level equal to, or above, that of other competitors. Occasionally renegotiation is required whenever the price of product or profit of the employer shows a substantial change, and a few agreements allow renegotiation whenever a decided change in general economic conditions can be demonstrated, such as inflation or deflation.

The *automatic type* is designed to adjust wage rates to purchasing power, to the ability of an employer to pay, or to escalator arrangements. Neither unions nor employers are keen for such automaticity because the theoretical flexibility may prove to be inflexible itself, that is, may freeze standards at existing levels or may involve excessive retroactive adjustment. Since job evaluation is a semiautomatic operating control of job grading, a union may fear that it will freeze present rates and retard any advance. The answer to this fear is to explain the whole procedure of community surveys (see Chapter 10).

A further reassurance can be secured by making a place for union-made surveys. This right is already common where there is machinery for hearings before an "impartial chairman" or other form of mediation and arbitration. Thus the essential bargaining is in no way hampered, but if the union has had a voice in shaping and accepting the plan most of the bargaining can be confined to the levels of key job rates. The rest will be worked according to plan and every employee will know that all individuals will be treated impartially under that plan. Unions have usually fought discrimination. If they are confident that the plan is well conceived and will be strictly followed, they will find that bargaining can be simplified without harm to their rights. The agreement itself can be shorter and decidedly more definite. Hence there will be less difficulty in interpreting the agreement and there will be fewer grievances.

Report on the Most Outstanding Case of Participation.
Elmer J. Maloy, Director, International Rate Adjustment Committee, United Steelworkers of America, has reported on the achievement of installing job evaluation jointly in the basic steel plants:

The problem of educating the vast number of people in the administering of this program was another major undertaking. The Union found it necessary to establish Rate Adjustors in each District, composed of competent Staff Representatives. We operated a school for these staff people for a full week and later sent International Committee people to each District to aid each of the three-man committees set up in each plant of the Companies where the Manual was agreed to. The fact that 150,000 jobs were classified by mutual agreement is a tribute to the very fine job done by the Rate Adjustors and Local Committee members, as well as the Top Committee in each Company. The Steel Manual, with its many adjustments, is now constructed to classify adequately any type of job found in the Industry.

Then in the summary of his report he says,

1. Job Descriptions for Bench Mark Jobs and for Gary Specimen Jobs were checked and approved by the Top Joint Committee in the United States Steel Corporation. All other Job Descriptions were prepared by the Company and negotiated locally by the grievance Committee of the Union and the Plant Superintendents. This procedure was also followed in all the other Companies.

2. The Steel Manual and all Bench Mark and Specimen Jobs were negotiated by the Top Joint Wage Rate Inequity Committee for U. S. Steel Plants. All other classifications were negotiated locally by a Joint Plant Inequity Committee composed of 3 members from the Union and 3 members from Plant Management. This procedure was also followed by all other Companies and Union Committees.

3. All disputes of job descriptions or classifications were settled by the Top Joint Committee or referred to Arbitration. It is a tribute to the honesty of purpose and the cooperative spirit of both sides that of the 150,000 jobs described and classified, a fraction of 1 per cent were referred to Arbitration.

4. A maximum of Union, Company and employee participation was used in the over-all program. I believe from the satisfactory results obtained that no part of the program should be done unilaterally by the Company, unless it is the preparation of descriptions and classifications, if the employees are to have the feeling that the program was installed fairly and honestly. In many small companies, the Union even wrote the descriptions and classifications to save the Company the expense of engineering consultants.

5. Finally, I believe the Companies and the United Steelworkers of America should make every effort mutually to maintain the splendid relationship of jobs brought about by the completion of the Program, and also the cooperation that was so manifest throughout all these negotiations.

Relation to Incentive Rates. Job evaluation should include base rates for incentives, which is the point raised in Question 10. Bonuses and premiums accentuate the importance of the rates upon which they are based. Hence unions have learned to be specific about these features in their agreements or to guard them negatively through grievance clauses. For some time many unions have been demanding the right to negotiate in advance all new incentive rates and from day to day all changes in such rates. This right has been generally conceded in the clothing, millinery, hosiery, shoe, and small steel products industries and some of these establish city-wide price schedules. A lesser degree of participation is being demanded in many other industries in the determination of piece rates. This perpetual bargaining is usually done in grievance committees and is not allowed to substitute for the regular negotiations over general wage levels described above. Advance notice of any proposed change in incentive rates, twenty hours to two weeks, is required to allow study of the facts. Employers are reluctant to make such advance announcement because it takes times to develop operative automaticity, and rates that may seem tight often prove adequate when the newness is worn off. The union may recognize this fact by allowing a thirty-day trial period at the end of which any questioned rate can be taken up by the grievance committeee.

Employers prefer to pay time rates during the learning period, a few hours to several weeks, and then determine the incentive rate. The underlying principle here is that no incentive rate shall be cut merely because an employee has earned more than was expected. It is just and fair that management should reduce the rate whenever it introduces equipment or method improvement, that is, when an old job is transformed into a new one. The distinction should be clear enough but many managements have tried to reduce labor costs regardless of the distinction and some unions have tried to force a sharing of gains regardless of the distinction. The true interests are mutual. Enlightened leaders from both groups want the distinction rigidly maintained. The usual answer is to guarantee rates against change for a period such as six months or, more reasonably, to guarantee all rates for their respective jobs indefinitely but allow new rates whenever there is a substantial change in capital resource creating a different job. In addition, it is wise to assure labor that it will suffer no reduction in daily earnings.

Guarantees. Under the Public Contracts Act and under the Fair Labor Standards Act employers subject to the acts are required to make good to the worker the difference when incentive earnings fall below the hourly minimum rate set for each class of work. State minimum wage laws require the same guarantee. These legal mandates make no distinction as to whether employee or employer may be to blame for the "fall-down," but the minimum amounts required are usually well below the normal earning of incentive workers. Some unions require that incentive rates be adequate to insure that a specified proportion of the employees, say 60 per cent, earn a certain amount above the minimum. This requirement aims at better management control but is more likely to tighten the standards of employee selection. One union conceded that "workers making less than 90 per cent of the average production in the plant shall be deemed substandard and the employer shall not be required to pay up to the minimum to these workers." All unions and all enlightened managements agree that there should be a higher guarantee to protect the employees for stoppages or slowdowns due solely to managerial faults. "A pieceworker unable to make reasonable wages through no fault of his own shall be paid at least his average daily earnings." "Incentive-plan workers who are qualified will be guaranteed 17½ per cent over their day rates on a weekly basis." These arrangements facilitate shifts between incentive and time-paid jobs to oblige management. When favors to management are not involved, 80 per cent of average earnings through the past four weeks is customary.

Thus the most liberal guarantee for incentive workers may be either some percentage of average earnings or a fixed percentage above base. But such arrangements are usually limited to cover failures of management and hence are restricted to short intervals. If an incentive plan includes a time rate guarantee to cover employee as well as managerial fault it is usually fixed at the base rate as per job evaluation, sometimes a percentage above the legal minimum.

All such rate setting may be indirectly affected by job evaluation. Management must formulate policies on these points that will be fair to both sides. When that is done there should be no fear as to the practice, but all points must be acceptable to labor and the responsibility for the "selling" or instructing still resides with management.

Reaction on the Grievance Procedure. The grievance procedure, or "machinery" as it is sometimes called, with which Question 11 deals, is all-important to a union. It must be respected and supported with full managerial cooperation. Job evaluation should certainly eliminate many petty grievances. Some unions may prefer to have many grievances in which case they will be against any form of job evaluation, and any attempt at winning them over will be fruitless, but it is inconceivable that unions of intelligent workers will persist in such perversity for long. They will hear of better ways in other plants and through their executive committees will demand a more constructive leadership. Most unions will welcome an undiscriminating, fact-based rate structure provided the grievance machinery is allowed to function also, and they would be right in wanting grievance machinery even if there were no serious grievances. Actually there are bound to be some grievances despite the best management, because there are intangibles in human relations that defy all prearranged system; there will at least be changing conditions, misunderstandings, different points of view, and the like. The answer to this question is therefore to welcome the grievance procedure and give it all the factual data pertinent to each case. Assure the shop stewards that job evaluation will help point the way to justice in their hearings. Tell them that if it comes to a question of system versus mutual satisfaction, the latter will prevail (see Chapter 9). A real system is not going to be upset by adjusting it to the larger justice. But a real system for evaluating jobs should bring a decided gain in justice.

Various Means of Winning Employee Support. There is no substitute for personal instruction but that can be supplemented by publicity through plant and union publications, employee letters (see Figure 17), questionnaires, and the showing of slides. For instance, the Sperry Company made slide and film records of the committee work from start to finish. This was done partly for immediate informational purposes and partly for future preparation of newcomers on committee work so that they might "all receive the same information, in keeping with the original intent." Most companies prepare a manual, or perhaps separate manuals, for hourly paid employees, for supervisors, and for salaried employees. An excellent example of the manual for hourly paid employees is *You and Your Wages* [7] in which cartoons are extensively used, even to illustrate the characteristics. The contents of this manual are as follows:

> You and Your Wages
> Job Evaluation
> Pay Grades (see Chapter 11, Figure 108)
> Merit Rating
> Periodic Merit Rating
> Wage Incentive

[7] American Seating Company of Grand Rapids.

JOB EVALUATION -- WHAT IS IT?

A program of Job Evaluations is being started in order to determine the value of each job in the plant. The purpose of it is to establish a sound wage policy which would accomplish:

1. A fair wage level equal to the rates paid for comparable work in similar industry in this area.

2. Establish a fair wage differential between jobs based on comparison of working conditions, responsibility, knowledge and experience and skill required for each job.

3. Eliminate any wage inequalities:

How will this program work?

1. In the first place, this program can work properly if you will participate actively. It is important that each person in the plant tells the committee in charge of Job Evaluation all about his job. Within the next few weeks you will answer personally a questionnaire and tell the committee what you do on your job, how you do it, and as the Job Evaluation Program progresses, you will participate in determining the value of your job.

2. A study and a survey will be made of various similar industries in this area and all the jobs in this plant will be compared with the jobs and the rates of pay of other companies. The names of companies and associations which will be used for comparison will be issued to you so that each individual will be able to check the findings of the committee and to see if they are correct.

3. Each individual will be given an opportunity for a hearing so that he can discuss and explain what he does on his job and what he thinks the value of his job is, in comparison with the rates paid in the area as well as other jobs in the plant itself.

4. In view of this big undertaking a number of committees will participate actively. The Foremen and Group Leaders Committee will handle their share of the program from the supervisory and departmental level. The Suggestion Committees will be assigned to handle the job so that the views and opinions of the people in all sections and floors could be gathered and transmitted. In addition, people will be appointed to act as information and clearing centers on each floor who will consequently inform you of what is going on and answer any questions. Mr. Harry Sherman, a member of the faculty of Brooklyn College, has been appointed to assist and coordinate the work of all these committees. He will be assisted by Mr. Henry Ries.

It is hoped that this program can be finished and in effect by January 15, 1951. As each step is taken in the Job Evaluation Program, its progress and workings will be explained to you in detail through reports in writing from the committees who will handle this project.

In trying to establish a sound wage policy for this plant, it is not the purpose of the Job Evaluation Program to reduce your present rate of pay. No one's wages will be reduced when the Job Evaluation Project is completed.

The Job Evaluation Program, which has for its objective a square deal in the matter of rates and pay for everyone in this plant, can only be as successful as the cooperation and the interest which you and every other Lewyt man and woman will give it.

FIGURE 17. BULLETIN ANNOUNCEMENT TO EMPLOYEES. (The Lewyt Corporation.)

Computing Your "Take-Home" Earnings
Miscellaneous Factors Affecting Wages

The Armstrong Cork Company has an excellent pamphlet which is published in full in the A.M.A. *Handbook of Wage and Salary Administration.*

The General Electric Company puts out a *Supervisor's Guide to G. E. Job Information.* This has 119 pages and no cartoons. Much space is given to "Don't Likes." It would be educational to many who are not supervisors.

The plant of the Celotex Corporation at Marrero, Louisiana, has a booklet entitled *Your Job and Its Evaluation* which indicates co-operation all along the line.

Last but not least, a great deal depends on the capabilities of the job analysts themselves. In the words of Dr. Leonard W. Ferguson [8] the analyst

. . . must be familiar with the general principles, the administrative techniques, and the technical details involved in a complete job evaluation program. A job analyst must possess sufficient tact to secure the cooperation of all levels within a company. He must be able to speak the language of employees and the language of management. He must be able to see the many sides of any problem, be able to make impartial judgments, and be able to sell all concerned on the purposes and merits of a job evaluation program.

[8] Life Office Management Association, Clerical Salary Administration, 1948.

6

SETTING UP MEASURING SCALES

The characteristics should be clearly defined and explained so that all connected with measuring and grading may have, as nearly as possible, a common viewpoint.

—W. D. STEARNS

No Real Measurement in Ranking. Under the ranking method predetermined degree definitions are superfluous. But the need for predetermined definitions of characteristics to be used as guides to proper ranking is now generally recognized. The earliest attempts at definition were crude. For instance, the Kimberly-Clark guide for "Probability and Consequence of Errors" read as follows: "Assuming that the occupation is filled by an experienced, conscientious employee, consider typical errors that are likely to be made and the consequences of each in terms of waste, damage to equipment, delays, complaints, confusion, spoilage of product, discrepancies, etc." Such guides may have focused appraisal but they failed to implement measurement as an aid to judgment. They did point up the need for real measuring scales.

Measurement Under the Straight Point Method. In the straight point method the concept of degrees was part of the plan itself so that it was natural to insert a definition in each box of the chart. This fact is illustrated in Figure 18. But as in the original method this measurement scale wholly neglects the relative difference in worth between the characteristics.

Measuring Scales Under Direct-to-Money Method. Under the direct-to-money method ten or more key jobs are selected and carefully described. A competent committee then ranks the jobs on each characteristic, members acting independently. This step has been called "the heart of the development." The final scores, 1 to 10, are averaged and the averages tabulated as in Figure 19. Then for each key job its existing rate per hour is distributed over the five characteristics by each member of the committee. This work should

89

Payroll Title_____

Rater's Name_____

	0	2	4	6	8	10
A. Education needed by person of average intelligence to do work.	Grammar School	2 years High School	High School Diploma	H. S. plus Business or Vocational School	College Degree	College Degree, plus technical training
B. Previous experience in same or related work.	None	1 year	2 years	3 years	4 years	Over 4 years
C. Time for person of average ability to be trained on the job.	None	1 week	1 month	3 months	6 months	Over 6 months
D. Precision and accuracy required (machine work).	Rough work		.01"	.005"	.001"	.0005"
E. Chance of damage to machines, materials, or products.	Under $50/yr.	About $50/yr.	About $500/yr.	About $1,000/yr.	About $2,500/yr.	Over $5,000/yr.
F. Extent to which unforeseen difficulties require initiative and ingenuity	Work is wholly routine	Routine work with occasional problems (weekly)		Routine work with daily problems		New problems met constantly
G. Versatility required (No. of operations involved e.g., milling, drilling).	1	2	3	4	5	6 or more

FIGURE 18. GRAPHIC SCALE FOR APPRAISING OCCUPATIONS AND POSITIONS, SAMPLE CHARACTERISTICS ONLY. (Clerical Salary Study Committee Report No. 1, Life Office Management Association.)

Key Jobs	Mental Effort	Skill	Physical Effort	Responsi-bility	Working Conditions
Pattern Maker........	9.4	9.4	3.9	8.2	2.5
Machinist No. 1......	8.1	9.1	5.7	7.5	5.6
Substation Operator...	8.9	7.3	1.0	9.7	1.2
Pipefitter No. 2......	6.0	7.0	6.4	6.8	6.3
Painter	5.4	6.6	5.3	5.3	6.1
Poleman	3.7	3.1	8.3	3.3	8.1
Drill Press Operator...	4.8	4.8	3.3	6.1	5.4
Rammer	1.6	1.8	9.3	2.2	9.1
Carpenter's Helper....	4.0	4.3	3.7	3.8	3.7
Laborer	3.1	1.6	8.1	2.1	7.0

FIGURE 19. AVERAGE RANKS OF TEN JOBS, SCALE OF 10

End Jobs	Mental Effort	Skill	Physical Effort	Respon-sibility	Working Condi-tions	Present Hourly Rate
Pattern Maker	30	33	9	14	6	
	27	32	11	15	7	92
	26	33	11	16	6	
Laborer	6	3	16	5	12	
	5	5	17	4	11	42
	4	4	18	4	12	

FIGURE 20. ESTIMATES OF RATER A ON ALLOCATION OF PRESENT HOURLY RATES IN CENTS

Key Jobs	Mental Effort	Skill	Physical Effort	Respon-sibility	Working Con-ditions	Present Hourly Rate
Pattern Maker......	26.8	33.4	10.2	15.8	5.8	92
Machinist No. 1.....	21.7	32.1	12.2	13.8	8.2	88
Substation Operator..	24.9	21.1	4.1	27.7	4.2	82
Pipefitter No. 2.....	11.1	20.1	14.0	12.2	10.6	68
Painter	10.1	18.8	10.8	10.6	9.7	60
Poleman	5.5	7.3	19.2	6.9	13.1	52
Drill Press Operator.	8.8	14.2	8.2	10.5	8.3	50
Rammer	3.2	4.2	21.9	5.0	13.7	48
Carpenter's Helper...	7.8	13.2	9.0	8.9	7.1	46
Laborer	5.5	3.0	17.7	4.0	11.8	42

FIGURE 21. POOLED ESTIMATES OF NINE RATERS ON ALLOCATION OF PRESENT HOURLY RATES IN CENTS.

(Three steps in making the measuring scale, Figure 22.)

Cents	Mental Effort	Skill	Physical Effort	Responsibility	Work Conditions
40					
39					
38					
37					
36					
35					
34					
33		Patternmaker			
32		Machinist No. 1			
31					
30					
29					
28				Substation Operator	
27	Patternmaker				
26					
25	Substation Operator				
24					
23					
22	Machinist No. 1		Rammer		
21		Substation Operator			
20		Pipefitter No. 2			
19		Painter	Poleman		
18			Laborer		
17					
16				Patternmaker	
15					
14		Drill Press Operator	Pipefitter No. 2	Machinist No. 1	Rammer
13		Carpenter's Helper			Poleman
12			Machinist No. 1	Pipefitter No. 2	Laborer
11	Pipefitter No. 2		Painter	Drill Press Operator	Pipefitter No. 2
10	Painter		Patternmaker	Painter	Painter
9	Drill Press Operator		Carpenter's Helper	Carpenter's Helper	
8	Carpenter's Helper		Drill Press Operator		Drill Press Operator
7		Poleman		Poleman	Carpenter's Helper
6	Poleman				Patternmaker
5	Laborer			Rammer	
4		Rammer	Substation Operator	Laborer	Substation Operator
3	Rammer	Laborer			

FIGURE 22. A MEASURING SCALE FOR THE BENGE PLAN. (Eugene J. Benge, *Job Evaluation and Merit Rating*, National Foremen's Institute Manual No. 931.)

be done several times with time intervals between trials. Three such distributions are shown in Figure 20 for two extreme key jobs. Next, these distributions of the hourly rates as of 1932 are adjusted and averaged as shown in Figure 21. When the whole committee is satisfied with the proportions the latter are rearranged in a form suitable for applying the Characteristic Comparison technique on any job in question (see Figure 22).

Percentage Scales. William D. Turner describes his method by applying it to twelve key jobs, in twelve steps, five of which follow:

Step 1. Select twelve key jobs which differ as to the characteristics.

Step 2. Each member of committee ranks the jobs independently on each characteristic. This is merely a rough move preparatory to Step 3.

Step. 3. On a separate percentage scale for each characteristic rate the lowest and highest jobs and then the rest of them by marking the respective job number at the appropriate point in each scale. These locations are not likely to be uniformly distributed.

Step 4. With ranking positions as ordinate and job numbers as abscissa headings, enter symbols for the characteristics. This shows ranking of characteristics for each job and is merely a preparation for Step 5.

Step 5. Have the committee rate all of each job's characteristics on a separate percentage scale for each job. Begin by assigning 100 per cent to the characteristic ranked highest in Step 4 and then locate the proportionate place for the other characteristics. These scales for the several jobs must not be considered equal in worth, nor are the ratings of Step 3 comparable with these of Step 5.

The results of Steps 4 and 5 are then combined through twenty-eight routine computations and entries in eleven tables, all of which are painstakingly shown [1] by Dr. Turner, but are too ritualistic to appeal to many managers.

First Step in Weighted Point Measuring. With Lott's development of the weighted point plan there came into use the principle of degrees, each of which was limited by a decimal range.

Exceptional	10–7 or 4
Above average	7–4 or 3
Average	3–1 or 2
Little or none	1–0 or 1

This degree scale was used as one axis and the subcharacteristics were used as a second axis. For instance, skill was subdivided into five components and these were entered as column headings as

[1] *Personnel,* XXIV, No. 6.

shown in Figure 23. Similar measures were set up for each characteristic, each of which was assigned an intercharacteristic weight by percentage. Thus the original plan of the Wright Aeronautical Corporation had thirteen characteristics weighted for patternmaker's job as in Figure 24.

	Dexterity	Precision	Versatility	Adaptation Period	Ingenuity
Exceptional	9	8 6	5	4	10 4
Above average.....	6 5 4	5 4	5 4	3	3 2
Average	3 2	3 2	3 2	2 1	1
Little or none.....	1 0	1 0	1 0	0	0

FIGURE 23. RELATIVE RATING OF SUBCHARACTERISTICS IN SKILL.

After determining these weights a committee of sixteen supervisors assigned rates from zero to 10 points to each job for each characteristic. They did this by first determining the job which, in the combined opinion of the committee, should have the maximum value of 10 points, and then evaluating all other jobs by comparison

Characteristics	Weight in Per Cent
1. Time required to learn trade........................	35.2
2. Time required to adapt skill to work..................	13.3
3. Difficulty in locating work elsewhere	.9
4. Educational requirements	7.4
5. Degree of skill and accuracy	19.5
6. Ingenuity	6.9
7. Cost of probable errors	4.4
8. Honesty of effort	1.7
9. Dirtiness of working conditions.....................	.8
10. Exposure to health hazard..........................	2.2
11. Exposure to accident hazard	2.5
12. Physical effort	4.5
13. Monotony of work.................................	.7

FIGURE 24. WEIGHTING OF JOB CHARACTERISTICS IN PERCENTAGE ACCORDING TO MODIFIED LOTT PLAN. (Wright Aeronautical Corporation—original plan.)

to it. To facilitate this rating, scales similar to Figure 18 were used. In fact, the characteristic "Time Required to Learn Trade" was evaluated by allowing one point for each year required, just as Lott suggested. The total points for each job were then found by multiplying each characteristic weight by the rate assigned to that particular job. The evaluation for patternmaker was as in Figure 25.

Characteristic	Rate	× Weight =	Total Points
1.	10.0	35.2	352.00
2.	3.5	13.3	46.55
3.	.0	.9	.00
4.	10.0	7.4	74.00
5.	8.5	19.5	165.75
6.	10.0	6.9	69.00
7.	1.0	4.4	4.40
8.	6.0	1.7	10.20
9.	2.0	.8	1.60
10.	1.0	2.2	2.20
11.	8.4	2.5	21.00
12.	1.0	4.5	4.50
13.	.0	.7	.00
Total.			751.20

FIGURE 25. DERIVATION OF POINTS FOR PATTERNMAKER'S JOB

Degrees Defined to Lessen Operating Judgment. Obviously the Lott technique was more elaborate than the results could justify. Each appraisal still depended solely on judgment. Some employers decided that the characteristic comparison technique gave just as accurate results with less figuring. Others sought to narrow the judgment by setting up a practical definition for each degree. The latter was the path taken by A. L. Kress.[2] At present the tendency is to accept the Kress definitions with little or no change. This we deplore, as many of the situations to which measuring is to be applied would be better served by reconsidering the definitions. It is, of course, helpful to take ready-made definitions as a starting point. With this advantage in mind, not as a final pattern for all applications, we reproduce in Figure 26 the Cole variation of degree definitions, adopted during World War II by eastern airplane companies. Points are identical with the Kress plan and definitions are nearly the same. Some companies have reduced the number of grades from twelve to ten, in which cases the point allotments differ.

[2] National Metal Trades Association *Bulletin* No. 3, Parts I to VII of the Industrial Relations Policies and Procedures. *Job Rating*, a pocket booklet of the same association. Also National Electrical Manufacturers Association, *Job Rating Manual*, and *Hourly Job Rating Plan 1953*, from NEMA Industrial Department.

1—EDUCATION

This factor appraises the requirements for the use of shop mathematics, drawings, measuring instruments, or trade knowledge.
0–14.
Requires the ability to read and write, add and subtract whole numbers.
15–28
Requires the use of simple arithmetic such as addition and subtraction of decimals and fractions, together with simple drawings and some measuring instruments such as caliper, scale. Equivalent to 2 years of high school.
29–42
Requires the use of fairly complicated drawings, advanced shop mathematics, handbook formulas, variety of precision measuring instruments, some trade knowledge in a specialized field or process. Equivalent to 4 years high school or 2 years high school plus 2 or 3 years trades training.
43–56
Requires the use of complicated drawings and specifications, advanced shop mathematics, wide variety of precision measuring instruments, broad shop trade knowledge. Usually equivalent to 4 years high school plus 4 years formal trades training.
57–70
Requires a basic technical knowledge sufficient to deal with complicated and involved mechanical, electrical, or other engineering problems. Equivalent to 4 years of technical university training.

2—EXPERIENCE

This factor appraises the length of time usually or typically required by an individual, with the specified education or trade knowledge, to learn to perform the work effectively. Do not include time required for apprenticeship or trades training which has been rated under Education.

Month		Points
1		8
2	1st degree	15
3		22
6		30
9	2d degree	37
12		44
24		55
36	3d degree	66
48		77
60	4th degree	88
6 yrs.		99
7 yrs.	5th degree	110

3—INITIATIVE AND INGENUITY

This factor appraises the independent action, exercise of judgment, the making of decisions or the amount of planning which the job requires. This factor also appraises the degree of complexity of the work.
0–14
Requires the ability to understand and follow simple instructions and the use of simple equipment involving few decisions, since the employee is told exactly what to do.

FIGURE 26. EXAMPLE OF DEGREE DEFINITION AND POINT ALLOTMENTS

15–28

Requires the ability to work from detailed instructions and the making of minor decisions, involving the use of some judgment.

29–42

Requires the ability to plan and perform a sequence of operations where standard or recognized operation methods are available, and the making of general decisions as to quality, tolerances, operation and set-up sequence.

43–56

Requires the ability to plan and perform unusual and difficult work where only general operation methods are available and the making of decisions involving the use of considerable ingenuity, and initiative and judgment.

57–70

Requires outstanding ability to work independently toward general results, devise new methods, meet new conditions necessitating a high degree of ingenuity, initiative and judgment on very involved and complex jobs.

4—PHYSICAL DEMAND

This factor appraises the amount and continuity of physical effort required. Consider the effort expended handling material (the weight and frequency of handling), operating a machine or handling tools, and the periods of unoccupied time.

0–10

Light work requiring little physical effort.

11–20

Light physical effort working regularly with light weight material or occasionally with average weight material. Operate machine tools where machine time exceeds the handling time.

21–30

Sustained physical effort, requiring continuity of effort working with light or average weight material. Usually short cycle work requiring continuous activity, the operation of several machines where the handling time is equivalent to the total machine time.

31–40

Considerable physical effort working with average or heavy weight material, or continuous strain of difficult work position.

41–50

Continuous physical exertion working with heavy weight material. Hard work with constant physical strain or intermittent severe strain.

5—MENTAL AND VISUAL

This factor appraises the degree of mental or visual concentration required. Consider the alertness and attention necessary, the length of the cycle, the co-ordination of manual dexterity with mental or visual attention.

0–5

Little mental and only intermittent visual attention since either the operation is practically automatic or the duties require attention only at long intervals.

6–10

Frequent mental or visual attention, where the flow of work is intermittent or the operation involves waiting for a machine or process to complete a cycle with little attention or checking.

FIGURE 26. (*Continued.*)

11–15

Continuous mental or visual attention where the flow of work is repetitive or the operation requires constant alertness.

16–20

Must concentrate mental and visual attention closely, planning and laying out complex work, or coordinating a high degree of manual dexterity with close visual attention for sustained periods.

21–25

Concentrated and exacting mental or visual attention, usually visualizing, planning and laying out very involved and complex jobs.

6—EQUIPMENT, PROCESS

This factor appraises the responsibility for preventing damage thru carelessness, to the equipment or process used in the performance of the job. Consider the probable amount of damage resulting from carelessness in handling setup, operation, etc., for any one mishap. Process relates to operations, such as plating.

0–5

Probable damage to equipment or process is negligible.

6–10

Probable damage to equipment or process is seldom over $25.

11–15

Probable damage to equipment or process is seldom over $250.

16–20

Probable damage to equipment or process is seldom over $1,000.

21–25

Probable damage exceedingly high, reaching several thousand dollars.

7—MATERIAL OR PRODUCT

This factor appraises the responsibility for preventing waste or loss of raw material or partially finished product thru carelessness. Consider the probable number of pieces which may be spoiled before detection and correction in any one lot or run, the value of the material and labor, the possibility of salvage. Do not use either maximum or minimum, but an average based on normal expectation.

0–5

Probable loss due to damage or scrapping of materials or product is seldom over $10.

6–10

Probable loss due to damage or scrapping of materials or product is seldom over $100.

11–15

Probable loss due to damage or scrapping of materials or product is seldom over $250.

16–20

Probable loss due to damage or scrapping of materials or product is seldom over $500.

21–25

Probable loss of material which may be damaged or scrapped is very high, up to several thousand dollars.

FIGURE 26. (*Continued.*)

8—SAFETY OF OTHERS

Careless operation of machine or handling of materials or tools by the employee on the job being rated, may result in injury to others. Accordingly this factor appraises (1) the care which must be exercised to prevent injury to others, and, (2) the probable extent of such injury. (Injury to the employee on the job being rated is to be considered under Unavoidable Hazards.)

0–5

Little responsibility for safety of others. Job performed in an isolated location, or where there is no machine involved and the material is very light.

6–10

Only reasonable care with respect to own work necessary to prevent injury to others, and accidents, if they should occur, would be minor in nature.

11–15

Compliance with standard safety precautions necessary to prevent lost-time accidents to others.

16–20

Constant care necessary to prevent serious injury to others, due to inherent hazards of the job but where such other employees may act to prevent being injured.

21–25

Safety of others depends entirely on correct action of employee on job being rated and carelessness may result in fatal accidents to others.

9—WORK OF OTHERS

This factor appraises the responsibility which goes with the job for assisting, instructing, or directing the work of others. It is not intended to appraise supervisory responsibilities for results.

0–5

Responsible only for own work.

6–10

Responsible for instructing and directing one or two helpers 50 per cent or more of the time.

11–15

Responsible for instructing, directing or setting up for a small group of employees usually in the same occupation, up to 10 persons.

16–20

Responsible for instructing, directing and maintaining the flow of work in a group of employees up to 25 persons.

21–25

Responsible for instructing, directing and maintaining the flow of work in a group of over 25 persons.

10—WORK CONDITIONS

This factor appraises the surroundings of physical conditions under which the job must be done and the extent to which those conditions make the job disagreeable. Consider the presence, relative amount of any continuity of exposure to dust, dirt, heat, fumes, cold, noise, vibration, wet, etc.

0–10

Ideal working conditions, complete absence of any disagreeable elements.

FIGURE 26. (*Continued.*)

11–20

Good working conditions. May be slightly dirty or involve occasional exposure to some of the elements listed above. Typical machine shop working conditions.

21–30

Somewhat disagreeable working conditions due to exposure to one or more of the elements listed above, but where these elements are not continuous if several are present.

31–40

Continuous exposure to several disagreeable elements or to one element which is particularly disagreeable.

41–50

Continuous and intensive exposure to several extremely disagreeable elements.

11—HAZARDS

This factor appraises the hazards, both accident and health, connected with or surrounding the job, even though all safety devices have been installed. Consider the material being handled, the machines or tools used, the work position, the possibility of accident, even though none has occurred.

0–5

Accident or health hazards negligible.

6–10

Accidents improbable, outside of minor injuries, such as abrasions, cuts or bruises. Health hazards negligible.

11–15

Exposure to lost-time accidents, such as crushed hand or foot, loss of fingers, eye injury from flying particles. Some exposure to occupational disease, not incapacitating in nature.

16–20

Exposure to incapacitating accident or health hazards, such as loss of arm or leg, impairment of vision.

21–25

Exposure to accidents or occupational disease which may result in total disability or death.

FIGURE 26. (*Concluded.*)

Before the reader appraises the degree definitions in the various exhibits he should be reminded that there are at least three ways of expressing them, namely:

1. In terms of average, one or two less, and one or two more than average.
2. In terms of job elements, such as: use heavy tools in rough work, use small tools and gauges in routine work, use precision tools in difficult work, etc.
3. In terms of specific operations or bench mark jobs.

The use of a point range for each degree as shown in the next illustrations is not usual because it allows subdivision of the measures and consequent higgling. The higher value for each degree is sufficient and much more clean cut.

Discussion of Point Allotments. NEMA and N.M.T.A., also most other users of the Kress type plan, use only the maximum number of points at each degree (see Figure 5). The point allotment principle has been much criticized. The criticisms are:

1. The values were arbitrary and set from a single set of jobs.
2. Because of the sudden acceptances, the allotments became frozen before they had been widely verified.
3. The progressions from one degree to the next are all arithmetic, whereas some should be exponential if not geometric.
4. Fixed definitions cannot be suitable to all kinds of jobs.
5. The maxima for characteristics prevent making headroom for new job contents.
6. The whole arrangement is rigid, makes classification automatic, and allows no flexibility.

We deny none of this except to say that Kress constantly has cautioned against being limited if breaking through is needed to do justice and bring mutual satisfaction. Beyond any doubt the plan has worked well, but there is room to improve or refit the scales and we think that should be done at time of adoption by any plant that has a competent set of analysts.

The Southern California Aircraft Industries Restudy Evaluation plan for hourly paid jobs employs 840 points for seven characteristics, thereby providing more leeway for measuring the skill sub-characteristics. This plan seems to have attained in part the simplicity of the Weed plan without resorting to the characteristic comparison technique. The degree definitions for this revised SCAI plan follow.

SKILL

SKILL is the technique acquired through training and experience. The amount of skill required for different jobs varies considerably. However, the amount of skill necessary for the satisfactory performance of any job can be measured with reasonable accuracy in terms of the length of time normally required for an average individual of normal mental capacity to acquire the necessary trade knowledge and training.

Training and experience are considered together, and the aggregate time required for both serves as the basis for the assignment of evaluation points. The table below indicates the points allocated to each month and year of experience and training required by the job.

2 weeks or less	40		2 years	230
1 month	57		2½ years	254
3 months	92		3 years	275
6 months	125		4 years	313
9 months	150		5 years	345
1 year	170		6 years	374
1½ years	203		7 years	400

MENTALITY

MENTALITY is the prerequisite mental capacity necessary to learn to perform a given job efficiently. Under this factor mentality is measured by educational attainment whether acquired through schooling or experience. The following degrees are defined:

1. Use simple arithmetic involving addition, subtraction, multiplication, or division of whole numbers and the addition and subtraction of decimals and fractions; includes direct reading of measuring instruments calibrated in decimal or fractional units. Understand simple verbal or written instructions.

2. To use arithmetic, to multiply and divide using fractions, decimals, and percentages or conversion of one quantity to another of equivalent value (such as the conversion of a common fraction to a decimal fraction). Use blueprints or production illustration to obtain easily identified reference information such as identification of parts and to determine primary dimensions (such as length and breadth). Also obtains processing, or material callout information, such as number of bolts per assembly, processing or finish specifications. Also ability to recognize part change notation.

3. To use arithmetic and algebra to solve equations and problems involving geometric formulas, ratios, and square root; to apply geometric propositions— includes use of sine bars following standardized computing procedure; does not include solving formulae requiring use of tables of natural trigonometric functions. Visualize three dimensions from flat views, interpret right angle projections and opposite hand views and meaning of standard symbols and codes. Understand simple technical instructions in such fields as electricity, hydraulics, chemistry, mechanics, radio, metallurgy, etc., where interpretation of terminology, symbols, or codes is necessary.

FIGURE 27. FACTORY SCAI RESTUDY EVALUATION PLAN.

4. Use trigonometry to solve right triangles for unknowns when the given parts are shown in the same plane. Interpret complex blueprints which are difficult to visualize; interpret all symbols, codes, engineering changes or variations, or use and work from lofting prints. Understand and apply basic technical knowledge in such fields as electricity, hydraulics, chemistry, mechanics, radio, metallurgy, etc., as applied to standard trade or craft practices.

5. Use trigonometry to solve for several interrelated dimensions in more than one plane and where projection and visualization of special relationships are necessary; solving of oblique triangles where given dimensions do not permit solving for right triangles. Interpret all information contained in any blueprint including complex electrical circuit diagrams, complex mechanical or installation drawings, and blueprints of intricate castings which require visualization of hollow core views, draft angles, and parting lines. Understand and use lofting practice and procedure. Understand and apply technical knowledge in such fields as electricity, hydraulics, chemistry, mechanics, radio, metallurgy, etc., where the solution of original problems is necessary.

Degree	1	2	3	4	5
Points	20	40	60	80	100

RESPONSIBILITY FOR MATERIAL AND EQUIPMENT

RESPONSIBILITY for material and equipment is the responsibility required by the job for preventing loss to the Company through damage to equipment, tools, material, or product.

"Equipment and Tools" include stationary and portable machines, material handling equipment, hand tools which are the property of the Company, and all tools, dies, jigs, and fixtures.

"Material and Product" include raw materials, supplies, work in process, and finished parts. Tools, dies, patterns, etc., are considered work in process for the department making them.

Evaluation Procedure

Estimate the cost to the Company of accidental damage to equipment and tools which could occur in the course of normal performance of the job. Consider only the damage for which the employee would be wholly responsible. Use an average top figure for a single occurrence—not an extreme maximum. Cover the cost of repairs necessary to restore the equipment to first-class operating condition and estimate the cost of accidental damage to material and produce on the same basis.

Degree	1	2	3	4	5
Dollar	0	51	251	501	1001
Range	50	250	500	1000	up
Points	20	40	60	80	100

FIGURE 27. (*Continued.*)

MENTAL APPLICATION

MENTAL APPLICATION is a measure of the degree of concentration and sensory alertness required by the job. Depending on the intensity, the frequency, and the continuity of concentration and sensory alertness, the following degrees are defined:

1. Minimum Mental Application. Operations requiring little attention and repeated successively at short intervals or nonrepetitive but of such a nature as to require little directed thinking.

2. Light Mental Application. Operations requiring intermittent attention to control machine or manual motions. Operations requiring intermittent directed thinking to carry out predetermined procedure or sequence of operations of limited variability.

3. Moderate Mental Application. Operations requiring almost continuous attention, but work is sufficiently repetitive that a habit cycle is formed; operations requiring intermittent directed thinking to determine or select materials, equipment or operations where variable sequences may be selected by the worker.

4. Very Close Mental Application. Operations requiring close and continuous attention for control of operations which require a high degree of coordination, or immediate response; operations requiring intermittent directed thinking to determine or select materials, equipment, or operations where highly variable sequence or close dimensions are controlled by the worker.

5. Intense Mental Application. Operations requiring sustained directed thinking to analyze, solve, or plan highly variable or technical tasks involving complex problems, machines, or mechanisms.

Degree	1	2	3	4	5
Points	10	20	30	40	50

PHYSICAL APPLICATION

PHYSICAL APPLICATION is a measure of the muscular exertion and physical strain required by the job. Depending on the intensity, the frequency, and the continuity of muscular exertion or physical strain, the following degrees are defined:

1. Slight physical exertion. Handling light (less than 10 lbs.) objects and/or tools, with worker having choice of working position; work operations do not involve elements of physical strain.

2. Light physical exertion. Handling, pushing, or pulling light to average weight (10 to 15 lbs.) objects and/or tools where elements of physical strain are slight or not involved; worker restricted in working position such as in continuous sitting or intermittent standing, walking, or climbing.

3. Moderate physical exertion. Occasional momentary moderate (15 to 25 lbs.) pushing, pulling, or lifting; almost continuous pushing, pulling, or lifting of light to average weight (10 to 15 lbs.) objects; perform work operations requiring almost continuous standing or almost continuous walking; work operations involve elements of physical strain or unnatural work positions at regularly recurring intervals.

FIGURE 27. (*Continued.*)

4. Strenuous physical exertion. Frequent momentary or occasional sustained heavy (25 lbs. or over) pushing, pulling, or lifting; performs work involving frequent physical strain or unnatural work position which causes more than normal fatigue.

5. Extremely strenuous physical exertion. Frequent or almost continuous sustained heavy pushing, pulling, or lifting; performs work operations approaching limits of normal capacity, normally works in such positions as to cause extreme physical exertion, or strain.

Degree	1	2	3	4	5
Points	10	20	30	45	60

JOB CONDITIONS

JOB CONDITIONS are the surrounding, or physical conditions, under which the job inherently must be performed, and which may affect the mental or physical wellbeing of the employee. The following factors are defined:

1. Good working conditions. No exposure to disagreeable elements or factors; removed from general factory conditions.

2. General factory working conditions. Exposure to general factory noise, dirt, fumes, vibration, temperature and dampness which surround the worker or which are inherent in the job but which are not disagreeable or irritating.

3. Occasional disagreeable working conditions. Occasional exposures to disagreeable or irritating elements or factors such as noise, dirt, fumes, vibration, heat, cold, dampness, flying particles, or wearing fatiguing or disagreeable protective devices.

4. Frequent disagreeable working conditions. Frequent exposure to disagreeable or irritating elements or factors such as noise, dirt, fumes, vibration, heat, cold, dampness, flying particles, or wearing fatiguing or disagreeable protective devices.

5. Continuous disagreeable working conditions. Almost continuous exposure to one or more disagreeable or irritating elements or factors, such as noise, dirt, fumes, vibration, heat, cold, dampness, flying particles, or wearing fatiguing or disagreeable protective devices, or almost continuous exposure to a combination of such elements or factors.

6. Extremely disagreeable working conditions. Exposure to disagreeable or irritating elements or factors which are present in such a degree and for a sufficient duration of time to cause extreme fatigue or excessive discomfort to the worker.

Degree	1	2	3	4	5	6
Point	5	15	25	35	50	65

FIGURE 27. (*Continued.*)

UNAVOIDABLE HAZARDS

UNAVOIDABLE OCCUPATIONAL HAZARDS are the possible injuries involved in the performance of the job. Depending upon the possibility, severity, and frequency of exposure to occupational hazards inherent in the job, the following degrees are defined:

1. Work having little or no accident hazard. Injury very unlikely.
2. Exposure to minor accident hazards such as surface cuts, bruises, minor abrasions, or burns which do not involve lost time.
3. Exposure to accident hazards involving lost time for a short period but from which complete recovery can be expected, such as lacerations, severe sprains, deep cuts and burns.
4. Infrequent exposure to accident hazards such as fractures, hernias, severe burns, or those causing some minor permanent physical disability such as loss of a finger.
5. Frequent exposure to accident hazards such as fractures, hernias, severe burns, or those causing some minor permanent physical disability such as loss of a finger or impairment of hearing.
6. Exposure to accident hazards involving major permanent disability such as loss of arm, hand, leg, hearing, foot, or sight of eye; exposure to accident hazards, the probable consequence of which is loss of life.

Degree	1	2	3	4	5	6
Points	5	15	25	35	50	65

FIGURE 27. (*Concluded.*)

Arbitrary Allotments. The most common practice weights the characteristics at the first degree in terms of percentage, namely, the sum of the first degree allotments is 100. Then the second degree allotments are derived by multiplying each first degree allotment by two, the third by three, the fourth by four, and the fifth by five. If a larger total is desired these figures are all multiplied by two or by three. Thus the total of points in the fifth degree for the Kress-Cole plan is 500 and for the Consolidated Water Power and Paper Company plan it is 1500. It is this assumption that the degrees ascend in constant ratio that makes these allotments so arbitrary, not the percentage weighting among the characteristics, although that should also be different as between any two differing sets of circumstances.

Ranking Technique Used to Determine Scales. So many companies have been content to adopt ready-made plans that it is refreshing to discover cases where plans have been locally developed. Nicholas L. A. Martucci [3] describes one case where this was done

[3]*Personnel*, XXIII, No. 2.

jointly by a four-plant manufacturing company and a local union which represented the labor in two of the plants. Officers of the national union at first declined to participate so the management went ahead with their other two plants, which were nonunion. Then when the union officials found that the management planned to use analysts from outside, that is, men who were strangers to the company, the union officials reversed their decision and allowed three of their men to go on the joint committee with three management men. One of the new analysts became chairman and head of the new job evaluation department. He reported to the manager of manufacturing, who was also a director of the company. A manual on job evaluation was used for instruction of the analysts and they in turn helped the supervisors to interest the stewards. Further development began by selecting and describing twenty-nine key jobs that would represent the spread of skill and ability from bottom to top. The analysts studied these jobs in all four plants and soon agreed on the final descriptions. In the meantime, all sorts of plans were considered, and a decision was reached to use a weighted-in-points plan. Next many characteristics were considered and from them twelve were selected that were common to all of the twenty-nine key jobs. The characteristics were then redefined to assure consistent interpretation. At this stage all members of the committee made independent allocations of percentage shares for the characteristics and checked their judgments against the twenty-nine job descriptions. This was repeated after a lapse of ten days. Results were tabulated, differences argued, and final judgments averaged.

The final step in developing the plan was to have the committee determine the division of the factor into degrees or levels in order that factor yardsticks might be designed for measuring the degree of each factor in all jobs. For this purpose, the brief narrative account of each factor for the key jobs, as written by job analysts, was transcribed on cards. The cards, identified according to factor and job title, were grouped to facilitate handling. Each committee member was given a group of twenty-nine cards, one for each key job, for each of the twelve factors included in the plan. The committee was directed to rank the twenty-nine jobs, one factor at a time according to the relative degree of the factor and compare the card content with the factor definition. The key jobs were ranked twice for each factor during a ten-day interval. Because judgments made by individual committee members were based on interpretation of available facts, the rankings were analyzed for statistical reliability in the same way as those for estimating factor percentage values. Again, it was necessary to return to the committee with the results of all judgments and reconcile differences of opinion.

Nature of Job	Degree of Possible Injury	Points Allowed			
		Persons Exposed			
		1	2	3	4+
A. Slight chance for injury Using hand tools, manual handling of light materials. Recording or observing.	A. Minor burns, cuts, bruises, etc.	2	3	4	6
	B. Injury causing one week or less of lost time.	5	6	8	10
	C. Injury causing over one week of lost time.	10	11	12	14
	D. Total or permanent disability.	15	17	18	20
B. Conditions quite safe Using power tools, spot welding, grinding, heating equipment, or the like.	A. Minor burns, cuts, bruises, etc.	4	5	7	10
	B. Injury causing one week or less of lost time.	7	8	10	13
	C. Injury causing over one week of lost time.	12	13	15	17
	D. Total or permanent disability.	17	19	20	23
C. Conditions generally safe Using power machine to process. Controlling boilers and electrical equipment. Handling large or heavy materials near others.	A. Minor burns, cuts, bruises, etc.	5	8	10	13
	B. Injury causing one week or less of lost time.	8	11	13	16
	C. Injury causing over one week of lost time.	13	15	18	20
	D. Total or permanent disability.	19	21	24	26
D. Conditions hazardous Alertness necessary to prevent injury. Moving materials with power mobile equipment.	A. Minor burns, cuts, bruises, etc.	8	11	13	16
	B. Injury causing one week or less of lost time.	12	14	16	19
	C. Injury causing over one week of lost time.	16	19	21	24
	D. Total or permanent disability.	21	24	26	29
E. Conditions very hazardous Extreme caution necessary at all times. Handling high-tension electricity or explosive and inflammable materials.	A. Minor burns, cuts, bruises, etc.	10	13	16	19
	B. Injury causing one week or less of lost time.	13	16	19	22
	C. Injury causing over one week of lost time.	18	20	24	27
	D. Total or permanent disability.	23	26	29	32

FIGURE 28. GUIDE CHART—RESPONSIBILITY FOR DETERMINING THE SAFETY OF OTHERS CHARACTERISTIC. (Sylvania Electric Products Company.)

Characteristics of Operation		Speed of Operation	Per Cent of Time Exercised				
			V	W	X	Y	Z
			0 10	11 30	31 50	51 70	Over 70
A—variations few and simple. Tasks become practically automatic. Duties highly repetitive and learned in a short time. Duties nonrepetitive but of such nature that methods are obvious. Decisions established by frequent repetition of similar conditions.	J—Immediate actions are not controlled by other men, processes or machines. Attention to coordinate actions with others are not required.	S—Moderate	1	5	10	15	20
		T—Fast	1	5	10	20	25
		U—Extremely fast	2	5	15	20	30
	K—Attention required to coordinate manual actions closely with other men, processes, or machines. Example: Catcher-piler.	S—Moderate	1	5	15	20	25
		T—Fast	2	10	15	25	30
		U—Extremely fast	2	10	20	30	40
	L—Makes routine decisions. Selects. Inspects and marks or assorts.	S—Moderate	2	10	20	25	35
		T—Fast	3	10	20	30	40
		U—Extremely fast	3	10	25	35	50
B—Tasks wherein variations are many and complex. Performance does not become automatic. Decisions not established by frequent repetition of similar conditions. Attention is required to vary speed, swing, or travel of power-driven equipment.	J—Immediate actions are not controlled by other men, processes, or machines, but duties are obvious or instructions are simple.	S—Moderate	3	10	25	35	45
		T—Fast	3	15	30	40	55
		U—Extremely fast	4	15	30	45	60
	K—Attention is required to coordinate closely manual actions with other men, processes, or machines. Attention constantly focused upon an operation to discern variations to which immediate response must be made.	S—Moderate	4	15	30	45	60
		T—Fast	4	20	35	55	70
		U—Extremely fast	5	20	40	60	80
	L—Attention to interpret detailed instructions. Attention to analyze and solve complex problems. Attention to plan complex operations.	S—Moderate	5	20	40	60	80
		T—Fast	6	25	45	70	90
		U—Extremely fast	7	25	50	75	100

FIGURE 29. GUIDE CHART FOR DETERMINING MENTAL EFFORT CHARACTERISTIC. (Original Plan of the U. S. Steel Corporation.)

Subdegrees. Some managements have tended to overdo good things, forgetting that system is never an end in itself, that there is a law of diminishing returns. Figure 28 is a three-layer measuring scale for the minor characteristic Safety of Others. This is one of 19 minor characteristics and carries a maximum weight of thirty-two points out of a theoretical total of 1,176 points. In fact, it is only one of four divisions under responsibility and yet it itself is sub-divided into five categories as to "Nature of Job," each of which is again subdivided into four degrees and each degree is given four conditions as to the number of persons for which the operator is responsible. This provides eighty different weights for one outcome. We present this one yardstick out of the whole set. If the company really wants all details this may be the way to get them, but the multiplicity reminds us of the man on the road to St. Ives.

Open to the same criticism is a four-layer scale (Figure 29) for Mental Effort. These four layers of subdivision run 2, 3, 3, 5, and give 90 different weights out of which only one answer is possible. Note the use of code letters. The latter can be used by the rater without recourse to the weights. This plan has been discarded.

The code letters also allow a further emphasis on adhering to the definitions, i.e., the letters and definitions can be separated from the

---

KNOWLEDGE (11—220)
  1. Intelligence
  (code) MNPRSTUWX
  2. Training and experience
  (code) ABCDEFGHJKL

RESPONSIBILITY (21—200)
  7. Safety of others
    Likelihood of injury
  (code) ABCDEF
  8. Supervision of others
    Supervisory units
  (code) LMNPRSTUVWX
  9. Material
    Likelihood of error
  (code) GHJK
  10. Equipment
    Care required
  (code) IOYZ

SKILL (23—300)
  3. Mental
  (code) HJKLMN
  4. Reacting Time
  (code) PRST
  5. Manual
  (code) ABCDEF
  6. Accuracy
  (code) XYZ

EFFORT (30—280)
  11. Mental
  (code) ABCDEF
  12. Physical
  (code) GHJKLM
    Fatigue
    (not measured separately)
  13. Surroundings
  (code) NPRST
  14. Exposure to accidents
  (code) VWXYZ
  Total of Maxima Values—1,000
    points

FIGURE 30. CHARACTERISTICS OF FRATER PLAN SHOWING CODE LETTERS FOR MEASURING SCALES

tables of points so that the evaluator will not be influenced by the thought of point results. The General Motors original plan included this precaution. Its characteristics were as in Figure 30.

In this plan there is no major characteristic for Working Conditions but (13) Surroundings and (14) Exposure to Accidents are tucked in with Effort. Broad skill is divided into Knowledge and Skill, each of which is again subdivided to make, in all, six minor characteristics. The code numbers for minor characteristics 1 and 2 are placed along two sides of a square table and the subsquares representing the various combinations are assigned point values as in other degree measures (see Figure 31). This is the simplest of the four measure tables. The largest one, with 1,056 subsubsquares, is for responsibility. Since there are four minor characteristics for one major characteristic, each side of the rectangular table carries two of the minor characteristics, one made subordinate to the other, and the coded degrees of the subordinate one are repeated under each degree of the other one (Figure 32).

		M	N	P	R	S	T	U	W	X
	A	11	18	26	35	45	57	70	86	105
	B	16	23	31	40	50	62	75	91	110
	C	23	30	38	47	57	69	82	98	117
	D	30	37	45	54	64	76	89	105	124
	E	38	45	53	62	72	84	97	113	132
	F	49	56	64	73	83	95	108	124	143
	G	60	67	75	84	94	106	119	135	154
	H	73	80	88	97	107	119	132	148	167
	J	88	95	103	112	122	134	147	163	182
	K	106	113	121	130	140	152	165	181	200
	L	126	133	141	150	160	172	185	201	220

KNOWLEDGE

Intelligence

Training & Experience

FIGURE 31. CODED TABLE OF DEGREE WORTHS FOR KNOWLEDGE. (*General Motors Job Evaluation Manual,* 3d ed.)

NOTES ON FIGURE 31

INTELLIGENCE

This factor is a measure of mentality or general intelligence required by the job for its successful performance. This faculty is usually held to be developed by education, but bear in mind that education need not necessarily be "formal" education. Required abilities have been listed in the chart but no degrees of "formal" education are indicated. If a job requires only one of the abilities for an established grade, it should receive the mark for that grade.

The job requires the employee to:

M. Carry out specific verbal orders.

N. Carry out simple written instructions; fill out a simple written report; carry out simple routine tasks not closely supervised.

P. Serve as a helper while learning a trade; operate on (or operate a machine on) repetitive work where no set-up is involved except the changing of tools or the setting of stops, etc., in a predetermined manner; deal with minor variations within a repetitive routine, as, bench assembly.

R. Add, substract, multiply, and divide; read dimensions and arrangement of "details" from blueprints; direct one or several helpers performing routine tasks; operate power equipment in loading and transporting materials in a routine manner; operate on (or operate machines on) one or more repetitive jobs where tool replacement or ordinary set-up only is involved; deal with variations within a repetitive routine, as, soldering, welding, testing, complicated assembly.

S. Set up automatic machinery for others; set up and operate machines on nonrepetitive work.

T. Make calculations involving fractions, decimals, and percentages; make general repairs to equipment requiring some knowledge of mechanical or electrical principles.

U. Read and analyze blueprints and follow out details on nonrepetitive work; use a thorough working knowledge of abstract mechanical or electrical principles.

W. Plan and direct the work of several others, both skilled and unskilled. (Example—Diemaker Leader)

X. Plan and supervise the work of skilled positions or large group of others. (Example—Assistant Foreman)

TRAINING AND EXPERIENCE

This factor is a measure of the practical knowledge required by the job for its successful performance. The relative evaluation of this factor should be based on the time ordinarily needed to acquire not only the experience prerequisite to assignment to the job, but also the time ordinarily required after assignment to learn to handle the job efficiently. Estimate the time required for the average employee to become proficient, to learn all the technical details required, and to acquire the necessary skills to successfully perform this job, and all necessary previous jobs leading to this job. A list of bench mark or example occupations to assist in selecting the proper mark should be worked out for each plant.

Months Necessary to Become Proficient on the Job, Before and After Assignment		Example Occupations
A	1 or less	
B	2	
C	3	
D	5	
E	8	
F	12	
G	18	
H	24	
J	36	
K	48	
L	Over 48	

		A						F		
		G	H	J	K		G	H	J	K
	I	21	28	36	45		47	54	62	71
L	O	28	35	43	52		54	61	69	78
	Y	36	43	51	60		62	69	77	86
	Z	45	52	60	69		71	78	86	95
	I	126	133	141	150		152	159	167	176
X	O	133	140	148	157		159	166	174	183
	Y	141	148	156	165		167	174	182	191
	Z	150	157	165	174		176	183	191	200

FIGURE 32. CODED TABLE OF DEGREE WORTHS FOR RESPONSIBILITY. (Sampled only by means of the four corner squares, out of the complete 66 squares.)

NOTES ON FIGURE 32

SAFETY OF OTHERS

This factor is a measure of the degree of care required by the nature of the job and the surroundings in which it is performed to prevent injuries or discomfort to *other* persons. The evaluation is based on the probability of accident and the seriousness of it. The direct acts or negligence only of the person performing the job should be considered.

LIKELIHOOD OF INJURY

On jobs requiring

A. Use of general hand tools, the handling of material manually, or the controlling of a process manually.

B. Use of edged hand tools, power-driven hand or machine tools, burning, welding, or heating equipment.

C. Use of hand or machine tools or the handling of material in positions above other persons.

D. Control of material through processing equipment, the material not being held in a fixed position.

E. Continuously moving or transporting of material with power-driven equipment.

F. Handling of highly inflammable materials, explosive materials; moving or controlling flow of molten materials.

SUPERVISION OF OTHERS

This factor measures the amount of responsibility inherent in the job or placed there by supervisory authority for the training, directing, and scheduling of other persons in order that the most effective use of their time and abilities can be secured and the most effective use of materials and equipment can be obtained. Supervision should not be confused with cooperation resulting in mutual direction between two workmen. The best approach to a proper evaluation of the amount of supervision inherent in a job is to measure the number and type of persons supervised.

> *General Labor*—All types of unskilled jobs requiring simple operations performed manually or with the aid of a few simple tools. Jobs that can be learned in less than three months.
>
> *Semiskilled Labor*—All jobs that normally can be classified as routine or involve the controlling of simple machine operations requiring some precision, mental application, responsibility, or knowledge of methods or materials. Jobs that are usually learned in three months to two years.
>
> *Skilled Labor*—All jobs requiring a high degree of skill and a wide knowledge of materials, equipment, or methods. Jobs that are usually learned in from two to four years.

Each job should be evaluated on a basis of two supervisory units for each general laborer, four supervisory units for each semiskilled laborer, and six supervisory units for each skilled laborer supervised. The total number of supervisory units will indicate the code letter to use in rating this factor. Jobs showing more than 50 supervisory units cannot usually be properly evaluated under this Manual.

Number of Employees Supervised	Class	Supervisory Units
	General Labor × 2 —	
	Semiskilled Labor × 4 —	
	Skilled Labor × 6	
	Total	

Supervisory Units	Code Letter	Supervisory Units	Code Letter
None	L	26 to 30	T
1 to 5	M	31 to 35	U
6 to 10	N	36 to 40	V
11 to 15	P	41 to 45	W
16 to 20	R	46 to 50	X
21 to 25	S		

PROCESSED AND PROCESSING MATERIALS

This factor measures the responsibility inherent in the job or placed there by supervisory authority for the care and prevention of damage to the processed and processing material. It can best be measured by considering the type of operation and the likelihood of damage. Responsibility cannot be considered as inherent in the job beyond the extent of a direct act of negligence on the part of the workman.

Processed material is that material which is being worked upon. Processing material is that material which is used as an aid in the performance of the requirements of the job. Processing material must not be confused with machinery and equipment.

Likelihood of error causing damage:

> G. Damage not likely to occur. Little attention required.
> H. Damage easy to avoid. Ordinary attention required.
> J. Damage fairly easy to avoid. Close attention required.
> K. Damage difficult to avoid. Extreme care required.

MACHINERY AND EQUIPMENT

This factor measures the responsibility for the prevention of damage to machinery and equipment and can be evaluated as a measure of the amount of care required to avoid damage.

Care required to avoid damage:

I. Working with machinery, tools, and equipment which are almost impossible to damage or in a manner in which damage is not likely to occur.
O. Ordinary attentiveness required to prevent damage.
Y. Damage fairly easy to avoid. Close attention required.
Z. Damage difficult to avoid. Extreme care required.

Trend Is Away from Complexity. We pointed out in our first chapter that job evaluation cannot be considered as scientific except in its objectivity. Most wage and salary administrators concur in this, but a few overzealous consultants still think that minute detail does make job evaluation scientific. Managers are usually practical enough to shun such plans, in fact, the Frater plan was never widely applied by its originating company. Since then similar efforts have appeared and this paragraph is written to discourage them. The reasoning of these overdoers is that "all job variables are solely linears." Thus they think that a multitude of finely divided measuring scales can be laid end to end without gap or overlap for accurate measurement of a whole job, omitting no detail. "The large number of points assists in the accurate evaluation of comparable jobs because minor differences of opinion on certain factors give rise to very small percentages of difference in the final result."

The latest of these efforts that has come to our attention uses 2455 points and divides skill into seven subcharacteristics as follows:

1. Knowledge—8 elaborately defined degrees, and each degree is subdivided for three speeds.
2. Experience—a two-way table, 12 x 10 values.
3. Contact—15 degrees with 3 speeds each.
4. Mental and Manual—11 degrees, each with 5 subdivisions, and each of these is given 5 subsubs.
5. Resourcefulness—15 degrees, each with a 3 x 9 table of values.
6. Analytical ability—9 degrees, with a 3 x 9 table of values.
7. Execution of Detail—5 degrees, each with 3 subdivisions and 5 speeds for each of those.

In addition to skill there are eight other characteristics, each with its microscopic measures!

The idea of bringing in speed variations is alone enough to queer any plan for evaluating a job. Necessary constant speed, as in keeping up with a mechanical process, or as a minimum coordination of sight and action, is legitimate, but *speed variation* is a man quality.

Tailor-Fitting Degree Definitions. It is fast, easy, and seemingly reassuring to accept the degree definitions and their point allotments from a plan already tried out elsewhere. The reassurance may, however, be short lived if the set of jobs to be evaluated differ in some unobserved aspects. We think the least that a management should do is to study each characteristic as it actually exists in his own set of jobs, determine the extreme limits, and then decide how the degree definitions should be written to include those limits and provide recognizable steps between. Our most successful analysts have insisted on listing an actual case to illustrate each degree range.[4] Paul M. Edwards, developer of the postwar steel plan jointly sponsored by "Big Steel" and the United Steelworkers of America, has gone much further in tailor-fitting. He has tested each proposed weight for correlation [5] with actual variations of all kinds in practice. It seems the union believes that "actual rates developed by supply and demand and bargaining in years past have recognized the nature of the problem better than the empirical job evaluation plan . . . [and this] makes it possible to pursue systematically in the future the same set of values that have governed both parties intuitively in the past." If pricing influences are to accompany the appraisal of job content, rather than to follow in negotiation, then no transference of a set plan to an entirely different application will be satisfactory.

In the particular case of basic steel the results have at least won bilateral acceptance. The joint committee started out with simple descriptions of one hundred and thirty "bench mark" jobs that existed in all forty-three plants of Carnegie-Illinois Steel Corporation. These pattern descriptions were checked and jointly approved. From these a system of degree values was developed (see end of this chapter) and put into a *Manual for Job Classification*. The *Steel Manual*, as it is called, was then checked against the same jobs in other plants and corrections were made until both parties accepted all the bench mark job descriptions and degree allotments. After several months more, 1250 bench mark jobs were described, rated, and added to the *Manual*. A further trial was made by applying the new system to the whole Gary works, and after seeing the results the U. S. Steel Corporation agreed to use the Gary job descriptions as

---

[4] For an elaborate check list to guide this preparation work see *Training and Reference Manual for Job Analysis*, War Manpower Commission, Bureau of Manpower Utilization, Division of Occupational Analysis and Manning Tables, June, 1944, pp. 10–52.

[5] P. M. Edwards, "Statistical Methods in Job Evaluation," *Advanced Management*, XIII, No. 4.

specimens for all its plants. A correlation check with jobs in other plants showed that about 80 per cent of all jobs were in line with the specimens.

By the spring of 1950 over 5,000 jobs had been classified, in 450 plants, which meant a coverage of about 450,000 employees, and "with satisfactory results both to the Companies and the Union members."

In general and as a matter of principle we have heretofore maintained that past pricing influences do not belong with the job characteristics. To whatever extent such influences do belong to jobs they belong only because of past precedents and customs which should not always be perpetuated, or they result from economic forces which change, and in either case we have believed they should be considered at the end, that is, they belong with the last step, which is the money pricing of objectively appraised jobs. In all transactions regarding property all agree that quality and weight or volume which constitute relative worth must be known before a price can be honestly set; otherwise the final results would be unreliable. Similarly the relative worth of jobs should, we have said, be established before a price is set. The question arises from the fact that jobs are human assignments and cannot be measured exactly. There is no disagreement in that, but experienced analysts know that because of the human aspect there is also a greater chance of error creeping into the values when they are set solely by bargaining. They claim that job evaluation has been mutually helpful because it has introduced a more objective and consistent means of deriving job worths. Hence they are apprehensive lest objectivity be lost. The difficulty is that no one can say with certainty which jobs have, and which have not, been appraised justly by past bargaining. If those who want past bargaining judgments retained through degree values will join with those who are apprehensive, and honestly sort out doubtful jobs so that the sure jobs only will be used for specimens, then perhaps both aims can be protected. In this new situation we recommend that, if characteristic and degree weightings are to be checked and readjusted so that they must evaluate specimen jobs as per custom and similar factors, great care be taken in the selection of specimens, or rather in the elimination of all prior job values that cannot be well substantiated. This requirement of itself seems almost prohibitive, but first class cooperation may achieve it and it looks as if basic steel has achieved it. Other unions that want past influences retained must be prepared to give equally constructive participation (see E. J. Maloy's report on participation in Chapter 5, page 83).

Measuring Scales for Weighted-in-Money Plans. What has been stated, in the paragraph just preceding this, is particularly pertinent here because, as Dr. Gomberg has aptly said, "The principal virtue of the factor comparison method when weights were distributed in money terms was that it lent itself readily to collective bargaining purposes." Elsewhere he states the reason as, "The factor comparison method is rooted in the existing wage structure of the firm."

Under this technique no predetermined degrees are used but each characteristic is carefully defined and ranges of points showing their relative worths may be used as guides to building the final measuring scales, which are sequences of well-described key jobs arranged according to rank for each characteristic, each key job weighted according to the proportion allowed for the given characteristic. Thus the final measuring scales, one for each characteristic, show definite measuring points from the lowest to the highest key job and thereafter any other job is measured on each characteristic merely by locating its proper position on the key job scale for the given characteristic. The final worth is a summation of all these characteristic measurements. As a sample of these key job measuring scales or ladder measures we select one for skill (Figure 33).

JOB	POINTS
	400
	380
Diemaker, combination dies, 1st	360
Patternmaker, wood, difficult	340
Toolmaker, 1st, complicated jigs Diemaker, 2d, irregular dies	320
Patternmaker, metal, difficult	300
Machinist, maint. 1st, diagnose, correct Patternmaker, wood, ordinary Boring mill, 1st, 16' stator frames Diemaker, 3d, stand. blkg. dies Machine operator, jig boring	280
Electrician, maint. 1st, lead. Toolmaker, 2d, complicated fixtures Patternmaker, metal, ordinary	260

FIGURE 33. LADDER MEASURE FOR SKILL

Plumber, st. fit. high press. san. Diemaker, 4th, plan shear dies Machinist, maint., 2d, rep. large mach. Tinsmith, maint., 1st, L/O develop. Planer 7' and over, fab. frames Lathe, engine, 1st, intricate	240
Carpenter, maint., 1st, fin. work Boring mill, 2d, loco. spiders & wheels Grind precision, 1st, gas eng. cranks Assembly, bench, 1st, fit scrape, align. Toolmaker, 3d, drill templates Auto. screw mach., 1st, die work & S. U. Lathe, turr. irreg. compl. arm. spiders Mill. machine, 1st, ordinary index	220
Machinist, maint. 3d, ordinary repairs Screw machine, 1st, micrometer & S. U. Assem. floor, 1st, align, large appara. Spray loco. finish large surfaces	200
Planer under 7', motor frames Lathe, engine, 2d, turn for grind Grind, precision, 2d arm, shafts Mill, machine, irregular, close	180
Boring mill, 3d, rough, fractional Milling machine, infixt, close limits Drill, radial, 1st, complicated, to L/O Assem. bench, 2d, gen. valve adjust.	160
Drill, rad. 2d, jig work, close Drill, sensitive, 1st, complic. to L/O Punch press, over 200 T. irregular	140
Craneman 200-ton double hook Weld, arc, gas, large mach. strength Mill, machine to fractional dimen.	120
Truck driver, licensed Milling machine, clearances Spray paint refrigerator cabinet Weld, arc or gas, repet. ref. cab.	100
Craneman 30 to 200-T. single hook Lathe, engine, 3d, rough off stock Auto. screw mach. no set-up Drill radial, 3d, clearance holes Punch press 80 to 150-T. blk. punch	80
Watchman, uniformed, patrol, dir. traffic Gateman, no patrol, directing visitors Truck driver, plant only Truck, shop electric Punch press, repet. strip or roll	60

FIGURE 33. (*Continued.*)

Job	Points
Assem. conveyor, simple, short cycle Spray apparatus, supply parts Grind small castings Weld, resistance and spot	40
Laborer, inside, bar stock Janitor—offices and lavatories Drill press, sensitive—simple	20
Sweeper, sweep and remove chips Labor, foundry, remove scrap, etc.	0

FIGURE 33. (*Concluded.*)

NOTE: Skill has been authoritatively defined as "Trade knowledge and the ability to apply it." The relative degree of skill required for dissimilar jobs and occupations can best be evaluated on the basis of length of training necessary for an individual of given mentality to be able to perform the work. (General Electric Company.)

Graphic Method of Determining Allotments. Daniel Weed was perhaps the first to turn to graphics for a solution to the problem of finding the true relationships between degrees and point allotments. Doubtless this early application was experiential rather than mathematical but it should have had greater influence. For instance, his study of Mentality and Training (see Figure 34) should have reminded all analysts that the effects of training are rapid through the first two years, after which they continue to increase, but at a nearly constant rate. The effects of mentality are less variable but show a steady gain in value for at least sixteen years. Three separate straight line graphs were set up to make the allotments for responsibility (see Figure 35). A curve that depicts ranking for the same characteristic is shown in Figure 36 (complete listing in Figure 37). There were other curves for the rest of the characteristics. They were used to guide the judgment of raters rather than as rigorous measures.

Several years ago, Paul M. Edwards published a curve for surroundings. Like the Weed curves it was plotted between degrees on the abscissa and weights on the ordinate and showed what all should have realized, that "ordinary working conditions call for little or no increment over ideal conditions, but that extreme conditions of disagreeableness require a heavier weighting compared with ordinary conditions, than any job evaluation plan has used." This high weighting does not apply to many jobs, but where such do exist the usual straight line allotments are likely to do some injustice.

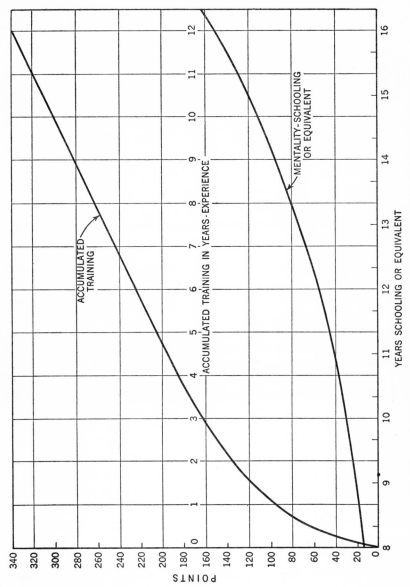

FIGURE 34. GUIDE CURVES FOR MENTALITY TRAINING. (General Electric Company.)

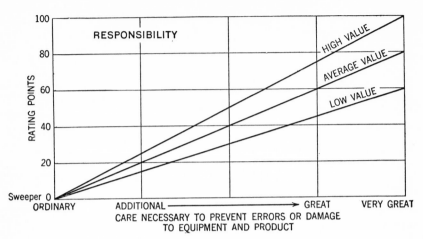

FIGURE 35. GUIDE CURVES FOR RESPONSIBILITY. (General Electric Company.)

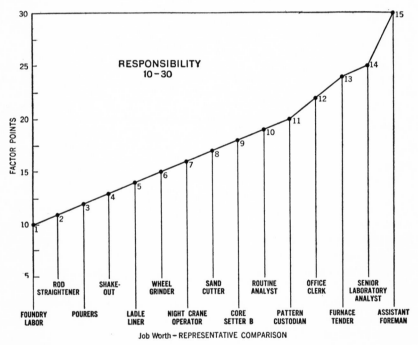

FIGURE 36. GRAPHIC RANKING ON RESPONSIBILITY. (National Founders' Association.)

CLASS	CLASS	CLASS
1. Sorter Cupola Helper Foundry Labor Coreroom Labor Cleaning Room Labor Yard Labor 2. Rod Straightener 3. Molder Helper Core Carrier Sandblaster Tumbling Sand Mixer (System) Scaler Furnace Charger (Helper) Cupola Charger (Helper) Furnace Helper Pourer Day Welder Night Welder Flask Carrier Maintenance Helper Core Sand Mixer Janitor 4. Machine Molder Machine Coremaker Core Blower	Core Paster Shakeout Washhouse Attendant 5. Squeezer Molder Ladle Liner Flask Maker Core Oven Attendant 6. Bench Molder A Machine Mold Finisher Bench Coremaker Facing Mixer Wheel Grinder Swing Grinder Chipper Electric Truck Operator Tester 7. Floor Molder A Floor Molder B Bench Molder B Sand Slinger Operator Floor Coremaker Senior Cupola Charger Night Crane Operator 8. Senior Furnace Charger Sand Cutter Mold Finisher	9. Core Setter A Core Setter B Core Assembler A Core Assembler B Truck Driver Pattern Maker 10. Routine Analyst Time Clerk 11. Inspector Day Crane Operator Senior Maintenance Man Pattern Custodian 12. Cupola Tender Office Clerk Shipping Clerk 13. Furnace Tender 14. Senior Laboratory Analyst 15. Assistant Foreman

FIGURE 37. FOUNDRY OCCUPATIONS CLASSIFIED BY RESPONSIBILITY. (A representative comparison of occupations selected from this list is shown in Figure 36.)

This curve for surroundings, with others, was derived by techniques of curvilinear correlation for which the reader is advised to consult a standard text on statistical methods. Incidentally when a degree-allotment curve shows a negligible rise for two or more degrees, those degrees can be combined into a single degree. If one can assume that geometric progression should be put into a degree measure a straight line should be located on a semilog grid from which geometric values can be determined. This was done long ago by A. W. Bass.[6] The semilog grid combines a logarithmic scale on the ordinate with a plain arithmetic scale on the abscissa so that a geometric series when plotted takes the form of a straight line or a

[6] *The Iron Age*, CXXXVIII, No. 11.

straight line provides geometric values. The desired number of degrees are equally spaced along the horizontal, proportionate values for known conditions of minimum and maximum degree worth are plotted vertically, and the two end points connected by a straight line. Values for the intermediate degrees are then read from the vertical magnitudes which correspond to the horizontal intervals, that is, according to the equally spaced points on the diagonal straight line. Job worths rated on such degree measures will fall into a straight line, or approximately so, when plotted on plain coordinates and there will be geometric progression in the rating.

Question of Exponential and Geometric Progressions. We postpone the main treatment of this question to Chapter 10 because putting such progression into the trend line can be done at that stage and that solution is least disturbing if you are remodeling a plan already established. When a plan is being designed, however, it is possible to achieve such progression at the source, that is, by arranging the degree allotments on a 1, 2, 4, 8, 16 relationship rather than on a 1, 2, 3, 4, 5 relationship. The Mills plan does this on some characteristics; for instance, responsibility has degrees of 1, 3, 5, 10, and 20 points.

There is one real advantage to leaving the solution to the last, namely, it may be impossible to put exact geometric progression into the degree allotments without resorting to fractions or without enlarging the amount of points used. Neither of these expedients is desirable. Psychologists tell us that the magnitude in characteristic worth of the highest job should usually not be more than three times that of the lowest job and should never be more than five- or sixfold. When a characteristic is valued at zero for the lowest job, the next lowest job, or the first to have a value, becomes the base for this check.

On the other hand, steps should not be less than 15 per cent. Thus if we call the first step unity, the maximum for step two would be 1.15, for step three 1.32, for step four 1.52, and for step five 1.75.

We have found a few plans which keep the relative weights down to two- or threefold and some plans which go to twentyfold, but general practice seems to lie between four- and sixfold and that certainly is enough for all hourly paid jobs. A limit to this relationship of, say, sixfold is therefore recognized by two professions which have had experience in observing job characteristics and it should be kept in mind. The rule is to establish both minimum and maximum values according to known conditions. Of course the maximum value need not be fixed for all time. Without these precautions one might make allotments for the degrees which would seem desirable on paper but which would be out of bounds as to actual relationships. It appears that this is one of the worst faults of some existing plans.

Measuring Degrees in Terms of Job Grade. Under the plan developed after 1944 by the United Steelworkers of America, CIO, and Carnegie-Illinois Steel Corporation, twelve characteristics are used with degrees varying from 3 to 9; the first degree is considered basic and the other degrees are allotted numerical values to total a theoretical maximum of 43, but no job has made a total above 32. These allotment job totals automatically classify the jobs from 1 to 32. Figure 38 is interesting in several respects: (1) Pre-

PRE-EMPLOYMENT TRAINING—I

Consider the mentality required to absorb training and exercise judgment for the satisfactory performance of the job. This mentality may be the result of native intelligence and schooling or self study.

Code	The Job Requires the Mentality to Learn To:	Bench Mark Jobs	Numerical Classification
A	Carry out simple verbal or simple written instructions necessary to the performance of a repetitive manual task, or a closely supervised nonrepetitive task. Make out simple reports such as crane reports and production cards. Operate simple machines and make simple adjustments where adjustments are limited. Use measuring devices such as scales, rules, gauges, and charts in the performance of work where action to be taken is obvious. Operate powered mobile equipment performing simple tasks where little judgment is required.	Stocker O. H. Laborer Loader-Shipping Thread. Mach. Oper. Barb Wire Mach. Oper. Pipefitter Helper Ingot Buggy Operator	Base
B	Perform work of a nonrepetitive or semirepetitive nature where judgment is required to obtain results. Lead or direct three or more helpers in a variety of simple tasks.	Pickler Stocker Keeper-B. Fce. Truck Driver Guide Setter-Bil. Slitter Operator	.3

FIGURE 38. SCALE FOR ONE OF TWELVE CHARACTERISTICS. (Taken from Collective Bargaining Agreement.)

Code	The Job Requires the Mentality to Learn To:	Bench Mark Jobs	Numerical Classification
	Exercise judgment in the operation of powered mobile equipment servicing a number of units or performing a variety of tasks. Set up and operate machines or processes requiring a variety of adjustments. Post detailed data to standard forms or write reports based on observation and judgment.		
C	Make general repairs to equipment involving the knowledge of mechanical or electrical principles. Interpret detailed assembly and complex part drawings such as involved in performing tradesman's duties. Direct the operation of a complex production unit which determines size, shape, analysis, or physical property of the product. Plan complex work details and procedures to obtain results.	Millwright B. M. Machinist "A" Heater-Hot Strip Tandem Mill Roller Moulder "A"	1.0

FIGURE 38. (*Continued.*)

employment Training has its degrees expressed in resulting abilities rather than in years of schooling, (2) under bench mark jobs there are job examples listed, and (3) the grade allotments are exponential or geometric. Two other characteristics are: Physical Effort and Surroundings have approximate geometric allotments as—base, .3, .8, 1.5, 2.5 and base, .4, .8, 1.6, 3.0 respectively. The other nine characteristics have arithmetic progression except for one or two larger jumps at the upper end in some cases, and in one case the interval is smaller at the lower end. The plan uses letters to code the levels, as *A, B, C* instead of first, second, and third (see Inequities Program—Agreements, Oct. 25, 1945 to Jan. 27, 1947.

7

JOB ANALYSIS—DESCRIBING AND SPECIFYING

The securing of the information and the writing of job descriptions is by far the longest and most important part of the program.

—W. J. Borghard

Job Analysis a Personnel Term. Time study men were called "job analysts" by some industrial engineers at the beginning but when referring to the job study itself the Taylor group stuck to "time study" and the Gilbreth group stuck to "motion study." From 1909 to 1912 a job study to aid job classifying, job rating, hiring, transferring, and promotion, that is, personnel functions, came into being. This development was originated under E. O. Griffenhagen [1] for the municipal service, at The Commonwealth Edison Company, Chicago, and carried to similar companies, and government offices, employing large clerical forces. As early as 1914 Harry A. Hopf was classifying clerical positions in banks and insurance offices.

In these large offices, where mechanized jobs were segregated, some real time study was done by industrial engineers and was duly called time study, but because most office work consisted of long and varied cycles there was a tendency to let nonengineering office specialists revamp methods and set tasks. Records of elapsed time or crude over-all timing was considered sufficient. Group tasks were much used. For instance, Wm. H. Leffingwell used a standardized work rate of clerical minutes per order (C.M.O.) for task. Like the emergency plant-wide tasks of 1944 it could be set without any analysis of individual jobs. In nearly all office studies the emphasis was on position classification and salary equalization, but the term *job analysis* was used regardless of emphasis or of scope.

---

[1] E. O. Griffenhagen, *Classification and Compensation Plans as Tools in Personnel Administration*, also A. M. A. Office Executive Series No. 17.

Hence in management literature the job study of industrial engineers was not always distinct from the job study of personnel men.

Confusion Has Arisen.[2] We recall all this merely to explain the confusion in terms that arose thereby. World War I caused a rapid growth in the new personnel movement and "job analysis" became one of its important activities.[3] The National Personnel Association in 1920 came out with a definition of job analysis which sounded in part like time study and this definition was widely accepted: "Job Analysis is that process which results in establishing the *component elements* of a job and ascertaining the human qualifications necessary for its successful performance." This definition was repeated in the committee report of 1922.[4] In professional addresses the term job analysis continued to be all-inclusive, that is, it covered every kind of job study, but as the personnel function grew the original personnel type of job study began to attract wider attention and to reclaim its name.

Factory Applications Restricted the Term. Although time study engineers had vied [5] with personnel people in the broad concepts of job analysis, in practice the former shunned the personnel term because their own motion and time study was narrower, that is, technical in purpose and restricted in scope. The main purpose of the latter was, and is, to improve tools and methods. The scope was, and is, to standardize the improved methods for determining tasks, using these for planning and rewarding but not as an aid to hiring people. When they extended their motion and time study to time-paid jobs the jobs would be no longer time-paid. Thus as the personnel movement slowly extended to factories, 1914 to 1919, their job analysis began to supplement the engineer's time study. Here the job analysis was definitely a review study of jobs which had already been standardized by time study or which did not justify any degree of time study. It was introduced solely for personnel purposes.[6]

Pioneering Completed by 1920. Many of our best-managed manufacturing companies shared in the development of personnel

[2] Roy W. Kelly, "Selecting and Training Interviewers," *Industrial Management,* April, 1919.

[3] Valentine and Gregg, *Outline of Job Analysis,* 1918, also *A Committee Report,* 1919, National Association of Corporation Schools.

[4] *Job Analysis,* National Personnel Association, 1922.

[5] W. O. Lichtner, "Time and Job Analysis in Management," *Industrial Management,* April, 1920.

[6] *Job Specifications,* Federal Board for Vocational Education, November, 1919.

functions. So far as we are informed, those which particularly contributed to the pioneer work of job analysis, 1914 to 1919, were:

Dennison Manufacturing Company
Detroit Steel Products Company
National Carbon Company
Youngstown Sheet and Tube Company
Westinghouse Electric & Manufacturing Company
American Optical Company
American Rolling Mill Company
International Harvester Company
Curtis Publishing Company
Cincinnati Milling Machine Company
National Cash Register Company
Leeds and Northrup Company

Before 1918 the job descriptions were in narrative form and not always confined to *minimum requirements of the job*. The National Carbon Company and the Youngstown Sheet and Tube Company introduced lists of paired opposites, such as standing-sitting, indoor-outdoor, and the Westinghouse Electric & Manufacturing Company divided such items into two groups, headed The Worker and The Work. This company also used square boxes for checking, which innovation was taken up by the Dennison Manufacturing Company, the International Harvester Company, and most others after 1918. This listing and checking was somewhat overdone, and left little space for the prose description of duties, but was better practice than some of the all-prose practice prevalent during World War II. The instructions which were used in 1919 were also pretty good (see Figures 39a and 39b). Soon after the deflation of 1920–22 every manufacturing company large enough to afford a personnel staff was using job analysis as its main source of data for personnel work. In fact, the personnel function may be said to have grown up during those memorable years 1922–29.

Terms Better Defined. Meanwhile in banks and insurance offices the office specialists continued their methods improvement, and classification, but found a new name for the combination, viz., "Salary Standardization."[7] J. K. Hackett, a member of the Job Analysis Committee already twice cited, wrote in 1923,[8] job analysis is "the determination of essential factors in a specific kind of work and of qualifications of the worker necessary for its component per-

[7] H. A. Hopf, *Salary Standardization,* Society of Industrial Engineers, 1921.
[8] *Management Engineering,* May, 1923.

JOB SPECIFICATIONS

Dennison Manufacturing Co.

THIS FORM IS EASY TO FILL OUT IF YOU FOLLOW INSTRUCTIONS CAREFULLY

1. GENERAL

NUMBER

DEPARTMENT NO.____SEC.____JOB NAME_____EMPLOYED____GRADE A B C SYMBOL

JOB DESCRIPTION_____

2. MINIMUM QUALIFICATIONS

☐ MALE   ☐ READ   ☐6   ☐2   ☐ BLUEPRINTS   PHYSICAL____
☐ FEMALE   ENGLISH   ☐ WRITE   SCHOOLING   ☐8   ☐4   ☐ SKETCHES   ____

TRADE EXPERIENCE_____ADVANTAGEOUS_____

3. NATURE AND CONDITIONS OF WORK

☐ PERMANENT	☐ FLOOR	☐ STANDING	☐ HEAVY	☐ VARIETY
☐ TEMPORARY	☐ BENCH	☐ SITTING	☐ MEDIUM	☐ REPETITIVE
☐ OVERTIME	☐ MACHINE	☐ WALKING	☐ LIGHT	☐ AUTOMATIC
☐ QUICK	☐ COURSE	☐ CLEAN	☐ HOT	☐ DUSTY
☐ SLOW	☐ FINE	☐ DIRTY	☐ MOIST	☐ ODORS
☐ DANGEROUS	☐ EXACTING	☐ GREASY	☐ WET	☐ GASES

MACHINES _____

PERSONAL TOOLS REQUIRED_____

TIME REQUIRED TO TRAIN A TOTALLY INEXPERIENCED MAN, PHYSICALLY AND MENTALLY CAPABLE, TO DO THIS WORK WITHOUT SUPERVISION OF INSTRUCTOR____

4. DUTIES AND QUALIFICATIONS

DUTIES	QUALIFICATIONS
JUST WHAT DOES HE DO WITH REFERENCE TO MATERIALS, MACHINES, EQUIPMENT, AND TOOLS?	WHAT QUALITIES SHOULD HE HAVE IN ORDER TO DO IT? CONSIDER TRADE EXPERIENCE, SCHOOLING, PHYSICAL QUALIFICATIONS AS EYESIGHT, HANDS, STRENGTH AND OTHER QUALIFICATIONS AS NEATNESS, PATIENCE, ETC.

5. RATES

☐ D. W.
☐ P. W.
☐ TASK AND BONUS   STARTING   NEXT
☐ TIME AND PIECE   WAGE_____   ADVANCE_____MAXIMUM_____
   RANGE   HOW SOON
   ON P. W._____PUT ON P. W._____

6. PROMOTION TO_____ HOW SOON_____ FROM_____

7. RELATED JOBS. WHAT OTHER JOBS IN THE PLANT USE TO ADVANTAGE EXPERIENCE GAINED IN THIS JOB?_____

8. EXITS. WHAT IS THE MOST COMMON REASON WHY WORKERS LEAVE THIS JOB?

9. REMARKS_____

DEPT. HEAD	FOREMAN	EMP. DEPT.	DATE

NOTE IF YOU THINK AGE, HEIGHT, WEIGHT, OR ANY OTHER QUALIFICATION, NOT PROVIDED FOR ABOVE, IS ESSENTIAL IN SELECTING A WORKER FOR THIS JOB, INDICATE THAT FACT UNDER REMARKS.

FIGURE 39*a*, JOB SPECIFICATIONS. (National Association of Corporation Schools, 7th Annual Convention (report), 1919.)

INSTRUCTIONS

GENERAL

1. It is necessary that the following instructions be carefully observed.
2. Write neatly and legibly.
3. Place a cross in the proper square when the item you are considering is helpful in selecting or training the worker for that job. Leave the square blank when it is unimportant.
4. Note carefully the information desired under each heading before writing. This will eliminate error and erasures.

WHAT IS WANTED

1. GENERAL
   Job Description should be brief, merely indicating the nature of the work. Do not put anything opposite *Grade A B C* or *Symbol*.

2. MINIMUM QUALIFICATIONS
   Be careful to distinguish between the qualifications of the worker who is on the job and the minimum requirements for another worker to do the job. For example, *English* □ *Read* ⊠ *Write* means that a worker *MUST* be able to write English before he can even be considered for that job. After *Schooling*, 6 and 8 refer to years of grade school, 2 and 4 to years of High School. *Trade experience* should be specified only when that experience is absolutely essential. After *advantageous* indicate any related work which may be helpful in this job.

3. NATURE AND CONDITIONS OF WORK
   Permanent means the *same* job month after month. In the square before *temporary* write the number of months.
   If the work is at a machine and on a bench put a cross in the square before *machine* and another cross in the square before *bench*. Make as many crosses as you think will help describe the work.
   Heavy, medium, and *light* refer to material or equipment hard to carry or move.
   Variety means different kinds of work, involving set-up and all adjustments necessary to completion of work; *repetitive* refers to straight production work involving only a small amount of adjustment and attention; *automatic,* doing identically the same thing in a purely mechanical way.
   Fine work demands care and neatness; *exacting* means continuous application to delicate or close up work.
   Dust includes sawdust, dust from polishing machines, dust from ground floors, etc.
   Fumes refer to objectionable smells, coming from ammonia, strong paints, glue, smoke, etc.
   Acids should be checked only when the worker handles acids as a part of his regular work.
   After *machines* write the different *KINDS* of machines used on the job, as lathe, printing machine, slitter, etc. If several machines operate together as one machine give the names of the separate machines. If the maker's name or the machine number is important, or if some special appliance on the machine makes it different from other machines of the same name, indicate that fact.

4. DUTIES AND QUALIFICATIONS
   Duties refer to the operations on the job and other things the worker has to do. Operations include make ready, actual operations on the job, and finishing up after the job. Other things he has to do include watching certain important things in the work, inspecting, or making adjustments during operations.
   Qualifications refer to such things as knowledge of material or machines, physical strength, quickness or delicateness of hands, ability to distinguish colors, other jobs that help the worker to do this job, etc. Give the qualifications of a first-class worker doing this job.

5. RATES
   Starting wage is the wage paid to a beginner with no experience that will help him on the job.

6. PROMOTION
   To what other jobs are workers promoted from this job? From what jobs are workers promoted to this job? Indicate preference for new or old workers.

7. EXITS
   Note if the job is one of the best in the department and much sought after.

8. REMARKS
   Include any special information which you think may be of interest, or helpful in selecting, training, or promoting work.

FIGURE 39*b*. INSTRUCTIONS TO ACCOMPANY FIGURE 39*a*.

formance." This definition omitted the "elements" which had always been the particular characteristic of good time study.

In factories time study was becoming influenced by Gilbreth's principles of motion economy. The present author, writing with Professor Joseph W. Roe in 1924, treated these complementary but at that time rival procedures, motion and time study, together under the end-step term *Job Standardization*.[9] Confusion as to the meaning of job analysis persisted, however, and in 1927 Charles R. Mann of the American Council on Education made the following plea: [10] "Reserve the term 'job analysis' for the various analyses of job descriptions made for special purposes afterwards." To this Mr. Hopf replied, "To me job analysis is a process, an approach to a situation; the job description or specification is the result of that process." In the *Handbook of Business Administration,* published by the American Management Association, 1931, E. O. Griffenhagen wrote:

> Where it is difficult to describe the common characteristics of a group of positions that are to be allocated to the same class in the process of classification, it is often possible to adopt the expedient of explaining the kind of ability, kind of experience, kind of skills, etc., that a person qualified to handle the work must possess. The first step in the process of classification is, therefore, *to learn all that is practical to learn regarding the duties of each position* in the service. The term job analysis, if it is to persist, ought to be restricted to this process.

Several years later Ralph C. Davis wrote:

> A job analysis is an investigation and analysis of a work assignment, and the conditions surrounding it, to determine its requirements from an organizational standpoint. In this respect it differs fundamentally from time and motion study. In most cases, it is used by the personnel department to procure information regarding the job and the worker that will facilitate employment, promotion, transfer, and training.

In short, job analysis had at last taken its place everywhere as a review study of duties subsequent to job standardization, and with the definite purpose of procuring all data on the man-job unit which the personnel staff needed. As such it became fundamental and, because it had also contributed to better classification, it shaped up as the basis of systematic job evaluation during the period 1931–37.

[9] See Section 15, "Operation Study and Rate Setting," *Management's Handbook* (New York: The Ronald Press Co., 1924.)

[10] *Improving Management Through Job Analysis,* by H. A. Hopf, Annual Convention Series No. 62.

We trust the term will hereafter stay put! For our own definition of job analysis see Chapter 1.

Earlier Job Analysis May Need to Be Discarded. Although modern job analysis is now hemmed in by job standardization on the one side and by job evaluation on the other side, it is still an inclusive term and as generally accepted covers job description, job specification, and job classification. Its scope begins with the preparatory work which precedes the gathering of preliminary job descriptions. If this preparatory work, the standardization of characteristics, the arrangement of the same on forms, and the like was completed before the proposed plan of evaluation was conceived there is little likelihood that such analysis can contribute, except by way of experience, to the further program. Even if the jobs are well described and classified, the data may be unsatisfactory. If it is worth while to have a new evaluation it will usually be best to start with no limitations. The reason is that the new plan may need to bring out certain data which were wholly lacking or not distinct on the old forms. Certainly it would be foolish to economize in the matter of foundational data for anything so important as a lasting job classification. With the same long-run view it is all-important to make the new preparation as sound and complete as foresight can allow.

Begin With Bench Mark Jobs. The first step in application of a job evaluation plan is to gather data from which a description and specification for each distinct or standardized job can be recorded, checked, and standardized. We say "standardized job" because it is a waste of time to describe jobs that are not reasonably definite. Preferably, a job should be made definite by the type of job study done by engineers, motion and time study. That precaution assures improved methods and something approaching stability. Hence a job study for the purpose of recording a final description is in the nature of a review and may be done by trained men, interviewers, investigators, analysts, etc., of the personnel staff. Usually the interviewer, investigator, or analyst will begin by listing all the jobs he thinks are distinct in a department, but it is better to compile, with the aid of supervisor and steward, a smaller list of "bench mark" jobs that are wholly distinct and common to several departments. This list can gradually be enlarged until all jobs are listed and checked by department heads, but if this work is new it is desirable to perfect the ways and means on a small list before going all out. Southern California Aircraft Industry used only twenty-eight key jobs for the whole industry.

Beware of assuming that like-titled jobs are always identical. In some establishments the payroll designations represent broad occupations, not specific jobs. If such is the case a tentative subdivision of each occupation may need to precede the solicitation of data. Four or five subdivisions, such as boring machine, labor grades 2, 4, 6, and 8, will usually suffice (see Figures 63 to 70, inclusive, for examples of these job descriptions).

Indicate the Kinds of Information Wanted. The information to be gathered must include (*a*) identifying data, namely equipment, operations, parts worked on; (*b*) job summary to show purpose and scope; (*c*) description of duties and responsibilities to clarify the nature of abilities necessary to meet requirements of *a* and *b;* and (*d*) specific data on all characteristics to allow definite appraisal as to kind and degree of each which may be involved. Note that for *d* there must be anticipation in the form or questionnaire of the predetermined degree definitions. If this is not made clear by the form or questionnaire the workers will not give all the needed data and information must be sought separately from the supervisor and others in a position to know. Some managements prefer this separation on the ground that, when a worker tries to furnish such data, they are unreliable and must be checked anyway. In that case the major part of the job description may be a prose statement of duties and responsibilities including both physical and mental demands of the job.

There are two difficulties in this. First, a worker may be superior to what the job actually requires and inclined to think of his own abilities rather than the minimum requirements. Such a description is exaggerated and is said to show a "halo effect." Second, he may be unused to describing anything accurately and be either too brief or downright garrulous without producing the desired facts.

A Manual Should Be Started. At this stage it may not be safe to complete a manual because eventually that will be the guide to harmonize the whole program, but it is necessary to have that part ready which defines the characteristics, their degrees if such are to be used, and relates to the degrees whatever scales are to be used for appraisal. This can be closed up by the top committee and officially accepted by top management. This is a prerequisite to the determination of procedure for gathering data and writing the descriptions. In the meantime the department analysts should, with supervisory advice, select the names and locations of the workers who are best suited to furnish the preliminary data.

Methods of Gathering the Data. There are four methods in use as follows:

1. Analyst calls employees to his desk where by use of a check list (see Figure 40) he solicits the information through an interview. This means several half-hour interviews for each job and considerable checking with the supervisors later on. It is not only time consuming, but is deficient in that the analyst may not envision the work place or influences affecting the actual performance.

2. Analyst interviews workers at their work places and fills out his prearranged headings (see Figure 41). This may take even more time, but it can bring better results because the analyst will see more than is told him. There is a two-way traffic in information.

3. Prepare an elaborate questionnaire such as Figure 42 or 52 and have the stewards help the workers fill them out. This has the advantage of transferring much of the judgment to the workers, but elaborate questionnaires alter the whole program and prevent simplification if they do not obscure important facts in a welter of details. Some employees are incapable of doing this as needed.

4. Supervisor has a group of employees who are on homogeneous jobs meet in a conference room where he and the analyst can talk to them for half an hour to give them much needed explanation concerning the program in general and the descriptions in particular. Each is then given a form and allowed to ask questions. They take the forms home to fill out or get the steward to help them. They are given a week or more for this. They return the rough drafts to their supervisor, who checks them in their presence and then hands them over to the analyst. The latter makes a composite description from the various ones entered for each job. When he is satisfied that these are complete and reliable he takes them back to the contributors for their final suggestions. Employee approval is important to the further procedure of the program. It is claimed that 30 to 60 per cent saving is made by this method.[11]

Principles of Form Design. As in the design of most forms the first principle (1) is to keep between excess complexity and excess brevity, that is, to provide for definite portrayal of all essential facts but no more. The second principle (2) is to arrange the essentials in the order which will facilitate the entry of data, the use of the information, and explanations of the results.

In endeavoring to keep within both principles there arises a choice between the use of prose and the use of a prearranged check list.

[11] J. E. Eitington, "Cutting the Cost of the Job Evaluation Program" *Personnel,* XXV, No. 4.

Job title ....

Alternate titles ....

Dept ....

Location ....

Normal force ....

Date ....

NATURE AND CONDITIONS OF WORK (Use ☐x to indicate; ☐XX to stress; or indicate percentage, e. g. ☐75 %)

Place
- ☐ Outdoor
- ☐ Indoor
- ☐ Platform
- ☐ Overhead
- ☐ Underground
- ☐ Scaffold
- ☐ Pit
- ☐ Unlocalized

Type
- ☐ Desk
- ☐ Bench
- ☐ Machine
- ☐ Counter

Activity
- ☐ Standing
- ☐ Sitting
- ☐ Hauling
- ☐ Climbing
- ☐ Lifting
- ☐ Walking

Operation
- ☐ Repetitive
- ☐ Varied
- ☐ Automatic
- ☐ Semi-Automatic
- ☐ Much activity

- ☐ Heavy
- ☐ Emergency
- ☐ Set-ups
- ☐ Layouts
- ☐ Templates
- ☐

Surroundings
- ☐ Clean
- ☐ Dirty
- ☐ Greasy
- ☐ Gangwork
- ☐ Crowded
- ☐ Orderly
- ☐ Distractions

Instruction
- ☐ Written
- ☐ Verbal

Illumination
- ☐ Natural
- ☐ Artificial
- ☐ Excellent
- ☐ Good
- ☐ Fair
- ☐ Poor
- ☐ Glare

Atmosphere
- ☐ Natural
- ☐ Ventilated
- ☐ Excellent
- ☐ Good
- ☐ Fair
- ☐ Poor
- ☐ Draughty
- ☐ Noxious Gas
- ☐ Fumes, odors
- ☐ Dust
- ☐ Very dry
- ☐ Humid
- ☐ Hot

Hazards
- ☐ Fire
- ☐ Electricity
- ☐ Hernia
- ☐ Eyes
- ☐ Ears
- ☐ Lungs
- ☐ Violence
- ☐ Hands

Remarks ....

OPPORTUNITIES:

Starting rate........per........Scheduled increases........Piece work........Av. weekly earnings........Inexperienced—time to learn........

REQUIREMENTS (Use X, XX, % or [R] —required; [P] —preferred)

Age	Height			Personal qualities	Experience
□ Max.	□ Max.	□ Bonded	□ Add and subtract	□ Unemotional	Kind
□ Min.	□ Min.	□ Color discrimination	□ Multiply and divide	□ Deliberate	....
Sex	Weight	Education—limits	□ Fract. and decimals	□ Quick	....
□ Male	□ Max.	Gr. 0 1 2 3 4 5 6 7 8	□ Percentage	□ Dynamic	....
□ Female	□ Min.	High 1 2 3 4	□ Shop arithmetic		□ Journeyman
Marital state		Coll. 1 2 3 4	□ Read blue prints	□ Tact	□ Apprentice
□ Single		Kind:—	□ Good handwriting		□ Inexperienced
□ Married		....	English	□ Patience	
Intelligence (fifth)		....	□ Understand		
□ Highest			□ Speak		
□ Second			□ Read		
□ Average			□ Write		
□ Low					
□ Lowest					

Special knowledge or experience........

....

Remarks ....

....

Name of
Interviewer ....

FIGURE 40. INTERVIEWER'S CHECK SHEET. (As used by E. J. Benge before 1932, *Industrial Relations*, III, No. 2.)

JOB EVALUATION AND DESCRIPTION SHEET		FACTORS	BASIS FOR RATING	PTS.
Job Title: VERTICAL BORING MILL OPR., SKILLED Departments: Planer (32)	KNOWLEDGE REQUIREMENTS	Education	Use complicated drawings shop math., arithmetic, equivalent to 2-yrs H.S.	
Brief description of Job: Works from complicated drawings, sets up own work on castings, forgings and some second operation work which is quite heavy.		Experience Required	2 - 3 years	
Required to work to very close tolerances - often .0005.		Initiative and Ingenuity	Perform and plan operations guided by general methods Decisions need ingen. & judgment.	
Grinds own tools, except special forming tools. Checks own work.	EFFORT	Physical	Continual physical effort handling medium and occas. heavy materials.	
Highly diversified and difficult set ups on a wide variety of irregular shaped parts; also tool room work when necessary.		Mental	Constant mental and visual attention.	
	RESPONSIBILITY	Material	$150 - $200.	
		Equipment	$250.	
		Safety of Others	Compliance with safety standards.	
Typical examples of work done: Cross slides, "A" type,		Minor Supervision or Training	Responsible for training of learners.	
Hex turret slides, rocker seats for sq.turrets. W.E. drums, rings, brackets, special pot and adjustable fixtures.				
Machines used if any: Vertical boring mill.	CONDITIONS	Working	Occasional disagreeable element. Vibration, dust, chips, heat, fumes.	
History of job Written by: (1) Grill (2) Gencope (3) Kingsbury Date		Hazards	Eye injury, hernia, loss of finger, crushed feet.	
Remarks:			Total Points	
			Approved by Committee Date	

W-S 582 10-44 SPS

FIGURE 41. KRESS SHORT FORM FOR GATHERING DATA. (Dartnell Personnel Administration Service.)

The latter certainly facilitates entries, and to a certain extent aids definiteness, thereby minimizing errors of interpretation, but some job duties cannot adequately be covered by a universal check list. Thus some combination of prose and check list is most satisfactory. The nature of the work involved and the thoroughness of treatment desired must determine the proportionate use of these two means of record. In all cases there must be harmony of order between related forms. This is important for entry, use, and explanation.

Besides the series of forms needed for job evaluation there are other forms to be made up using some of the same original data. We will therefore pause here to survey these other uses of the data.

1. Occupational or job class information as an aid to normal selection and placement; also as a guide to utilization of disabilities, and the like.
2. Information as to levels of skill, responsibility, and other abilities, as a basis for the revamping of jobs.
3. Information as to kind and degree of skill, responsibility, and other abilities, as a basis for planning transfer and promotion; hence a guide to training.

JOB RATING DATA SHEET

Occ. No. _____
Dept. _____
Class _____
Points _____
Grade _____

Job Name _____

Job Description:

FACTOR	D	POINTS
EDUCATION		
EXPERIENCE		
INITIATIVE		
PHYSICAL		
MENTAL		
EQUIP		
MATERIAL		
SAFETY		
W OF O		
WORK CON		
HAZARDS		

Typical Examples:

I. EDUCATION OR TRADE KNOWLEDGE

_____ Able to read, write
_____ decimals, fractions
_____ shop arithmetic
_____ handbook formulas
_____ geometry, trigonometry
_____

Explain use:

Drawings

	Simple	Ordinary	Complex
_____ sketches	___	___	___
_____ drawings	___	___	___
_____ number of dimensions	___	___	___
_____ wiring diagrams	___	___	___
_____ specifications	___	___	___

Extent used:

Measuring Instruments

_____ rule, scale, calipers, square
_____ micrometers
_____ fixed gauges—plug, ring, snap
_____ dial indicator
_____ vernier-height
_____ vernier-calipers
_____ bevel protractor
_____ sine bars
_____ jo-blocks
_____ pyrometer
_____ weigh scales
_____ shrink rule
_____

Trade Knowledge

_____ feeds, speeds, tools, work holding methods on specialized machine operation

_____ fundamentals of construction and operation of _____

_____ broad knowledge of _____
requiring _____ years apprenticeship or trades training covering

_____

_____

---

2. EXPERIENCE

Analyze job to determine the length of time usually required to learn to do the job duties satisfactorily, over and above any trades training where required.

_____ up to and including 1 month   _____ over 1 year up to 3 years
_____ over 1 month up to 3 months   _____ over 3 years up to 5 years
_____ over 3 months up to 6 months   _____ over 5 years
_____ over 6 months up to 12 months

Do not include apprenticeship or trades training in experience. Consider it under Education.

FIGURE 42. KRESS-COLE FORM FOR GATHERING DATA. (Dartnell Personnel Administration Service.)

3. INITIATIVE AND INGENUITY

Analyze the job as to complexity, variety of work assigned, standardization of duties, length of cycle per unit, amount and kind of planning required, kinds of decisions made, diagnosing and remedying trouble.

Work Assignment

Who directly assigns work?   How often?
Who checks work?   How often?
Describe inspection, if any:

Variety of Work: Quantity of Lots   Approximate Time Per Unit   Tolerances

Highly Repetitive   _____   _____ _____
Repetitive   _____   _____ _____
Short Runs   _____   _____ _____
Jobbing   _____   _____ _____
Repair & Maintenance   _____   _____ _____
                          (jobs per day)

Planning Work: State typical examples of planning that job requires.

Decisions Required:
    Examples   Effect of Error in Judgment

Trouble Shooting: State below typical examples of diagnosing and remedying trouble

4. PHYSICAL DEMAND

Analyze job requirements as to work position, elements of work which produce physical strain or fatigue, lifting, bending, etc.

Work Position   Percent of Time

Material Handling				
Weight of Material	N	O	F	C
Up to 1#				
1 to 5#				
Over 5 to 25#				
Over 25 to 60#				
Over 60#				

____ Sit   _____
____ Stand   _____
____ Walk   _____
____ Bend-Stoop _____
____ Lift-Handle _____
____ Hold   _____
____ Shovel Sand _____
____ Ride   _____
____ Push or Pull _____
____ Carry _____ lbs _____
     Arms in Unsupported
____ Position   _____

N = Up to 5% of time
O = 5% to 20% of time
F = 20% to 50% of time
C = 50% or more of time

Explain use of any material handling equipment, such as hoists or cranes. Describe any difficult work positions which may produce physical strain or fatigue.

FIGURE 42. (*Continued.*)

5. MENTAL OR VISUAL DEMAND

Analyze job as to mental or visual attention and alertness required.

Degree:
_____ Little - up to 20% of time   _____ Close attention on complex work
_____ Frequent - 20% to 50%   _____ High manual dexterity - close visual attention
_____ Continuous - over 50%   _____ Concentrated and exacting attention on very complex jobs as _____

Reasons:
_____ Intermittent duties   _____ Parts or equipment difficult to manipulate
_____ Length of cycle   _____ Tolerances difficult to maintain
_____ Handle small parts   _____ Machine adjustments necessary
_____ Check work   _____ Coordinate hand and eye - highly repetitive
_____ Speed of manipulation

Operating Points
Requiring Attention:

6. RESPONSIBILITY FOR EQUIPMENT

Equipment Involved	How can it be damaged through Carelessness	Estimated Cost to Repair

7. RESPONSIBILITY FOR MATERIAL

Analyze job for causes of scrap or rework caused by carelessness on the job. Consider amount of spoilage that may occur before detection, the value of labor and material up to this point, the salvage value if any and cost to repair.

Causes	Where discovered and by whom	Scrap or Rework	Probable Loss

8. RESPONSIBILITY FOR SAFETY OF OTHERS

Analyze job to see how some employee may be hurt through carelessness on this job. What care must be used to prevent injury to others?

Hazard Causing Injury	Who can be Injured	How can they be Injured
_____ Air Hose		
_____ Dropped Tools		
_____ Dropped Work		
_____ Electric Shock		
_____ Flying Part or Chips		
_____ Flying Work		
_____ Hot Material		
_____ Molten Metal		
_____ Wheel Breakage		
_____		

9. RESPONSIBILITY FOR WORK OF OTHERS

Is employee responsible for directing other employees? _____
How Many?

If so, describe nature of duties:

FIGURE 42. (*Continued.*)

10. WORKING CONDITIONS

Analyze job to see what disagreeable elements there are in working conditions
N = Up to 5% - O = 5-20% - F = 20-50% - C = Over 50%

Element	Cause or Source	Degree	Percent of Time Exposed	Remarks
Acid				
Cold				
Dust				
Fumes				
Grease				
Heat				
Noise				
Oil				
Steam				
Vibration				
Water				
Weather				
Respirator				

11. UNAVOIDABLE HAZARDS

Analyze job for possible hazards, either accident or health, even though safety devices are in use.

Hazard	Cause	How Can Employee be Injured
Abrasions		
Burns - Minor		
Burns - Major		
Crushed Fingers		
Crushed Toes		
Cuts		
Eye Injury		
Falls - Ladder, Etc.		
Fractures		
Hernia		
Loss Fingers, Toes		
Loss Arm, Leg		
Shock		

Employees Who Regularly Do This Job   Remarks:

Man No.	Day	Rate Base	Earn.	Man No.	Day	Rate Base	Earn.

Approvals

I approve the facts and ratings unless otherwise noted above.

_____

_____

		Date	Man
Written Up			
Rated			
Checked			
Typed			
Revised			

FIGURE 42. (*Concluded.*)

4. Information on which to base a system of merit rating; hence a guide to systematic follow-up and morale building.

5. Indication of working conditions which may be the source of occupational diseases, fatigue, or industrial injuries; hence the improvement of preventive action.

A general plan for all these personnel activities should be outlined at this stage of development so that a unified set of forms can be laid out.

Examples of Preliminary Job Descriptions. A good example of the use of prose and check list, neither of which is elaborate, is Figure 43, put out as a sample by the Civilian Personnel Division Headquarters, Services of Supply, War Department.

PRELIMINARY JOB DESCRIPTION SHEET

Establishment __Philadelphia QM Depot__   Present Payroll Designation _____Railroad Trackman_____

Section ___Utilities Railroad___   Proposed Change In Designation _____

Title of Immediate Supervisor _____Foreman Railroad Trackmen_____

GENERAL NATURE OF WORK

1. Under immediate supervision of Foreman Railroad Trackmen, maintains or installs railroad tracks within Depot. Works in group of from 6 to 15 individuals.

2. Maintains tracks by jacking and placing ballast under ties. Unspikes and respikes rails to correct gages. Removes worn ties and replaces with new ties by jacking rails, removing spikes, and respiking rails to new ties. Replaces worn or broken rails by unspiking and removing them and by placing, gaging, and spiking the new rails.

3. Installs new track by performing operations similar to above.

4. This is essentially a heavy labor job.

Precision (tolerances) required:

Check Working Conditions	Check Type of Supervision	Check Extent of Inspection
1. Inside	1. General	1. Immediately after—1
2. Outside—2	2. Immediate—2	2. After other operations
3. Abnormal temperatures	3. Continuous—3	3. 100% inspection—3
4. Unusual noise	4. Intermittent	4. Sampling or spot check
5. Fumes, dust, etc.	5. Written Instructions	
6. Unusual hazards (describe below)	6. Oral instructions—6	

Danger from moving heavy rails and from swinging sledge

FIGURE 43. PRELIMINARY JOB DESCRIPTION SHEET

a. The upper portion identifies the job, indicates its general place in the organization, and gives the title of the immediate supervisor.

b. Space is next provided for full outline of the duties performed. As will be noted in the job description of a Railroad Trackman, the duties performed may be described according to the order of their importance. Duties of another type of work might be described according to the sequence of operations. Note also that it is customary to begin each sentence with a verb and to eliminate unnecessary words. Most important is that this portion of a job description be factually accurate, not a matter of opinion or an ideal assignment of duties. The use of adjectives to compare the job in question with another job should be kept at a minimum. Instead, exact examples of duties performed prove more useful. One company supplements its prose examples with picture examples. A complete description should indicate what work is done, and if significant, how, when, and where the work is carried on and within what precision tolerances or limits of decision. Occasionally, it may be helpful to indicate also the reason for an operation and its relation to other work of the establishment.

c. On the back of the job description (at bottom here) space is provided for certain detailed information relating to the degree of supervision, machines or equipment used, materials worked upon, specific precision requirements, inspection of work, and working conditions, such as indoor or outdoor, abnormal temperatures, unusual noise, fumes, dust, or hazards.

Filling Out the Form. If the form is to be filled out by the interviewer, as intended in Figure 43, all explanations can be oral, but it is better to prepare a manual. If a form is to be filled out by the employees it must carry written explanations or be so explicit that there is little room for misunderstanding. It is not practical, however, to eliminate all personal explanation because, left to himself, the employee is likely to overstate the importance of his job or to omit pertinent details, often both. Under guidance an employee-filled blank, at the work place, has several advantages: the direct contribution of data gives him a sense of participation, brings out details which might otherwise be overlooked, and provides a better background for subsequent analysis. Always the immediate supervisor, and sometimes others who may be involved, should be consulted. The job description form (Figure 44), which is really a standardized arrangement for answers and checks, is a good compromise between the extremes of complexity and brevity. It is meant to be filled out by the employees but with the aid of an investigator.

JOB DESCRIPTION FORM

NAME_____TITLE_____

DEPT._____DATE_____

1. DESCRIPTION OF DUTIES:

   A. DAILY

   B. PERIODIC

   C. OCCASIONAL

2. MINIMUM STARTING REQUIREMENTS FOR POSITION:

   (Note: Do not state your own personal education, experience, etc., unless it coincides with the minimum requirements.)

   A. MINIMUM EDUCATION—Check one
      1. Read, write, and speak English
      2. Grammar school
      3. High school
      4. College
      5. Graduate work or special courses

   B. MINIMUM EXPERIENCE—Check one
      1. Less than one month
      2. One to three months
      3. Three months to one year
      4. One, to two years
      5. Over two years

3. RESPONSIBILITY

   A. SAFETY OF OTHERS—Check one
      1. None.
      2. Up to five persons
      3. Six to ten persons
      4. Eleven to fifteen persons
      5. Over fifteen persons

   B. WORK OF OTHERS—Check one
      1. None
      2. Up to five persons
      3. Six to ten persons
      4. Eleven to fifteen persons

   List names of jobs and describe briefly the duties of these jobs.

FIGURE 44. JOB DESCRIPTION FORM

C. EQUIPMENT OR PROCESS—Check the approximate value that you are responsible for.

1. None
2. Up to $25.00
3. $26.00 to $250.00
4. $251.00 to $1,000
5. Over $1,000

Please name equipment or process that is your responsibility.

D. MATERIAL OR PRODUCT—Check the approximate value that you are responsible for.

1. None
2. Up to $25.00
3. $26.00 to $250.00
4. $251.00 to $1,000
5. Over $1,000

Please name material or product that is your responsibility.

4. EFFORT

A. WHAT PORTION OF YOUR TIME IS SPENT:

Standing_____%   Sitting_____%   Climbing_____%
Lifting_____%   Walking_____%   Other_____%

B. WHAT PHYSICAL REQUIREMENTS ARE NECESSARY FOR THE PROPER PERFORM-
ANCE OF YOUR DUTIES—(Strength, height, dexterity, etc.)?

5. WORKING CONDITIONS

A. PLEASE STATE YOUR REGULAR WORKING HOURS

B. HAZARDS—Check the ones that you are subject to.

1. Machine hazard
2. Acid fumes
3. Heavy lifting
4. Heat
5. Wet
6. Dust
7. Nerve strain
8. Eye strain
9. Others

6. WHERE DO YOU GET YOUR WORK?

7. WHERE DOES IT GO?

8. TO WHOM ARE YOU IMMEDIATELY RESPONSIBLE AND WHAT IS HIS
POSITION?

9. CAN YOU SUGGEST ANY IMPROVEMENTS WHICH CAN BE MADE IN
PERFORMING YOUR WORK?

FIGURE 44. (*Concluded.*)

Several of these answers per job are then built into a single composite record acceptable to all concerned and summarized on the job specification form (Figure 45). A form to be filled out independently by three analysts is shown in Figure 53.

JOB SPECIFICATION

Job
No.....................

Rate per hour...........

Job
Title............................. Dept.............................

Duties...

....

....

....

....

Skill	Responsibility	Effort	Working Conditions
Education required	Safety of others	Kinds: Standing _____% Sitting _____% Climbing _____% Lifting _____% Walking _____%	Place Type Surroundings
Experience required	Work of others	Bending _____% Other _____%	Atmosphere
		Repetitive _____ Intermitt. _____	Hazards
	Kind of equipment or process	Varied _____	
		Age _____to_____ Height _____ Weight _____ Sex _____	Other
	Kind of material or product	Light thinking Average thinking Deep concentration	
	Other responsibilities		

FIGURE 45. JOB SPECIFICATION

Some have made a distinction between the terms *description* and *specification*. We do not think this is important. When the distinction is made description refers to the recording of conditions, duties, etc., while specification refers to designation of qualifications needed for satisfactory performance of duties.

A combined description-specification, but to be filled out by the interviewer, is shown in Figure 46*a*. This is essentially a check list on which there is some prose description so that there is none on the rating sheet, Figure 46*b*. Together they constitute a complete job specification. The same can be said for Figure 47 but it should allow for prose description to show certain aspects not otherwise provided for.

JOB DESCRIPTION FORM

Job Title—Gear Cutter

1. EDUCATION OR TRADE KNOWLEDGE
    - ✓ Read and write or follow verbal instructions.
    - ✓ Add and subtract whole numbers.
    - ✓ Multiply and divide.
    - ✓ Fractions and decimals.
    - ✓ Handbook formulas.
    - ___ Advanced shop mathematics and trigonometry.

    - ✓ Read blueprints—Simple.
    - ___   "   "   Fairly complicated.
    - ___   "   "   Very complicated.

    - ___ Education equivalent to two years of High School.
    - ✓   "   "   " four   "   "   "   "
    - ___   "   "   " one   "   " trades training.
    - ✓   "   "   " four   "   "   "   "
    - ___   "   "   "   "   "   " technical university training.

    Trade Knowledge Necessary
    - ✓ Some in a specialized field of process.
    - ___ Broad shop trade knowledge.
    - ___ Technical knowledge to deal with involved engineering problems.

    Gauges and Instruments Used

✓	Scale	___	Sine bar
✓	Caliper	___	Plug, ring, snap gauge
___	Depth gauge	___	Thread plug gauge
___	Dividers	___	Gauge blocks
___	Combination square	___	Dial bore indicator
✓	Feeler gauges	___	Vernier protractor
___	Surface gauge	___	Indexing head
___	Dial indicator	___	Mechanical comparitor
✓	Micrometer caliper	___	Optical comparitor
___	Vernier height gauge	___	Brinell hardness tester
___	Vernier micrometer caliper	___	
___		___	

FIGURE 46*a*. A SPECIAL CHECKLIST FOR GATHERING JOB DATA FOR AN N.M.T.A. RATING.

2. EXPERIENCE TO ATTAIN PRODUCTION AND QUALITY

___ Up to three months.
___ Over three months up to one year.
_√_ Over one year up to three years.
___ Over three years up to five years.
___ Over five years.

3. INITIATIVE AND INGENUITY

Must keep four gear shapers in operation at all times, each cutting a different type of gear. Must change the setup for each machine on the average of once per day.

Must keep in mind the capabilities of each machine in assigning work to machines.

In changing the setup of the machine the operator must keep in mind the difference in machines since each gear shaper is a different model.

4. PHYSICAL DEMAND

Most gears are light (10 pounds) and can be easily lifted by hand.

About 25 per cent of the work consists of heavy gears (up to 70 pounds). These gears must be lifted by hand since no crane is available. A helper is required on the heavy gears in lifting them to the machine.

Requires constant moving in checking and loading each of four machines.

5. MENTAL OR VISUAL DEMAND

Must constantly refer to charts during setup, in order to get the correct gear train.

Must check the first gear of each lot for the correct number of teeth after the first revolution of the table. Must check the correct over the pin size on the first and every tenth gear.

6. RESPONSIBILITY FOR EQUIPMENT OR PROCESS

___ Probable damage to equipment or process is negligible.
___   ”   ”   ”   ”   is seldom over $25.
_√_   ”   ”   ”   ”   ”   ” $250.
___   ”   ”   ”   ”   ”   ” $1000.
___ Probable damage is exceedingly high, reaching several thousand dollars.

7. RESPONSIBILITY FOR MATERIAL OR PRODUCT

Probable loss due to damage or scrapping of materials or product is seldom over:

___ $10
___ $100
_√_ $250
___ $500
___ very high, up to several thousand dollars.

8. RESPONSIBILITY FOR THE SAFETY OF OTHERS

Only reasonable care to own work necessary to prevent injury to others, and accidents, if they should occur, would be minor in nature, such as cuts, bruises, abrasions, etc.

FIGURE 46a. (*Continued*)

9. RESPONSIBILITY FOR THE WORK OF OTHERS

_√_ Responsible only for own work.

___ Responsible for instructing and directing one or two helpers 50% or more of the time.

___ Responsible for instructing and directing up to 10 persons.

___   "   "   "   25   "

___   "   "   "   over 25   "

10. WORKING CONDITIONS

What part of the day on the average up to:

	Some	Much	Half	All
Harmful fumes, gases, smoke, and odors..	___	___	___	___
Dirt, dust, and grease	_√_	___	___	_√_
Oil....................................	___	___	___	___
Acids	___	___	___	___
Harmful weather conditions—Outside	___	___	___	___
Heat	_√_	___	_√_	___
Cold	___	___	___	___
Humid	___	___	___	___
Drafts	_√_	___	___	_√_
Water	___	___	___	___
Noise	___	___	___	___
Vibration	___	___	___	___
Chips and shavings	___	___	___	___
Special clothes, Goggles, Respirators	___	___	___	___
Eye strain	___	___	___	___
Illumination Excellent	___	___	___	___
Fair	___	___	___	_√_
Poor	___	___	___	___
Surroundings Crowded	___	___	___	___
Orderly	___	___	___	_√_

11. HAZARDS

___ Accident or health hazards negligible.

_√_ Accidents improbable, outside of minor injuries, such as abrasions, cuts, or bruises. Health hazards negligible.

___ Exposure to lost-time accidents, such as crushed hand or foot, loss of fingers, eye injury from flying particles. Some exposure to occupational disease, not incapacitating in nature.

___ Exposure to health hazards or incapacitating accident, such as loss of arm or leg.

___ Exposure to accidents or occupational disease which may result in total disability or death.

FIGURE 46a. (*Concluded*)

Job Title—GEAR CUTTER

Factors	Degrees					Points
	1	2	3	4	5	
SKILL						
1. Education			√			42
2. Experience			√			66
3. Initiative and Ingenuity			√			42
EFFORT						
4. Physical Demand			√			30
5. Mental or Visual Demand			√			15
RESPONSIBILITY						
6. Equipment or Process			√			15
7. Material or Product			√			15
8. Safety of Others		√				10
9. Work of Others	√					5
JOB CONDITIONS						
10. Working Conditions		√				20
11. Unavoidable Hazards		√				10
Labor Grade __6__	TOTAL					270

FIGURE 46b. JOB RATING SHEET. (The National Metal Trades Association)

Writing the Official Description—Specification. Figure 47 is the form originally used by Kress and hence the pattern for all NEMA, N.M.T.A., and Cole Panel (airplane companies) applications. In practice one whole page or more may be used for the prose description, but if so it must be abbreviated to be put on the Kress Job Rating Specification sheet. Figure 48 is an actual worker's preliminary description of his job made without assistance. It would be rewritten in less than 300 words by the analyst and still further abbreviated as already explained. Any data called for in the form and not provided by the preliminary description must be procured by the analyst from the supervisor and/or from other reliable sources. In the case of hourly paid jobs it is unlikely that there will be any misunderstanding of who supervises a job, but all job descriptions must be reconciled with existing organizational understandings or vice versa, so the analyst must be sure where every job belongs, and where responsibilities start and stop.

The existing job title may need simplifying and harmonizing with other titles, that is, it should be expressed in terms of the occupational class of work within which it falls and should distinguish it from kindred job titles by the addition of a modifying adjective such as Assembler—Wire, Cable, and Hose, or so far as practicable by nothing more than the grade number, such as: Carpenter, 1 (NEMA and Cole start grade numbers from the top, N.M.T.A. from the bottom). Sometimes a series of occupational code numbers may be established which can be associated with all job titles and used on payroll records. This is particularly desirable where tabulating equipment is used. The new title and date of writing should head the official job description.

Getting the description into satisfactory shape takes care and time. It may have to be rewritten three or four times.[12] NEMA suggests beginning with "Under direct supervision of. . . ." Then list basic duties. Begin each sentence after the first with a word which denotes action, such as: Prepare, Perform, or whatever active verb is most helpful in the elaboration of the basic duties already listed. Avoid inconsequential items that add nothing important and discard a description every time there is a minor change in job content. Avoid abstract phrases or any words you or the users do not understand. When the description really gives a thumbnail picture of the job, and distinguishes it from jobs related to it, approval

[12] Jack Grady, "How to Write Good Job Descriptions," A.M.A. Management Review 6/1948, and NICB Studies in Personnel Policy No. 72 "Job Descriptions."

should be obtained from the supervisor, and eventually from the department head. Figures 49 and 50 give a fair representation of good description practice. Other examples, with job ratings added, will be shown in later chapters.

JOB RATING SPECIFICATION

Occ. No.＿＿＿＿＿＿＿＿＿

Job Name   Dept.＿＿＿＿＿＿＿＿＿

Description   Class＿＿＿ Grade＿＿＿＿＿＿＿

Points＿＿＿＿＿＿＿

Factor	Specifications	Rating	
		D	Pts
Education			
Experience			
Initiative and Ingenuity			
Physical Demand			
Mental or Visual Demand			
Responsibility for Damage to Equipment.			
Responsibility for Material or Product...			
Responsibility for Safety of Others			
Responsibility for Work of Others			
Working Conditions ...			
Hazards			

FIGURE 47. NEMA FORM FOR FINAL WRITEUP

FACTORY EVALUATION DATA

Job Title_____Date_____Analyst_____

SKILL

Determine training and experience necessary for an inexperienced employee to satisfactorily perform the job (assume employee has average intelligence, aptitude, and is afforded normal supervision).

MENTALITY

Determine level of mathematics used—why?
Determine type and complexity of reference documents used (blueprints, wiring diagrams, sketches, DATs, etc.).
Determine degree and type of technical knowledge required (Electricity, Chemistry, Metallurgy, etc.).

RESPONSIBILITY

Average top loss including general overhead resulting from damage to items listed below for a single occurrence for which employee could be wholly responsible.

Item	Possible ($) Loss *	Actual Experience
Tools		
Machines		
Equipment		
Material		
Product		

* Repair or replacement, whichever is least.

MENTAL APPLICATION

What portion of employees' assignments require mental application (consider intensity, frequency and continuity)? Is employee required to make machine setups or layouts, determine operational sequences, select materials, etc.?

PHYSICAL APPLICATION

What type and degree of physical exertion is required (lifting, pushing, walking, awkward working positions, etc.)?

Type	Explain Degree (i.e. lift over 25 lbs.)	Frequency

JOB CONDITIONS

Disagreeable Element	Intensity	Frequency

Does job require wearing of any protective devices: Yes ☐   No ☐
Explain if "Yes":

UNAVOIDABLE HAZARDS

Type Accident	Frequency of Exposure	Severity	Frequency of Occurrence

FIGURE 47a. FORM FOR GATHERING EVALUATION DATA. (The Lockheed Aircraft Corporation.)

MAINTENANCE MECHANIC—HI-LO FORK TYPE
ELETRIC LIFT TRUCKS

Scope

There are six trucks to maintain and the job covers four fields:

1. Battery upkeep and repair
2. Electrical maintenance
3. Hydraulic maintenance
4. Mechanical maintenance.

Battery Upkeep

I have to service and charge the batteries. Add distilled water. See that I have proper solution points (gravity) per cell. I remove and replace defective elements. This means removing straps, cover, element. I check and replace worn separators. I solder lugs on, clean batteries. Once a month I equalize the battery charge. I have to maintain the charging equipment. There is a Hobart charger. I have to test it with a voltmeter, adjust contactor, replace brushes. If commutator is rough, I turn it down on a bench lathe. I undercut the mica; sand and clean the commutator and put it back in the motor. Also replace bearings. On the rectifier, I have to check charging rate, adjust it to taper off for proper charge level.

Electrical Maintenance

The biggest job is diagnosing and remedying trouble. Contactors in function box get worn; I have to clean, adjust, and replace them. If voltmeter shows trouble at the drive or lift motor, I check the commutator and do the same as on the Hobart charger commutator. I check the forward and reverse switches. The contacts get dirty or burned so I check the points, clean and replace them.

Hydraulic System

I have to service the hydraulic system. I replace fluid, repack valves and pump, replace broken lines, connections. I replace broken springs on the valve control and adjust the control to maintain flow of oil and pressure in lines. Also replace bearings and pump rotors on the hydraulic pump. This is all important.

Mechanical

I grease and oil them. Re-tire wheels pressing on the tires. Diagnose and remedy trouble with brakes, steering gear. On the brakes, there are two systems on different make trucks. One is hydraulic. Here I check the valves, replace valve rubbers, clean and flush lines, add fluid; also bleed the lines and adjust brakes to $\frac{1}{16}$". I have to remove and re-face the clutch sometimes. On the other type of brakes, I replace the brake linings and clutch facings. Also adjust pedals, steering system for alignment. All this keeps me busy.

FIGURE 48. PRELIMINARY DESCRIPTION SUBMITTED BY ONE WORKER

Labor Grade 3   Code 8452

INSPECTOR—FLOOR—MFG.
INS-F-MFG

Job Description

Perform inspection checks on all operations on any part manufactured in department. Is responsible for the inspection of first piece produced on each new setup and also for first piece made by each operator at the beginning of the shift.

Inspect part visually for finish, mutilation, burns, etc. Check the operation for detailed dimensions such as diameters, radii, thread, and concentricity. Read a variety of blueprints, operation sheets, service, and blue orders to get dimensional limits and tolerances. Must know effect of substandard operation on a later operation.

Use various standard and special gauges in checking operations, such as inside and outside micrometers, verniers, plug and snap gauges, thread gauges, and indicating gauges. For inspection of parts without complete tooling, set up work on surface plate, between centers, or on Vee blocks. Use verniers, height gauges, and protractors for checking the operation. Use ingenuity in devising proper setup for checking such parts.

Do some paper work such as signing operator's job card, if operation is O.K.; handling service and blue orders, making out salvage and rework tickets. Work with minimum supervision.

Check blueprints for engineering changes and see that any special gauges used conform with new specifications. Check special gauges for tool inspection stamp which certifies their accuracy.

1. *Education*

Use advanced shop mathematics. Read complicated drawings and have knowledge of machine shop methods. Use a wide variety of precision measuring instruments.

2. *Learning Period*

Approximately 4 years on varied inspection work. Inspect operations performed on all types of machines.

3. *Initiative and Ingenuity*

Plan and perform a series of diversified inspection operations on the machine shop floor. Usually has standard inspection procedures and tooling, but occasionally use considerable judgment to improvise inspection methods on special parts. Decide whether to allow off-size part to remain in production or send to salvage. Occasionally do layout work for checking purposes. Work with minimum supervision.

FIGURE 49. EXAMPLE FROM COLE APPLICATION. (Wright Aeronautical Corporation.)

4. *Physical Demand*

Light physical effort handling average weight material and parts. Almost continuous walking from machine to machine.

5. *Mental and Visual Demand*

Concentrate mental and visual attention closely inspecting, laying out parts, and studying blueprints.

6. *Resp. for Equipment or Process*

Careless handling of gauges and precision measuring instruments may cause damage. Seldom exceeds $25.

7. *Resp. for Material or Product*

Errors in inspection or poor judgment in passing parts may necessitate scrapping or reworking a large number of pieces. Seldom exceeds $800.

8. *Resp. for Safety of Others*

Little responsibility for the safety of others.

9. *Resp. for Work of Others*

Occasionally assist or instruct others.

10. *Working Conditions*

Good. Walk around machines and handle parts which are somewhat oily.

11. *Unavoidable Hazards*

May crush hands or feet handling parts.

FIGURE 49. (*Concluded.*)

Labor Grade 10   Code 8512

JANITOR
JAN

—Job Description—

Perform any or all of the following jobs, as assigned:

Sweep, mop, dump refuse in barrels, move and replace furniture and equipment, dust and clean working areas.

1—*Education*
Read, write, and follow simple direct instructions.

2—*Learning Period*
Approximately 1 month to learn duties.

3—*Initiative and Ingenuity*
Repetitive work. Work from simple instructions in sweeping, mopping, dusting, moving and replacing furniture or equipment. Work with occasional supervision.

4—*Physical Demand*
Sustained physical effort sweeping, mopping, and moving furniture and equipment. Usually work with brooms, mops and shovels.

5—*Mental and Visual Demand*
Frequent visual and some mental attention to maintain clean conditions in area assigned.

6—*Resp. for Equipment or Process*
Negligible.

7—*Resp. for Material or Product*
Negligible.

8—*Resp. for Safety of Others*
Reasonable care in the use of broom and mop and in the placing of pails and equipment required to prevent injury to others.

9—*Resp. for Work of Others*
Responsible only for own work.

10—*Working Conditions*
Somewhat disagreeable. Some exposure to dirt, heat, water, oil, dust, noise, etc.

11—*Unavoidable Hazards*
Slips and falls on oily floors, or falls from ladders.

FIGURE 50. EXAMPLE FROM COLE APPLICATION. (Wright Aeronautical Corporation.)

Job Description by Code Letters. Some of the most conscientious job analysis is done by finding the degree definitions which fit the conditions of a job and then recording the identification by means of code letters. The purpose of this is to make sure that all pertinent questions will be answered and that the degree definitions will be carefully applied at the source without any influence from point weightings. The latter are tabulated separately and kept out of reach of the interviewers. Later the code letters, which have been recorded on a standard work sheet (Figure 51) by way of job description, are located in the tables and the corresponding weight combinations are entered on the job specification for adding. General Motors' instructions for using this kind of form are as follows:

The value and accuracy of this analysis are dependent on the care exercised in evaluating the various factors. Differences of opinion and judgment will practically disappear if reasonably intelligent and thorough consideration is given to each item.

1. Enter at the top of the third column of the center page any remarks or special notes that will help to indicate just what this job is.
2. Enter the code letter for the chosen degree of each job factor in the space marked "Code" on the center sheet.
3. Enter, in the space immediately below, your comments on what you found in observing or considering the job that caused you to select the code letter you have just entered. Keep in mind that these comments collectively form a sort of job description and should tell the story of the job.
4. At the foot of each column, enter after the word "Code" all the code letters appearing in the column above, as "JDRY." There should be 14 code letters.
5. Points should be entered from the point charts only after the first rating and the review have been made.

The degree definitions with their code letters,[13] also the tables of weights, are given for the characteristics Knowledge and Responsibility, Chapter 6, Figures 31 and 32. We have a high regard for the managements which have adopted this procedure but we still doubt the necessity of using such fine scales and of the consequent large number of total points. The ratio between the lowest worth and highest worth is also very high.

Putting Measuring Scales in Hands of Operatives. Complete inclusion of all measuring scales in the questionnaire which goes to employees seems to violate Principle I for design of forms but in exceeding limits there it narrows the limits elsewhere and in effect

[13] In practice these as well as the instructions are attached to each work sheet.

JOB ANALYSIS WORK SHEET

DIVISION_____ PLANT_____ JOB_____ CODE_____

SKILL		RESPONSIBILITY FOR PEOPLE		REMARKS OR SPECIAL NOTES	EFFORT	
MENTAL SKILL	CODE	SAFETY OF OTHERS	CODE		MENTAL EFFORT	CODE
MANUAL SKILL	CODE	SUPERVISION OF OTHERS	CODE		PHYSICAL EFFORT	CODE
		RESPONSIBILITY FOR PROPERTY		PROFICIENCY		

DEXTERITY	CODE	PROCESSED AND PROCESSING MATERIALS	CODE	INTELLIGENCE	CODE	SURROUNDINGS	CODE
ACCURACY	CODE	MACHINERY & EQUIPMENT	CODE	TRAINING & EXPERIENCE	CODE	HAZARD	CODE
CODE	POINTS	CODE POINTS	CODE POINTS	CODE	POINTS	CODE	POINTS
First Rating by: ______		Reviewed by: ______		Approved by: ______		TOTAL POINTS	
Date ______		Date ______		Date ______			

FIGURE 51. JOB ANALYSIS WORK SHEET IN CODE. (General Motors Corporation.)

gets compensations which are claimed to be net gains. By way of analogy it is a change from full table service to complete automat. The service in this case is the work of the job analysts; their judgment is needed only in allotting weights to the degrees in general. For any specific job the degrees are indicated by the employees on the blanks. Of course the variations between employee recordings must be adjusted. This is done by the committee on a summary sheet (Figure 52), which is much like the original questionnaire. There are seven major headings, most of which have several subdivisions and most of those are given predetermined degree definitions. Users of this procedure are enthusiastic for it. Besides the elimination of much judging on the part of the management the users claim that the questionnaire can be tailor-fitted to special conditions and thereby meet all needs better than any other procedure. By the way, this tailoring may be aided by the shop stewards as well as by the foremen so that all sources of job knowledge can be brought to bear on the plan before it is frozen. Actually the tailoring is a matter of detail rather than alteration of the major characteristics. The allocation of weights need not be done in advance of recording, but while the employees are working out their recordings. The trouble with this procedure is that the fine subdivisions obscure overlaps and necessitate overlarge point totals.

Instructions to Employees. A paragraph on each characteristic, to guide employee judgment as to degrees, is sent along with the questionnaire, also a word of encouragement which might be termed an apology for the lengthy procedure. The employee is not given the general weightings until after he has made the recording.

Although the questionnaire is long, it is not difficult to fill out. Most of the questions can be answered by just marking "yes" or "no" or by checking. If a question does not apply to your job, answer "no" or "none." If there is any doubt in your mind about how to answer, or if you do not understand the questions, ask your Steward to help you. The success of the whole plan depends upon the way the questionnaires are answered. Be frank, be honest, and do not exaggerate.

Keep the questionnaire for a day or two. Consider your answers carefully. If you like, seal your questionnaire in the envelope or hand it in as it is. The important thing is to return it. Give your filled-out questionnaire to your Steward. He will turn it in to the Evaluation Committee. The questionnaires are going to be checked by the Committee to assure the correctness and accuracy of the information given.

Please give us your fullest cooperation—this is your plan—you are helping to build it.

THE EVALUATION COMMITTEE

JOB EVALUATION SUMMARY SHEET

Date...

Job Title...

Job No............................ ....Department...

Job Description:

Factors	Evaluated Points
I Working Conditions	... .
II Responsibility	....
III Leadership	....
IV Physical Effort	....
V Mental and Visual Effort...	....
VI Knowledge and Experience..	....
VII Manual Skill	. ...

Total............................

Job Class.. Job Rate............................

FIGURE 52. JOB EVALUATION SUMMARY SHEET. (The M. W. Kellogg Company.)

I. A. Is this job injurious or uncomfortable in comparison with other jobs in this plant, and to what extent?

	Some	Much	What Part of the Day On the Average Up to ½	All	
1. Harmful Fumes and Gases, Smoke and Odors	☐	☐	☐	☐	....
2. Dirt, Dust and Grease					....
3. Oil					....
4. Acids					....
5. Harmful Weather Conditions—Outside					....
6. Heat					....
7. Eye Strain					....
8. Water					....
9. Special Clothes, Goggles, Respirators					....
10. Chips and Shavings					....
11. Noise					....
12. Drafts					....
13. Vibration					....

Total I A ....   ☐

I. B. What is the probability of the following accidents occurring on this job?

	Slight	Average	Above Average
1. Minor Cuts, Burns or Bruises, etc	☐	☐	☐
2. Eye Injuries, Severe Strains or Burns, etc	☐	☐	☐
3. Amputations and Permanent Disabilities	☐	☐	☐
4. Fatalities	☐	☐	☐

Total I B ....   ☐

I. C. Can the following personal property, not supplied by the company, be spoiled or worn out on this job and to what extent?

Yearly Value of Spoilage

Clothing, Shoes and Tools..................................... ....

Total I C ....   ☐

Total I Working Conditions...............

II. A. What degree of responsibility is required on this job in connection with the following?

	Slight	Average	Above Average	Extreme	
1. Hand Tools	☐	☐	☐	☐	....
2. Jigs and Fixtures	☐	☐	☐	☐	....
3. Equipment or Machines	☐	☐	☐	☐	....
4. Product or Material	☐	☐	☐	☐	....
5. Clerical Detail or Records	☐	☐	☐	☐	....

Total II A ....   ☐

II. B. How many other persons are simultaneously exposed to probable injury because of the nature of this job, and to what degree?

	Persons 1 - 3	4 - 10	11 and over
1. Minor Cuts, Burns or Bruises, etc	☐	☐	☐
2. Eye Injuries, Severe Strains or Burns, etc	☐	☐	☐
3. Amputations and Permanent Disabilities	☐	☐	☐
4. Fatalities	☐	☐	☐

Total II B ....   ☐

Total II Responsibility...............

III. A. How many employees are supervised on this job?

1 - 3	4 - 10	11 - 20	21 - 30	31 and over
☐	☐	☐	☐	☐

Total III A ....   ☐

III. B. Is the nature of work supervised:

	Part Time	Full Time
Routine or repetitious	☐	☐
Variable	☐	☐
Complicated	☐	☐

Total III B ....   ☐

FIGURE 52. (*Continued.*)

III. C. Are any of the following functions a regular part of this job?

Part Time   Full Time

1. Teach employees their jobs?... ☐   ☐ ....
2. Select the operator for the job?... ☐   ☐ ....
3. Decide which job is to be done next?............................. ☐   ☐ ....
4. Decide the method and machines to be used?............. ☐   ☐ ....

Total III C .... ☐

Total III Leadership... ═

IV A. Is this job performed in the following manner?

What Part of the Day - On the Average
Up to ¼   ½   ¾   All

1. Sitting .... ☐   ☐   ☐   ☐ ....
2. Standing . ... ☐   ☐   ☐   ☐ ....
3. Awkward Position .... ☐   ☐   ☐   ☐ ....
4. Mostly Walking .... ☐   ☐   ☐   ☐ ....

Total IV A .... ☐

IV. B. Does this job require:

What Part of the Day - On the Average
Up to ¼   ½   ¾   All

1. Light Physical Effort........................... ☐   ☐   ☐   ☐ ....
2. Average Physical Effort....................... ☐   ☐   ☐   ☐ ....
3. Heavy Physical Effort.......................... ☐   ☐   ☐   ☐ ....
4. Extra Heavy Physical Effort.............. ☐   ☐   ☐   ☐ ....

Total IV B .... ☐

Total IV Physical Effort... ═

V A. Does this job require:

What Part of the Day - On the Average
Up to ¼   ½   ¾   All

1. Following written or verbal orders.............. ☐   ☐   ☐   ☐ ....
2. Performing routine operations................. ☐   ☐   ☐   ☐ ....
3. Performing clerical duties....................... ☐   ☐   ☐   ☐ ....
4. Analyzing variable problems................... ☐   ☐   ☐   ☐ ....
5. Analyzing complex problems................... ☐   ☐   ☐   ☐ ....

Total V A .... ☐

V. B. In which of the following ways are the eyes used on this job?

What Part of the Day - On the Average
Up to ¼   ½   ¾   All

1. Ordinary use, walking, etc.................... ☐   ☐   ☐   ☐ ....
2. To position pieces in machinery, jigs, etc............. ☐   ☐   ☐   ☐ ....
3. Keeping records and reading blueprints.............. ☐   ☐   ☐   ☐ ....
4. For ordinary inspection, etc.................... ☐   ☐   ☐   ☐ ....
5. For very close inspection requiring the use of
precision instruments .... ☐   ☐   ☐   ☐ ....

Total V B .... ☐

Total V Mental & Visual Effort... ═

VI. A. How much schooling or self-training is required for this job?

1. Read and write or follow verbal instructions... ☐
2. Add, subtract, multiply and divide... ☐
3. Use fractions and decimals and read ordinary blueprints........................... ☐
4. Repair machinery or parts.. ☐
5. Do complicated shop mathematics and read complex bluprints .... ☐
6. Do tool and die work.. ☐

Total VI A .... ☐

VI. B. How many months or years of shop training and experience are required to do this job?

Months....................... Years.......................

Total VI B .... ☐

FIGURE 52. (*Continued.*)

VI. C. What type of decision is necessary on this job and how frequently?

	Seldom	Often	Very Often
Simple—Repetitive operations, methods worked out by others	☐	☐	☐
Routine—Repetitive operations, with some variations like changes in speed, temperature, etc......................	☐	☐	☐
Variable—Considerable variations in method required because only general instructions can be given....	☐	☐	☐
Complex — Considerable variations. not previously worked out	☐	☐	☐

Total VI C .... ☐

Total VI Knowledge & Experience.................... =

VII. A. What degree of coordination of hands and eyes does this job require to obtain normal production?

Some	Average	Above Average	High
☐	☐	☐	☐

Total VII A .... ☐

VII. B. What accuracy is required on this job?

Approximate	Close	Very Close	Exact
☐	☐	☐	☐

Are jigs, gages, fixtures or machine stops used to obtain accuracy?

No	Yes
☐	☐

Total VII B .... ☐

VII. C. 1. Does this job require the use of more than one type of machine tool?

Sometimes	Often	Very Often
☐	☐	☐

....

2. Does this job regularly require doing different types of operations?

Sometimes	Often	Very Often
☐	☐	☐

....

3. Does this job require:

	Sometimes	Often	Very Often
Routine set-up or layout........	☐	☐	☐	....
Complicated set-up or layout.....................................	☐	☐	☐	....
Grinding of tools...	☐	☐	☐	....

Total VII C .... ☐

Total VII Manual Skill................................ =

FIGURE 52. (*Concluded.*)

A Combination Procedure. Listing three ways of gathering data for a job description-specification, that is, analyst-supervisor conference, analyst interview, and employee questionnaire, the Clerical Salary Study Committee of the Life Office Management Association [14] gave a thorough discussion of the advantages and disadvantages of each procedure and then described an example of a combination of the three procedures developed by an anonymous company as follows:

1. The employee fills out a two-section form, the first section covering the job description, the second section the job specification. [15]

2. The supervisor fills out only the job specification form. This limitation of his contribution acknowledges his inability to know in detail the work of all of the employees under him.

3. The employee description and specification form and the supervisor's specification form are returned directly to the Personnel Department where they receive careful study by the job analyst assigned to that particular department.

4. The job analyst supplements the information obtained on the two forms by an analyst interview. Having the previous knowledge of the job obtained from the employee description and specification and the supervisor's specification he is able to proceed much more rapidly toward a well-rounded description of the job.

5. The job description written by the analyst after the analyst interview is referred to the employee for his acceptance.

6. The approved job description is then referred by the job analyst to the supervisor. Such revisions as the latter thinks necessary are made and he then indicates his approval by signing the description.

It will be seen that this combined method maintains the advantages claimed for the employee questionnaire and adds to it most of the advantages of the analyst interview. However, because of the number of original forms, this method does require more writing to develop a finished description than does the plain analyst interview.

Description by Means of Standard Data. Most large companies make some use of standard data in determining tasks for new or

[14] Report No. 1, September 1, 1938.
[15] We do not recognize this distinction.

altered jobs. Perhaps many job descriptions will eventually be built up by the same means. Such procedure has not yet seemed feasible to most of us because this project is only in its "teens" and also because the "basic elements" are considerably less definite than those coming from good time study. Nevertheless a tryout was made.[16] The Edo Aircraft Corporation made descriptions of all basic units rather than of complete jobs. Each of these is termed a "basic operation evaluation study" and is recorded on Form A. They are then classified and all of a class are listed on a "schedule of basic job/operations by class." This Form B carries a code number for each basic operation, shows the degree for each of eleven minor characteristics, and in the last column gives the labor grade. The term *class* here means the kind of operations, such as preparation, cutting, forming, drilling, fitting, fastening, etc. Form C is another "schedule of basic/operations by labor grade." There are twelve labor grades and sequences within each grade, the latter being identified by a second number. For instance 10–63 means labor grade 10, sequence No. 63. Point values are included on this form, also class symbols. Form D, "departmental check list" collects all the operations for each department. Form E, "work sheet," is used to build up a total job value from the basic data and Form F is a "worker classification notice."

This job evaluation system was designed, studied, and installed at Edo before the war as Mr. Bostwick's answer to the special problems encountered there. With the advent of the preparedness program, however, rather than go through the long drawn out official sanctioning process for getting such a program approved for the huge flow of government work, Edo installed the government-recommended Cole plan. It is regrettable that Mr. Bostwick's plan did not function through such a good proving period as the war years offered. It would have presented the best of opportunities for testing the principles involved in the system. The normal conditions of production may in the future again suggest use of this kind of plan.

Practice in Writing Job Descriptions. The following data on two jobs have been used by NEMA to provide new analysts practice in writing up a job. Through the courtesy of Dr. John Donald we now offer them to users of this text. They will be most valuable to graduate classes.

---

[16] Stanley E. Bostwick, "The Principle of Basic Element Standards Applied to Job Evaluation," *Advanced Management*, IX, No. 2.

I. PAINTER-SPRAYER

In the manufacture of electric ranges, hot water heaters, washing machines, one of the important operations from a quality control standpoint is the spray painting of the outside parts with white baking enamel. This is usually done on a moving conveyor in a "water wash booth." The fumes and spray from the paint are "caught" by the water wash.

Here are notes made by a job analyst.

1. Spray paint prime and finish coat on outer jackets with white enamel.
2. Revolve part on conveyor hanger. Move spray gun up and down to apply evenly.
3. Blow off or wipe surfaces to remove dirt or foreign matter before painting.
4. Dismantle and clean gun; see it is kept clean; adjust air regulator to control spray.
5. Mix paint; add solvents to keep required consistency.

Following preparatory and cleanup work is required.

1. Clean out water wash booth at end of shift.
2. Put in clean screen, remove screen and put accumulated paint in barrel.
3. Drain system; clean out all excess paint and refill with water.
4. Strip protective lining from booth once a week; apply grease and paper to top, sides, and floor of booth.
5. Start and stop conveyor, fans, water circulatory pump.
6. Keep work area clean and orderly.

Write a job description for this job.

II. TESTER, A.C. DIESEL GENERATOR UNITS

This company makes internal combustion engines. One of the departments assembles 4, 6, and 8 cylinder gas and diesel engines to generator units to make up a "power plant."

You are asked to write up a job description to cover the job of Tester, with the above title. The job involves final test and check to assure conformity with specifications prior to shipment.

You decide to ask the Engineering Department for a copy of the test procedure to save your time. In this way you do not need to observe every step in the testing. You are given the attached test specification.

Write up a job description of 250 to 350 words. The Tester has to read voltmeters, ammeters, wattmeters, frequency meters, current and potential transformers. He keeps log sheets.

Test Specifications—OG-183.

GENERAL TEST PROCEDURE FOR A.C. DIESEL
GENERATOR SETS

ENGINEERING DEPARTMENT may modify these test requirements on certain units to check performance and conformity to customers' requirements and specifications.

1. Fill cooling system and check for leaks. When required, connect external cooling system and provide thermometers in outlet and inlet.

2. Fill crank case with URSA Two Star SAE 30 Lub. Oil. Lubricate fuel pump and governor with the same grade Lub. Oil. Lubricate charging generator and starter and other engine accessories with a proper grade lubricant.

Do not depend upon any bearing being previously lubricated; check each point and be sure before starting the engine.

3. See that the main generator is lubricated in accordance with instructions supplied by the manufacturer.

See that the exciter brushes are in good condition and well seated. The pig-tails should be free from interference and firmly fastened to their relative connections. Check the connections to the brush holders; see that they are firmly fastened. Check the air gap in the alternator and exciter and see that no foreign matter exists, such as fiber blocking strips, nuts, bolts, washers, or any material that could damage rotating parts. See that the rotating parts do not touch any wiring, studs, covers, or brush holders. See that the commutators and slip rings are clean.

4. Connect the fuel system to the floor connections. All engines will be required to run their log time lifting the fuel from below the floor level.

5. Connect the generator to a load suitable to give Buda name plate full load rating, plus $\frac{1}{4}$, $\frac{1}{2}$, $\frac{3}{4}$, and $\frac{5}{4}$ loads. Provide volt meters, amp meters, watt meter, frequency meter, current transformer, and when necessary, potential transformers.

The voltage leads shall be connected directly to the generator terminals and not at the end of the load cables.

List on the back of the log sheet the style and serial number of instruments used, also the ratio and multipliers used.

6. Connect batteries with correct number of cells for the charging and starting system. Start the engine and warm up.

After determining that the unit is functioning properly, check the phase rotation on poly phase machines with a suitably calibrated instrument. If not standard rotation, change lead markings on the generator, change switchboard leads if the unit has paralleling requirements. Mark on log sheet that phase rotation has been checked and correct, and if change in load markings has been necessary.

7. Apply full-rated load at the rated voltage and speed; check the switchboard instruments against the portable standards. Make sure the standard instruments are in the same phase circuit as the panel instruments. The switchboard instruments shall be accurate within 3% of their full scale markings at the point of the rated load and voltage. They shall be accurately set on zero when not in operation. Check the various switches and switchboard equipment and see that they are functioning properly. With the governor set at rated speed full load, the no load speed shall be within plus 5% of the rated full load speed. The governor shall be stable within .5 cycles and no periodic surge at any speed from no load to 25% overload. The smoke stop shall be set to enable the engine to carry 25% overload and not more than 30% overload.

Have the inspector check the appearance of the exhaust and record O.K. on log sheet.

8. Have the inspector sign the start of the log. Record for two hours on standard log sheet at 15-minute readings; standard meter readings, multipliers, calculated readings, and switchboard meter readings. Record volts, amps, KW, PF, frequency, engine temperature, oil pressure, charging amps, room temperature, and, where applicable, oil temperature, top radiator temperature, and inlet and outlet of cooling water of separately cooled units.

At the end of the full load run check the ceiling voltage of the generator at full Buda name plate rated load in KW and PF. The generator shall be capable of at least 10% over voltage under these conditions. Record on log sheet ceiling voltage, KW, PF, and speed of this test.

The regulation test will now be made recording volts, amps, KW, and speed at zero ¼, ½, ¾, ⁴⁄₄, and ⁵⁄₄ loads. The full load shall be accurate within plus or minus 3% in KW and PF. The other loads other than full load may vary plus or minus 5% of the full load rating in their percentage of load, but attempt to keep uniform PF.

After the regulation test, run the unit at 25% overload for 30 minutes, recording the proper data at 15-minute intervals.

9. All safety equipment supplied with the unit shall be tested under operating conditions. Adjust safety equipment to normal safety settings and record settings on log sheet.

10. Correct any leaks, make minor repairs, seal governor. Have the inspector check the log sheet and the unit. Have the inspector check for the nonexistence of any water in the Lub. oil or excessive oil in the cooling water.

11. Have the inspector's signature on the log. Flush the engine in accordance with the specification listed on the B.M. Upon completion of the flushing, the inspector will put a test O.K. tag on the unit. It may then be disconnected and removed from the test floor.

8

RATING THE JOBS

> It is clear that the extent to which each item or factor contributes to the total cannot be determined by inspection of the scale alone and that the end result may yield results different from those intended by the makers of the scale.
>
> —C. H. LAWSHE

Rating Cannot Rise Above Preparation. It should be obvious from the previous chapters that when a framework of values for job characteristics is set, be it in the form of a ladder scale or in the form of degree definitions, what remains to be done in rating is largely a matter of identifying the subdivisions of job content and applying to each subdivision the corresponding value from the scale. This, of course, explains labor's anxiety about job content, but it should also remind management that erroneous rating can be caused either by unreliable descriptions of content or by inappropriate scale values. Of these two determinates the matter of job content is likely to be the more important, partly because content is expressed in words which can fail for many reasons, and partly because even a poor scale will at least show consistent variations in relative worths. So we give a last warning to those who set the scales and to those who write the subdivisions of job content. Management is responsible here for what follows in the way of good or bad rating and its consequences.

Training Is Very Important. The full time analysts usually do most of the original rating and the chief analyst must, therefore, provide such training and practice for them that they can in due time be trusted to do as intelligent and conscientious rating as he himself would do. But this is not enough. All members of the job evaluating committees and any department heads, supervisors, and other personnel who are likely to be asked about job content should eventually be coached as to the pitfalls in subdividing content and rating the subdivisions against the various scales. Much of this coaching

172

may have to be done individually but time can be saved by producing a clarifying manual and discussing it with small groups. Whatever explaining is necessary should be done one step at a time, and in short sessions. When the time comes for the rating every one should be asked to rate a series of jobs with which he is familiar. This can be made interesting by assigning several identical key jobs common to all so that comparison of the ratings will be possible. The old practice of having each one rerate the same jobs after a lapse of several days is disillusioning. The beginners are sure to disagree with one another on the key jobs and probably with themselves on the repeated trials. That is discouraging at first but discussion should soon show up the directions of error, teach the need for real objectivity, and impress all with the necessity of pooling judgment. Of course, this practice will help in the matter of describing and subdividing content as much as or more than in the rating. The former, as we have implied, is of primary importance. Don't hurry through this practice period. It should begin as soon as the scales and forms have been set, if not before, and continue until all concerned have learned to distinguish the degrees without hesitation, and until objectivity becomes habitual.

Precautions Needed in Any Type of Plan. Under the Weighted-in-Money method (Factor Comparison) the greatest danger is that the raters will cling too much to the present money rates. For the trial rating of select specimen jobs this may be desirable, that is, while determining the scales, but it is not permissible thereafter for any jobs. Explain that if unreliable values are retained job evaluation might as well be dispensed with. Under the Weighted-in-Points methods—no separation of universal requirements—the greatest danger is that the raters will get careless, will think they know the degree distinctions when they do not, and thereby drift farther and farther away from the correct scales. The only way to head that off is to remind the raters of their responsibility. Remind them that such looseness will take money from one job and put it on another, which amounts to taking cash out of one man's pocket and putting it in another's. In short, insist on conscientious adherence to the scales and, by close checking at first, random checking ever after, enforce meticulous rating.

The Lockheed Aircraft Corporation organizes its raters in squads of three. After each of these has rated a set of jobs independently, the three then discuss and compare, characteristic by characteristic, so that the final rating is the result of pooled judgment and that is reached before memory of job content can lapse (see Figure 53).

EVALUATION, FACTORY 1951

Job Title: _____ Using Depts. _____

Evaluation By		Date		Date		Date		Final Date	
Factor		Degrees	Points	Degrees	Points	Degrees	Points	Degrees	Points
Skill									
Mentality									
Responsibility									
Mental Application									
Physical Application									
Job Conditions									
Occupational Hazards									
Total Points									
Evaluated									
Rate Range									

Remarks:

FIGURE 53. FORM FOR POOLING THE RATINGS OF THREE ANALYSTS. (Lockheed Aircraft Corporation.)

174

In the case of a multiple duty job the degrees should be determined by the highest requirements included even if such portions of the job are not in effect much of the time.

Explanation of Weighted-in-Money Rating. In Chapter 3 we have described the Benge method of rating key jobs and from those ratings building the ladder scales. The rating of other jobs is essentially a matter of interpolating the characteristics of the given job within those that have been located on the ladder scales.

Prior to the actual evaluating the analysts reread the job descriptions of all the original and supplementary key jobs as a general refresher. Then each analyst evaluates all the remaining jobs; he starts with those jobs for which he prepared the job descriptions because of his greater familiarity with them. In either case, he arranges the group of job descriptions in a rough sequence with those of lowest possible grade on top. Taking one job description at a time, the analyst compares each characteristic of the job with the corresponding scale. In this comparison account is taken not only of the characteristic itself but also of the intensity with which it applies. By intensity is meant the proportion of the total time during which the ability or endurance must be used on the job.

After the comparison is computed the standard step, established in accordance with the preferred number series, which seems most correct for the job being evaluated is selected. This value, or step in the scale, is then recorded both on the job description itself and on a "Cross Index Form." The "Cross Index Form" lists on one card all those jobs having the same value for a particular characteristic and is used as a reference in further evaluation. This procedure is followed for each of the five characteristics for one job before proceeding to the next job.

After all the remaining jobs are evaluated by each of the analysts the results are compared and correlated. If the five individual ratings for any job characteristic fall within three successive steps in the corresponding scale then the five ratings are averaged out. This average value when rounded off to the nearest standard step is taken as the final judgment of the analysts. Those job characteristic values falling beyond three successive steps in the corresponding scale are discussed and then revalued. If after the third evaluation there is still discord, the analysts refer back to the job description and make whatever changes may be necessary to reconcile the differences of opinion. When all the jobs have been so evaluated the executive committee is obliged to review each of the job characteristic lists agreed upon by the analysts. After the executive committee has approved each of these lists the five values are added to get the final total value for any one job.[1]

Examples of Kress Type Job Rating. Examples of rating taken from one case should not be applied to any other case, so we caution the users of this book and the users of other wage and salary literature to study such examples, but not to accept them as correct for their own jobs. The nine we present next come from NEMA, except that of "Burrer-Bench," which comes from the Wright Aeronautical Corporation, where the Cole form of the same plan is used. These nine jobs fall into consecutive grades Nos. 2 to 10. The description subdivisions are definite and easily identified with the predetermined degree definitions given in Chapter 6. We suggest that the numerals representing degrees and points be covered or folded out of sight when using Figures 54 to 62 for training.

JOB RATING SPECIFICATION

(Hourly Rated Jobs)

Job Title: MACHINIST (MAINTENANCE)   GRADE 2
                                                POINTS 340

Job Description:

Plan and perform all operations necessary to the construction, repair, and maintenance of important and expensive standard and special machinery and equipment. Must be able to diagnose and correct difficult mechanical trouble. Involves accurate fitting and aligning. Work from complicated drawings, sketches, and samples, or where design information is incomplete.

Factor	Specification	Evaluation	
		Deg.	Pts.
Education	Requires trades training such as Machinist. Interprets complex machine drawings and makes calculations, using advanced shop mathematics.	4	56
Experience	In addition to trades training, satisfactory performance can be attained after a period of 3 to 4 years consisting of experience on lower graded work as a machinist and training on this job.	4	88

[1] For further details of rating under this type of plan see E. N. Hay, "Techniques of Securing Agreement in Job Evaluating Committees," *Personnel*, XXVI, No. 4.

FIGURE 54. EXAMPLE OF NEMA RATING

Factor	Specification	Evaluation	
		Deg.	Pts.
Initiative and Ingenuity	Uses high degree of judgment in diagnosing machine difficulties on complicated equipment and takes corrective action on own initiative. Handles unusual or very difficult jobs on a wide variety of shop machinery requiring considerable ingenuity.	4	56
Physical Demand	Occasionally handles heavy machine parts and motors; however considerable time is spent planning operations and directing helpers and co-workers in performing the physical work.	2	20
Mental and/or Visual Demand	A high degree of concentrated mental and visual attention is necessary to determine cause of machine trouble and plan course of action in making repairs.	4	20
Responsibility for Equipment or Process	Uses tools such as portable drills, machines such as grinders, and instruments such as micrometers. Damage to equipment will normally range between $5.00 and $20.00 for any one loss because of carelessness.	2	10
Responsibility for Material or Product	Makes repairs and instructs others in making repairs to expensive machines. Carelessness resulting in damage to equipment and tieup of production may cause losses from $250.00 to $350.00 but seldom over.	4	20
Responsibility for Safety of Others	Care required in properly fastening, tightening, and balancing revolving machine parts, and installing guards securely to insure safety of others and prevent lost-time accidents.	3	15
Responsibility for Work of Others	Responsible for instructing and directing helpers and co-workers who may be assigned to work with Machinist.	2	10
Working Conditions	Maintenance and repair work on machine shop equipment and machines involves dirty, oily, or noisy conditions that are somewhat disagreeable.	3	30
Hazards	Exposed to lost-time accidents, such as eye injury, severe abrasions of hand, loss of fingers and hernia from awkward lifting, while making repairs to, trying out, or operating machines.	3	15

FIGURE 54. (*Concluded.*)

JOB RATING SPECIFICATION
(Hourly Rated Jobs)

Job Title: TOOL, DIE, OR GAUGE MAKER   GRADE 3
                                                 POINTS 330

Job Description:

Plan and perform all bench and required machine operations, including experi-mental work, to construct, alter, or repair tools, jigs, fixtures, dies, molds, and gauges, involving ordinary skill and knowledge. Generally of average design and construction such as box or stand type drill jigs, milling fixtures, single and com-bination perforating and blanking dies, the simpler types of die casting or molding dies and average location gauges or profile gauges, etc.

Factor	Specification	Evaluation	
		Deg.	Pts.
Education	A broad trades training as commonly required for Toolmakers is necessary to interpret com-plex tool drawings, understand operation of a variety of machine tools, fitting and assembling procedures, and tool construction.	4	56
Experience	In addition to trades training, satisfactory per-formance can be attained after a period of 3 to 4 years consisting of experience on a wide variety of lower graded toolmaking and training on this job.	4	88
Initiative and Ingenuity	Requires a high degree of ability to plan course of action and sequence of diversified operations in the absence of general instructions. Uses in-itiative and ingenuity in determining need for and taking independent action in clearing diffi-culties and occasionally developing methods of procedure, working without aid of direct super-vision.	4	56
Physical Demand	Involves frequent handling light tool details in performing operations and occasional handling of heavier tool details and machine attachments. Involves standing, walking, and sitting on an intermittent basis.	2	20
Mental and/or Visual Demand	Concentrated mental and visual attention re-quired to interpret information, plan and lay out work, perform machine and bench opera-tions, and maintain close dimensional require-ments.	4	20
Responsibility for Equipment or Process	Uses a wide range of machine tools and pre-cision measuring instruments, where failure to exercise proper care in setup or operation could result in damage. Cost of repair and replace-ment of defective and damaged parts would sel-dom exceed $250 for any one loss.	3	15

FIGURE 55. EXAMPLE OF NEMA RATING

Factor	Specification	Evaluation	
		Deg.	Pts.
Responsibility for Material or Product	Failure to exercise proper care in planning and laying out work, setting up and operating machines, or in checking work could result in defective tool details or damage to details with considerable previous work completed, where cost of repair or loss of material and labor could reasonably exceed $250 in any one case.	3	15
Responsibility for Safety of Others	Considerable care required in setting up and operating machines and in moving machine attachments and heavier tool details to prevent lost-time injuries to others in the nature of broken bones and eye injuries from flying parts, broken tools, and contact with revolving parts or parts dropped during handling.	3	15
Responsibility for Work of Others	Involves responsibility for instructing lower graded Toolmakers assigned to assist with the job (up to 2).	2	10
Working Conditions	Involves good working conditions with minor exposure to oil and grease on machines and tool details and to low-level machine shop noise.	2	20
Hazards	Involves exposure to loss of fingers and broken bones in operating machines and handling machine attachment and heavier tool details, and to cuts, bruises, and abrasions when using hand tools, and from sharp edges or burrs on material.	3	15

FIGURE 55. (*Concluded.*)

JOB RATING SPECIFICATION
(Hourly Rated Jobs)

Job Title: BORING MACHINE OPERATOR—   GRADE 4
HORIZONTAL   POINTS 306

Job Description:

Set up and operate 3½″ x 36″ Giddings and Lewis horizontal boring machine, to bore and face a variety of parts where accuracy of bores and interrelated surfaces must be held to close tolerances. Setups exacting, requiring care to avoid distortion, assure rigidity, and maintain alignment between several interrelated surfaces. Work from layout or locating surface. Usually fixture work, using blocks, shims, parallels, clamps, bolts, indicators, level to set up. Select tools, speeds, and feeds. Check work to assure sufficient stock to clean up on later operations. Bore, face, drill, tap, straddle mill; use tools such as boring bars, fixed and floating cutters, fly cutters, face mills, drills, taps, reamers. Tools ground by others. Load and unload work; gauge from time to time. Keep machine clean and lubricated. Tolerances as close as plus or minus .001″; usually .002″ to .005″.

Factor	Specification	Evaluation	
		Deg.	Pts.
Education	Use shop arithmetic. Work from drawings. Use rule, micrometers, dial indicator, depth gauges. Knowledge of shop practice, cutting qualities of metals, tooling, feeds, speeds on horizontal boring mill. Equivalent to 2 years high school plus 2 to 3 years trades training.	3	42
Experience	3 to 5 years.	4	88
Initiative and Ingenuity	Plan and perform difficult work where only general methods are available. Make decisions which require considerable ingenuity and judgment to make complicated setups involving careful blocking to avoid distortion, plan sequence of cuts, select speeds, feeds, tools, diagnose and remedy trouble to correct distortion or misalignment. Independent action required in dealing with new problems.	4	56
Physical Demand	Most of time light physical effort operating machine, checking, adjusting, waiting for cuts. Handle clamps, blocks, tools during setups. Heavy work handled by crane.	2	20
Mental and/or Visual Demand	Continuous mental or visual attention to make setups, adjust cutters, check work, load work.	3	15
Responsibility for Damage to Equipment	Careless setup or operation may result in breaking gears, feed mechanism, damage to boring bars or tools. Probable damage seldom over $250.	3	15

FIGURE 56. EXAMPLE OF NEMA RATING

Responsibility for Material or Product	Careless setup or operation may result in under-size work, boring or reaming oversize, poor fin-ish, or wrong dimensions. Probable loss seldom over $250.	3	15
Responsibility for Safety of Others	Compliance with standard safety precautions necessary in loading and unloading work and handling tools to prevent lost time accident to others.	3	15
Responsibility for Work of Others	None.	1	5
Working Conditions	Good working conditions.	2	20
Hazards	Exposed to crushed fingers or toes handling material, clamps, tools, possible eye injury from flying chips, finger or hand injury from rotating tools, any of which may result in lost-time acci-dent.	3	15

FIGURE 56. (*Concluded.*)

JOB RATING SPECIFICATION
(Hourly Rated Jobs)

Job Title: WELDER—ARC OR ACETYLENE

GRADE 5
POINTS 285

Job Description:

Arc or acetylene weld, braze or metallize a variety of castings to be salvaged which have been machined over-size or which are cracked. Mostly all downhand weld-ing. Prepare castings for welding; drill, tap, and plug large cracks; grind out cracks with portable grinder; clean with wire brush; chip out any defect to bright metal; select welding rod, adjust and set voltage for thickness of material; select flux, tips, pressures, gas mixtures. Maintain arc or flame and speed to produce sound weld of proper thickness, penetration, and fusion. Clean flux accumulations, grind weld to smooth finish; metallize as required. Spot- or torch-anneal parts such as gears on shafts, end of shaft. Use a variety of hand and power tools such as flexible shaft grinder, chisels, hammer, file, wire brush, emery wheel. Keep work area and equipment clean and orderly.

Factor	Specification	Evaluation	
		Deg.	Pts.
Education	Use shop arithmetic. Work from drawings, sketches, specifications, instructions. Use rule, scale, square, calipers, level, plumb bob. Trade knowledge of welding methods. Equivalent to 2	3	42

FIGURE 57. EXAMPLE OF NEMA RATING

Factor	Specification	Evaluation	
		Deg.	Pts.
Experience	years high school plus 2 to 3 years trades training in welding methods. 1 to 3 years.	3	66
Initiative and Ingenuity	Plan and perform a sequence of operations where standard methods are available. Make general decisions which require initiative and judgment to determine sequence of welding, set up work, prepare surfaces, select size and type of rod, set current, select tips, pressures, determine number or passes; maintain alignment and size; assure homogeneous weld; check work. Independent action required within limits of standard methods.	3	42
Physical Demand	Sustained physical effort handling and positioning work, holding welding rod or torch steady, using hammer, chisel, wire brush, bending, stooping. Sometimes difficult work positions.	3	30
Mental and/or Visual Demand	Must coordinate a high degree of manual dexterity with close visual attention to effect successful weld.	4	20
Responsibility for Equipment or Process	Careless operation handling or moving work may result in burning out or damaging arc welder, damage to cable, electrode holders, tips, regulators. Probable damage seldom over $25.	2	10
Responsibility for Material or Product	Careless welding may result in cracked or burned welds, distortion, misalignment requiring rework. Probable loss seldom over $100.	2	10
Responsibility for Safety of Others	Compliance with standard safety precautions necessary in handling and moving work, using tools to prevent lost-time accident to others.	3	15
Responsibility for Work of Others	None.	1	5
Working Conditions	Somewhat disagreeable due to noise, dirt, fumes from electrodes, torch, flashes from electric arcs, none of which is continuous.	3	30
Hazards	Exposed to crushed fingers or toes, handling and moving work, burns, eye injury from intermittent flashes, any of which may result in lost-time accident.	3	15

FIGURE 57. (*Concluded.*)

JOB RATING SPECIFICATION
(Hourly Rated Jobs)

Job Title: TESTER—GENERATOR UNITS   GRADE 6
                                                       POINTS 258

Job Description:

Perform standardized test for AC diesel-generator sets to check performance and conformity with specifications prior to shipment. Set unit on test stand; fill cooling system, check for leaks; use thermometers in outlet and inlet as required. Fill crankcase with oil; lubricate fuel pump and governor, charging generator, starter, accessories, before starting engine. Check main generator for lubrication; check exciter brushes, air gap in alternator and exciter, assure no foreign matter present; check to see rotating parts do not touch wiring, covers, brush holders. Connect fuel system to floor connections. Connect generator to load, connect voltage leads, batteries. Start engine and warm up. See that unit functions properly. Check phase rotation on polyphase units; change lead markings on generator, change switchboard leads. Apply full-rated load at rated voltage and speed; check switchboard instruments against portable standards; see that switches and switchboard equipment function properly. Record at specified time intervals standard meter readings, multipliers, calculated readings, switch board meter readings, volts, amperes, kilowatts, power factor, temperatures, oil pressure. Run unit for regulation and overload test. Test and adjust safety equipment; record settings. Make minor repairs, correct leaks, seal governor. Flush engine on completion of test, disconnect unit, remove from test floor. Use voltmeters, ammeters, wattmeters, frequency meters, current and potential transformers. Keep log sheets. Keep work area clean and orderly.

Factor	Specification	Evaluation	
		Deg.	Pts.
Education	Use shop arithmetic. Work from assembly drawings, wiring diagrams. Use electrical measuring instruments, temperature and thermometer gauges. Trade knowledge of elementary electricity. Equivalent to 2 years high school plus 2 to 3 years trades training.	3	42
Experience	6 to 12 months.	2	44
Initiative and Ingenuity	Plan and perform a sequence of operations where standard methods are available. Make general decisions which require initiative and judgment to perform standard tests, diagnose and remedy trouble as short in wire, motor off scale, current breakers open up before full load, open fuses, engine or governor trouble. Independent action required within limits of standard methods.	3	42
Physical Demand	Light physical effort on the average. Heavier work while setting engines on test stand (1 or 2 a day). Most of time spent observing tests, reading data.	2	20

FIGURE 58. EXAMPLE OF NEMA RATING

Factor	Specification	Evaluation	
		Deg.	Pts.
Mental and/or Visual Demand	Continuous mental or visual attention to perform assigned duties.	3	15
Responsibility for Equipment or Process	Careless operation may result in damage to measuring instruments. Probable damage seldom over $100.	3	15
Responsibility for Material or Product	Carelessness in performing test may result in damage to engine or require field service. Probable loss seldom over $250.	3	15
Responsibility for Safety of Others	Compliance with standard safety precautions necessary in handling or moving generator sets, connecting up engines, to prevent lost-time accidents to others.	3	15
Responsibility for Work of Others	None.	1	5
Working Conditions	Exposed to some noise, fumes, heat, which makes job somewhat disagreeable.	3	30
Hazards	Exposed to crushed fingers or toes handling engines, possible burns from exhaust pipe, exposure to possible shock, any of which may result in lost-time accident.	3	15

FIGURE 58. (*Concluded.*)

JOB RATING SPECIFICATION

(Hourly Rated Jobs)

Job Title: BURRER—BENCH

GRADE 7
POINTS 240

Job Description:

Remove burrs, hangers, break sharp edges, form and blend radii according to specifications on a variety of parts. Use various types of scrapers, files, air guns, flexible shafts, etc., equipped with burring tools, small abrasive wheels, etc. Shape wheels to suit job. Select proper type of tool for various jobs and occasionally make up a simple special tool. Occasionally use dental lights and mirrors while performing internal burring operations.

Parts are placed on bench or on holding fixture where applicable. May mount part in speed lathe to facilitate burring operation. Use tampico brush (mounted on polishing jack) or emery cloth to finish some surfaces after breaking edges.

Factor	Specification	Evaluation	
		Deg.	Pts.
Education	Use decimals, fractions and scale. Read simple blueprints and operation sheets.	2	28
Learning Period	Approximately 9 months to meet production standards.	2	44
Initiative and Ingenuity	Repetitive work. Follow detailed instructions. Some judgment in the use of hand operated tools to remove burrs, hangers, break all sharp edges, corners, and blend radii. Use care to avoid mutilating finished surfaces.	2	28
Physical Demand	Sustained physical effort working on average to heavy weight parts.	3	30
Mental and/or Visual Demand	Continuous visual and some mental attention to remove all burrs and hangers, break all sharp edges, and blend radii.	3	15
Responsibility for Equipment or Process	Possible damage to hand tools, such as files, gauges, scrapers, flexible shaft tools. Seldom exceeds $25.	2	10
Responsibility for Material or Product	Mutilation of finished surfaces or excessive grinding may scrap part. Seldom exceeds $150.	2	10
Responsibility for Safety of Others	Flying particles from grinding wheels or from hand tools may cause eye injury to others.	4	20
Responsibility for Work of Others	Occasionally assist or instruct others.	2	10

FIGURE 59. EXAMPLE OF COLE RATING

Factor	Specification	Evaluation	
		Deg.	Pts.
Working Conditions	Somewhat disagreeable. Exposed to dust from grinding and burring. Tampico brushes used on some jobs throw emery powder and metal particles onto clothing and body. May require wearing a respirator at times. Suction fans are provided on some benches.	3	30
Hazards	Possible eye injury from flying particles or emery. May receive cuts on fingers or hands from sharp edges on parts. Possible abrasions from flexible shafts or burring tools. Crushed hand or foot handling heavy parts.	3	15

FIGURE 59. (*Concluded.*)

JOB RATING SPECIFICATION
(Hourly Rated Jobs)

Job Title: METALLIZER   GRADE 8
                                                        POINTS 225

Job Description:
Operate metallizer gun to metal spray a variety of parts such as machined surfaces, bearings, shafts, cylinder blocks for repair or straightening, using copper, zinc, steel, and stainless steel wire. Metallize castings which show sand holes, porous metal defects, welded cracks. Build up shafts, machined surfaces, to proper thickness. Prepare parts for metallizing; clean, grind, wire brush surfaces. Insert wire in metallizing gun; set air and flame to desired pressure; apply coating uniformly. Handle heavy work with hoist. Keep equipment and work area clean and orderly.

Factor	Specification	Evaluation	
		Deg.	Pts.
Education	Use simple arithmetic. Work from drawings, sketches, standard practice instructions. Use rule, square, calipers. Equivalent to 2 years high school.	2	28
Experience	3 to 6 months.	2	44
Initiative and Ingenuity	Work from detailed instructions given by Foreman. Make minor decisions which require some judgment to set up machine, set rotating speed, current, voltage on fuse bonder; check work for uniform metallizing. Repetitive nature of work	2	28

FIGURE 60. EXAMPLE OF NEMA RATING

Factor	Specification	Evaluation	
		Deg.	Pts.
	limits independent action to minor decisions not difficult to make.		
Physical Demand	Light physical effort on the average, lifting and handling light and average weight parts, holding metallizing spray gun.	2	20
Mental and/or Visual Demand	Must coordinate a high degree of manual dexterity with close visual attention to assure uniform thickness of metal, watch flame.	4	20
Responsibility for Equipment or Process	Careless handling of spray gun, tubing may result in damage seldom over $25.	2	10
Responsibility for Material or Product	Careless operation, failure to build up metal evenly, may result in re-work or scrap. Probable loss seldom over $25.	2	10
Responsibility for Safety of Others	Compliance with standard safety precautions necessary in handling and moving work, using tools to prevent lost-time accident to others.	3	15
Responsibility for Work of Others	None.	1	5
Working Conditions	Somewhat disagreeable due to noise, fumes from electrodes, flashes from electric arcs, none of which is continuous.	3	30
Hazards	Exposed to crushed fingers or toes handling and moving work, burns, eye injury from intermittent flashes, any of which may result in lost-time accident.	3	15

FIGURE 60. (*Concluded.*)

JOB RATING SPECIFICATION

(Hourly Rated Jobs)   GRADE 9
                              POINTS 195

Job Title: INSPECTOR AND/OR TESTER

Job Description:
Visual, mechanical, or electrical inspection and check, using standard methods, on somewhat diversified work under frequent supervision involving handling of average weights. Work from simple to average drawings and specifications. Use simple gauges and DC or simple AC test sets.

Factor	Specification	Evaluation	
		Deg.	Pts.
Education	Requires reading and interpreting simple assembly drawings, manufacturing layouts and specifications to check for requirements.	2	28
Experience	Requires 8–9 months experience and job training to become familiar with the various types of work inspected, requirements and the setup and operation of test sets used.	2	44
Initiative and Ingenuity	Some judgment is required and minor decisions must be made in rejecting defective work or determining acceptability of products.	2	28
Physical Demand	Work requires continuous handling of lightweight material; occasional handling of average weight.	2	20
Mental and/or Visual Demand	Continuous visual and mental attention required to read drawings, layouts, and test set values and to inspect for proper completion of operations.	3	15
Responsibility for Equipment or Process	Damage to test equipment would seldom involve loss over $25.00.	2	10
Responsibility for Material or Product	Failure to detect improper work could result in losses which could exceed $10.00 in performance of subsequent operations but would seldom exceed $10.00 in any one instance.	2	10
Responsibility for Safety of Others	Involves minimum responsibility for the safety of others as work is performed at an individual work position.	1	5
Responsibility for Work of Others	No responsibility for work of others.	1	5
Working Conditions	Good shop conditions involving some noise from adjacent machines and some dirt and grease from work inspected.	2	20
Hazards	Carelessness in handling items inspected could result in minor cuts, bruises or abrasions.	2	10

FIGURE 61. EXAMPLE OF NEMA RATING

JOB RATING SPECIFICATION

(Hourly Rated Jobs)

Job Title: ASSEMBLER—WIRE, CABLE & HOSE   GRADE 10
                                                                         POINTS 173

Job Description:

Perform various bench operations to make up a wide variety of wire, cable, and hose assemblies for all types of engines. Refer to sketches, drawings, or specifications to ascertain lengths and types of terminals. Measure wire and cable to specified lengths; strip insulation from ends, attach and solder terminals; tape ends; bundle and tag assemblies by sets. Cut hose to specified lengths. Use a variety of hand tools such as pliers, file, hammer, rule, soldering iron, shears, electric saw, and wire stripper. Keep work area clean and orderly.

Factor	Specification	Evaluation	
		Deg.	Pts.
Education	Use simple arithmetic to compute dimensions. Work from simple drawings and specifications to select dimensions. Use rule. Equivalent to 2 years high school.	2	28
Experience	Up to 3 months.	1	22
Initiative and Ingenuity	Work from detailed instructions. Make minor decisions which require some judgment to measure material to correct lengths, select material specified, select correct couplings, inserts, clamps, connections, bundle, and tag sets. Repetitive nature of work limits independent action to minor decisions not difficult to make.	2	28
Physical Demand	Light physical effort most of time assembling wire, cable, hose with couplings, inserts, clamps, connections.	2	20
Mental and/or Visual Demand	Continuous mental or visual attention to cut material to proper lengths, select proper type and fittings, assemble.	3	15
Responsibility for Equipment or Process	Little probable damage to equipment.	1	5
Responsibility for Material or Product	Careless cutting of wire, cable, hose or use of fittings may result in scrap or re-work. Probable damage seldom over $25.	2	10
Responsibility for Safety of Others	Only reasonable care necessary to prevent injury to others. Work in isolated location, seldom any other employees around.	2	10

FIGURE 62. EXAMPLE OF NEMA RATING

Factor	Specification	Evaluation	
		Deg.	Pts.
Responsibility for Work of Others	None.	1	5
Working Conditions	Good working conditions.	2	20
Hazards	Accidents outside of minor abrasions, cuts or bruises improbable.	2	10

FIGURE 62. (*Concluded.*)

Occupation	Labor Grade	Job Rating Points	Description
BORING MILL OPERATION	2	343	A. Highly diversified. Turn, bore, and face wide variety of large and expensive parts. Close tolerances. Difficult setups requiring blocking and aligning of parts of irregular shape. Determine feeds, speeds, tooling, operation sequence for considerable range of unusual and difficult operations. (Usually very large mills such as 16′ or 20′.)
	4	311	B. Highly diversified. Turn, bore, and face wide variety of intricate castings of medium size. Close tolerances. Difficult setups requiring extensive blocking and aligning of parts of irregular shape. Determine feeds, speeds, tooling, operation sequence for considerable range of unusual and difficult operations. (Usually 6′ to 12′ mills and vertical turret lathes.)
	6	265	C. Turn, bore, face small and medium size parts. Close tolerances. Setups exacting but not usually involved or difficult. Determine speeds, feeds, tooling, operation sequence for variety of ordinary operations where a large number of cuts need not be made.
	8	225	D. Repetitive types of turning, boring, and facing operations. Fairly close tolerances. Simple setups or use of fixtures. Speeds, feeds, tooling prescribed.

FIGURE 63. FAMILY OF BORING MILL JOBS, LABOR GRADES 2, 4, 6, AND 8. This is an occupation summary made from the data on four separate job descriptions shown below. Together they are a sample of analyzing a family of jobs. (National Metal Trades Association.)

Occ. Code No._____

Dept._____

JOB RATING—SUBSTANTIATING DATA

Job Name___Boring Mill Operator—Vertical (Usually 16′ and up)___ Class___A

FACTORS	DEG.	BASIS OF RATING
EDUCATION	3 (42)	Use shop mathematics, charts, tables, handbook formulas. Work from complicated drawings or job layouts. Use micrometers, depth gauge, surface gauge, vernier calipers, bevel protractors. Knowledge of turning, boring, facing methods; cutting tools; cutting qualities of metals. Equivalent to 2 years high school plus 2 to 3 years trades training.
EXPERIENCE	5 (110)	5 to 8 years on a wide variety of vertical boring mill work, including very large mills.
INITIATIVE AND INGENUITY	4 (56)	Wide variety of very large and expensive parts. Close tolerances. Difficult setups, requiring extensive blocking of irregularly shaped parts. High degree of ingenuity and judgment to plan and lay out varied and unusual operations, handle very large work. Select speeds, feeds, tools. Check castings or parts to insure adequate finish allowance.
PHYSICAL DEMAND	2 (20)	Handle large clamps, blocks, tools, during setup. Climb over large work during operation. Most of time light physical effort operating machine, checking, adjusting, waiting for cuts.
MENTAL OR VISUAL DEMAND	4 (20)	Must concentrate mental and visual attention closely to a large number of details, making setups, planning complex operations on diversified work, checking, adjusting to close tolerances.
RESPONSIBILITY FOR EQUIPMENT OR PROCESS	4 (20)	Careless setup or operation, jamming of tools, dropping castings on table, allowing clamp to strike ram, breaking worm feed on ram may cause damage. Probable damage seldom over $500.
RESPONSIBILITY FOR MATERIAL OR PRODUCT	4 (20)	Careless setup or operation may result in spoilage and possible scrapping of expensive castings, forgings, etc. Probable losses seldom over $500.
RESPONSIBILITY FOR SAFETY OF OTHERS	3 (15)	Flying chips may cause burns, cuts, or eye injuries. Clamps or rail may be set in such a position as to injure employee walking past machine. Careless handling or setup may be hazardous to others.
RESPONSIBILITY FOR WORK OF OTHERS	1 (5)	None.
WORKING CONDITIONS	2 (20)	Good working conditions. May be slightly dirty, especially in setups. Some dust from castings.
UNAVOIDABLE HAZARDS	3 (15)	May crush fingers or toes in handling heavy castings; dropped tools or clamps may cause injury. Possible burns, cuts, or eye injury from flying chips and particles.
REMARKS	343–2	

FIGURE 64. JOB RATING—SUBSTANTIATING DATA

Occ. Code No._____

Dept. _____

JOB RATING—SUBSTANTIATING DATA

Job Name __Boring Mill Operator—Vertical__   Class ___B___

FACTORS	DEG.	BASIS OF RATING
EDUCATION	3 (42)	Use shop mathematics, charts, tables, handbook formulas. Work from complicated drawings or job layouts. Use micrometers, depth gauge, surface gauge, vernier calipers, bevel protractor. Knowledge of turning, boring, facing methods; cutting tools; cutting qualities of metals. Equivalent to 2 years high school plus 2 to 3 years trades training.
EXPERIENCE	4 (88)	3 to 5 years on a wide variety of vertical boring mill work.
INITIATIVE AND INGENUITY	4 (56)	Wide variety of castings and parts of complicated form requiring considerable amount of turning, boring, facing, etc. Very close tolerances. Difficult setups requiring extensive blocking of irregularly shaped parts. High degree of ingenuity to plan and lay out varied and unusual operations. Select speeds, feeds, tools. Check castings or parts to insure adequate finish allowance.
PHYSICAL DEMAND	2 (20)	Handle clamps, blocks, tools during setup. Most of time light physical effort operating machine, checking, adjusting, waiting for cuts.
MENTAL OR VISUAL DEMAND	4 (20)	Must concentrate mental and visual attention closely to a large number of details, making setups, planning complex operations on diversified work, checking, adjusting to close tolerances.
RESPONSIBILITY FOR EQUIPMENT OR PROCESS	3 (15)	Careless setup or operation, jamming of tools, dropping castings on table, allowing clamp to strike ram, breaking worm feed on ram, may cause damage. Probable damage seldom over $250.
RESPONSIBILITY FOR MATERIAL OR PRODUCT	3 (15)	Careless setup or operation may result in spoilage and possible scrapping of expensive castings, forgings, etc. Probable losses seldom over $250.
RESPONSIBILITY FOR SAFETY OF OTHERS	3 (15)	Flying chips may cause burns, cuts, or eye injuries. Clamps or rail may be set in such a position as to injure employee walking past machine. Careless handling or setup may be hazardous to others.
RESPONSIBILITY FOR WORK OF OTHERS	1 (5)	None.
WORKING CONDITIONS	2 (20)	Good working conditions. May be slightly dirty, especially in setups. Some dust from castings.
UNAVOIDABLE HAZARDS	3 (15)	May crush fingers or toes in handling heaving castings; dropped tools or clamps may cause injury. Possible burns, cuts, or eye injury from flying chips and particles.
REMARKS	311–4	

FIGURE 65. JOB RATING—SUBSTANTIATING DATA

Occ. Code No._____

Dept._____

JOB RATING—SUBSTANTIATING DATA
MASTER SHEET

Job Name Boring Mill Operator—Vertical   Class   C

FACTORS	DEG.	BASIS OF RATING
EDUCATION	3 (42)	Use shop mathematics, charts, tables, handbook formulas. Work from ordinary drawings or job layouts. Use micrometers, depth gauge, surface gauge, vernier calipers, bevel protractor. Knowledge of turning, boring, facing methods; cutting tools; cutting qualities of metals. Equivalent to 2 years high school plus 2 to 3 years trades training.
EXPERIENCE	3 (66)	1 to 3 years on a variety of vertical boring mill work.
INITIATIVE AND INGENUITY	3 (42)	Variety of castings, forgings, parts. Setups exacting but not usually difficult. Close tolerances. Select speeds, feeds, tools. Judgment to plan and perform a normal range of operations, including multihead work, where a large number of interrelated dimensions need not be considered.
PHYSICAL DEMAND	2 (20)	Handle large clamps, blocks, tools during setup. Climb over large work during operation. Most of time light physical effort operating machine, checking, adjusting, waiting for cuts.
MENTAL OR VISUAL DEMAND	3 (15)	Continuous mental or visual attention setting up, operating, checking, and making adjustments.
RESPONSIBILITY FOR EQUIPMENT OR PROCESS	3 (15)	Careless setup or operation, jamming of tools, dropping castings on table, allowing clamp to strike ram, breaking worm feed on ram. Probable damage seldom over $250.
RESPONSIBILITY FOR MATERIAL OR PRODUCT	2 (10)	Error in setup or checking may result in spoilage and possible scrapping of castings, forgings, etc. Probable loss seldom over $100.
RESPONSIBILITY FOR SAFETY OF OTHERS	3 (15)	Flying chips may cause burns, cuts, or eye injuries. Clamps or rail may be set in such a position as to injure employee walking past machine. Careless handling or setup may be hazardous to others.
RESPONSIBILITY FOR WORK OF OTHERS	1 (5)	None.
WORKING CONDITIONS	2 (20)	Good working conditions. May be slightly dirty, especially in setups. Some dust from castings.
UNAVOIDABLE HAZARDS	3 (15)	May crush fingers or toes in handling heavy castings; dropped tools or clamps may cause injury. Possible burns, cuts, or eye injury from flying chips and particles.
REMARKS	265–6	

FIGURE 66. JOB RATING—SUBSTANTIATING DATA—MASTER SHEET

Occ. Code No._____

Dept. _____

JOB RATING—SUBSTANTIATING DATA

Job Name Boring Mill Operator—Vertical   Class   D

FACTORS	DEG.	BASIS OF RATING
EDUCATION	2 (28)	Use simple shop arithmetic. Work from simple drawings. Use micrometers, scale, and calipers. Equivalent to 2 years high school.
EXPERIENCE	2 (44)	6 to 12 months on simple vertical boring mill work.
INITIATIVE AND INGENUITY	2 (28)	Repetitive turning, boring, and facing operations. Simple setups, or use of fixtures. Fairly close tolerances. Speeds, feeds, tools prescribed. Minor decisions to check work and make machine adjustments, replace dull tools.
PHYSICAL DEMAND	3 (30)	Sustained physical effort handling tools and material during setup, operating machine and making adjustments. Short cycle work.
MENTAL OR VISUAL DEMAND	3 (15)	Continuous mental or visual attention setting up, operating, checking, and making adjustments.
RESPONSIBILITY FOR EQUIPMENT OR PROCESS	3 (15)	Careless setup or operation, jamming of tools, dropping castings on table, allowing clamp to strike ram, breaking worm feed on ram may cause damage. Probable damage seldom over $100.
RESPONSIBILITY FOR MATERIAL OR PRODUCT	2 (10)	Careless setup or operation may result in spoilage and possible scrapping of castings, forgings, etc. Probable losses seldom over $100.
RESPONSIBILITY FOR SAFETY OF OTHERS	3 (15)	Flying chips may cause burns, cuts, or eye injuries. Careless handling or setup may injure others.
RESPONSIBILITY FOR WORK OF OTHERS	1 (5)	None.
WORKING CONDITIONS	2 (20)	Good working conditions. May be slightly dirty, especially in setups. Some dust from castings. May use coolants.
UNAVOIDABLE HAZARDS	3 (15)	May crush fingers or toes in handling heavy castings; dropped tools or clamps may cause injury. Possible burns, cuts, or eye injury from flying chips and particles.
REMARKS	225–8	

FIGURE 67. JOB RATING—SUBSTANTIATING DATA

Page No. ___2250___

File Code ___BG 0930 or___
                   0940 (CWSB)

Department ___TEMPER PASSING & COLD ROLLING___

Sub Division ___SHEET MILL COLD REDUCTION___

Job Title (Std.) ___ROLLER—COIL TEMPER MILL___

Job Title (Plant) ___ROLLER—COILS___

JOB DESCRIPTION

PRIMARY FUNCTION

Operates a four-high temper mill in processing coil product to obtain desired flatness, surface, and physical properties.

TOOLS AND EQUIPMENT

Uncoiler, four-high single stand temper mill, recoiler, stripper, auxiliary equipment, etc.

MATERIAL

| | Stainless Coils | | Regular Low Carbon Coils | |
	Min.	Max.	Min.	Max.
Gauge	.015	.125	.015	.060
Width	20″	48″	24″	80″

SOURCE OF SUPERVISION

Supervised by turn foreman.

DIRECTION EXERCISED

Closely directs one catcher and three feeders.

WORKING PROCEDURE

Charging coil—Remains at mill controls while crew threads strip through mill to delivery reel.

Acceleration—Drafts and starts mill. Operates controls adjusting strip tension between entry reel and mill, and mill and delivery reel, inspects surface of strip and adjusts draft and strip tension to obtain desired flatness, surface, and physical requirements.

Rolling—Observes mill load, tension fluctuation, and strip shape. Inspects for flatness, strip shape, and surface defects. Observes closely for trouble that may occur due to a bad coil end. Operates controls in running up screws. Checks elongation using scribe.

Removing coil—Operates controls in stripping coil off delivery reel.

Roll Change—Selects rolls for correct crown, finish desired, hardness, and size. Directs craneman and crew in roll change. Drafts mill after roll change.

Weighs and identifies each coil or directs members of crew to perform these tasks and makes out a complete production report of material rolled during turn.

FIGURE 68. SPECIMEN EXAMPLE OF JOB DESCRIPTION AND CLASSIFICATION. (Represents an Actual Case in Fact.)

JOB CLASSIFICATION

Factor	Reason for Classification	Code	Classification
Pre-Employment Training	Requires mentality to learn to: Read gauges, meters, micrometers, calculate elongation, adjust mill.	C	1.0
Employment Training and Experience	Requires experience of up to 30 months on this and related work.	F	2.0
Mental Skill	Considerable judgment and planning required in determining proper draft, tension, and rolls to obtain desired results.	D	2.2
Manual Skill	Requires high degree of coordination to manipulate controls at rapid pace when starting mill and in making of adjustments to mill.	C	1.0
Responsibility for Material	Damage material by failure to obtain correct temper, roll marks strip thus reducing material to rejects. Estimated Cost ¼ turn before detection = 25 ton $45 cost/ton $27/ton rejects 25 × ($45–$27) = $450 regular estimated stainless—100 15 ton $550 total	E	4.5
Responsibility for Tools and Equipment	High degree of care required on a high speed production unit to prevent damage to rolls and equipment.	MED E	2.0
Responsibility for Operations	Sets pace on a major production unit and is responsible for production.	E	3.0
Responsibility for Safety of Others	Considerable care and attention required to prevent injury to others while changing rolls, starting and stopping mill.	C	.8
Mental Effort	Close mental and visual application required to plan drafting and roll shape to obtain proper elongation and surface rolling of coils at high speed, direct roll changes, control mill while threading strip, standing and observing operations, coil changes, strip coil, adjust reel and minor adjustments.	D	1.5
Physical Effort	Minimum physical exertion required to observe, direct operations, inspect rolls, inspect product, and assist in roll changes (operate controls during threading).	A	Base
Surroundings	Slightly dirty and noisy—good plant conditions.	A	Base
Hazard	Works in close proximity to moving strip. Subject to cuts, punctures, and bruises, also exposed to crane hazards during roll changes.	B	.4

Job Class   18   Total   18.4

FIGURE 68. (*Concluded.*)

Page No._____

File Code____LM-0010 ZA-03_____

Department____MAINTENANCE_____

Sub Division____COKE PLANT_____

Job Title (Std.)____LEAD BURNER_____

Job Title (Plant)____LEAD BURNER "A"_____

JOB DESCRIPTION

PRIMARY FUNCTION
To inspect, dismantle, install, repair, fabricate, and test any type of lead lining or parts for process equipment.

TOOLS AND EQUIPMENT
Hydrogen torch and tanks, shears, forming tools, miscellaneous hand tools, etc.

MATERIALS
Lead or lead alloy sheet, pipe, rod, pig, and bar stock oxygen, hydrogen, etc.

SOURCE OF SUPERVISION
Foreman or immediate supervisor. Performs work with a minimum of direction.

DIRECTION EXERCISED
Works alone or directs helpers and other workmen as required.

WORKING PROCEDURE
Receives blueprints, sketches, and instructions regarding work assignment. Inspects equipment, interprets prints, and plans working procedure and tool and material requirements.

Removes damaged sections; lays out, cuts, and forms new lead sheet or piping for any size, shape, or type of process vessel such as stills, agitators, saturators, drain tables, troughs, etc. Scrapes, bevels, and drosses edges for making joint.

Fits new sections of lead sheet or pipe into position. Molds and fuses lead bar into joint, skillfully using hydrogen torch in down-hand, vertical, or overhead position. May prefabricate linings or sections of linings before installation in equipment or build up directly as work progresses in either open or partially closed vessels.

Fabricates lead or lead alloy parts and equipment such as pipes, valves, open and closed containers, protective coatings for fans and fan casings, etc.

Makes lead or lead alloy castings as required.

Performs work requiring a thorough knowledge of the various lead forming and burning techniques, physical and working properties of lead and lead alloys, and the skillful use of tools and equipment used in the trade.

FIGURE 69. SPECIMEN EXAMPLE OF JOB DESCRIPTION AND CLASSIFICATION. (Represents an Actual Case in Fact.)

JOB CLASSIFICATION

Job Title (Plant)   LEAD BURNER "A"   File Code   LM-0010 ZA-03

Factor	Reason for Classification	Code	Classi-fication
Pre-Employment Training	Requires mentality to learn to: Read blue prints, lay out and accurately form lead sheets.	C	1.0
Employment Training and Experience	Requires experience on this and related work of 37 to 48 months of continuous progress to become proficient.	H	3.2
Mental Skill	Plan work detail in installing and repairing lead lining.	E	2.8
Manual Skill	Uses hand tools, lead burning torch, mallet, and forms in forming, shaping, and applying lead lining to close tolerances.	D	1.5
Responsibility for Material	Requires close attention for majority of turn. Lose labor and material by improper cutting or forming. Estimated Cost: $250 or under.	D	1.6
Responsibility for Tools and Equipment	Some attention and care to prevent damage to torch, regulators, tanks, etc., by careless or improper use.	B LO.	.2
Responsibility for Operations	Performs tradesman's work to get the producing unit into operation.	C	1.0
Responsibility for Safety of Others	Works as a member of crew where individual acts may injure others. Ordinary care and attention required.	B	.4
Mental Effort	Close mental or visual application required in layout from blue print details and in forming sheets.	D	1.5
Physical Effort	Moderate physical exertion in using torch, and in shaping lead.	C	.8
Surroundings	Exposed to considerable fumes.	C	.8
Hazard	Exposed to lead fumes, severe cuts and bruises. Exposed to burns from molten metal.	D	1.2
Job Class 16 Total			16.0

FIGURE 69. (*Concluded.*)

Page No. _____

File Code ___LCX 0010 CWSB___

Department ___MAINTENANCE_____

Sub Division ___ELECTRIC SHOP_____

Job Title (Std.) ___ELECTRICIAN (ARMATURE WINDER)_____

Job Title (Plant) ___ARMATURE WINDER_____

JOB DESCRIPTION

PRIMARY FUNCTION

To test, dismantle, repair, rewind, and assemble armatures, stators, rotors, commutators, and field coils for any size, type, and style of electric motors and generators in shop or field.

TOOLS AND EQUIPMENT

Soldering equipment, preheating torch, testing apparatus, arbor press, commutator under cutting machine, handing lathe, drill press, saw, hand tools, etc.

MATERIALS

AC and DC armatures, stators, rotors, various types of coils, commutators, commutator parts, solder, insulating materials, banding wire, etc.

SOURCE OF SUPERVISION

Foreman or immediate supervisor. Performs work with a minimum of direction.

DIRECTION EXERCISED

Works alone or directs work of helpers and other workmen as required.

WORKING PROCEDURE

Receives instructions, winding diagrams, and work orders. Inspects and tests equipment to determine extent of damage and nature of repairs necessary, basing decisions on a thorough knowledge of armature winding principles and established shop practice.

Reads and interprets any type of winding diagram or makes sketch of windings to aid in reassembly when prints are not available.

Strips down, repairs, or rewinds armatures and coils for any type of motor, generator, transformer, or solenoid-operated equipment. Repairs, replaces, or fabricates, fits, and assembles replacement parts as required. Repairs or restacks laminated iron cores. Dismantles, replaces segments, or rebuilds commutators as required, fabricating mica V-rings when necessary. Cleans and tins risers. Winds, insulates, shapes, varnishes, and bakes form and hand-wound coils. Assembles coils in slots and insulates, wedges, and bands into position.

Solders leads to commutator or groups connections and brings out to leads of slip ring.

Turns commutators, under-cuts mica, straightens journals, checks fit on bearings, and balances armatures for rated speed.

Tests for polarity, grounds, shorts, and brake load and adjusts equipment for proper operating characteristics. Changes windings on AC machines to suit voltage and speed requirements.

Does "on the job" planning.

Analyzes trouble on emergency breakdowns, cuts out faulty coils, and makes temporary repairs on equipment still in service to minimize operating delays until such time as equipment may be shut down for complete overhaul.

FIGURE 70. SPECIMEN EXAMPLE OF JOB DESCRIPTION AND CLASSIFICATION. (Represents an Actual Case in Fact.)

JOB CLASSIFICATION

Job Title (Plant)   ARMATURE WINDER   File Code   LCX 0010 CWSB

Factor	Reason for Classification	Code	Classi-fication
Pre-Employment Training	Requires the mentality to learn to: Make sketches of wiring. Read drawings and diagrams. Dismantle and repair armatures, stators, etc.	C	1.0
Employment Training and Experience	Requires experience on this and related work of from 37 to 48 months of continuous progress to become proficient.	H	3.2
Mental Skill	Read drawings and diagrams. Make sketches of wiring. Use testing equipment, determine correct winding procedure. Dismantle and repair motors and generators.	E	2.8
Manual Skill	Use tradesman's tools in a wide variety of tasks. Test, dismantle and repair armatures, stators, motors, etc.	C	1.0
Responsibility for Material	Use close attention for majority of turn. May damage insulation or make wrong connection resulting in burned-out coils. Repair or rewind—labor and material. Estimated Cost: $250 or under.	D	1.6
Responsibility for Tools and Equipment	Moderate attention and care to prevent damage. May damage hand tools by careless or incorrect use. Damage testing equipment by overloading.	C MD.	.7
Responsibility for Operations	Repair mill motors and generators. Occasionally works on rush jobs for mill departments.	C	1.0
Responsibility for Safety of Others	Little care required to prevent injury to others. Usually works alone.	A	Base
Mental Effort	Close mental and visual application, wind, undercut commutators, make connections, wedge, solder, trace connections, and make electrical tests. Strip and clean coils. Read wiring diagrams. Hook up for crane. Get supplies.	D	1.5
Physical Effort	Light physical exertion. Read drawings and plan work. Use light hand tools. Clean motors. Wind armatures. Cut commutator slots. Dismantle and assemble motors or generators.	B	.3
Surroundings	Inside—machine shop conditions.	A	Base
Hazard	Works on electric equipment. Cuts, punctures, bruises. Subject to shock.	C	.8
	Job Class 14 Total		13.9

FIGURE 70. (*Concluded.*)

Page No.

File Code   HAX 0011 CWSB

Department   MAINTENANCE

Sub Division   FOUNDRY

Job Title (Std.)   CORE MAKER

Job Title (Plant)   CORE MAKER

JOB DESCRIPTION

PRIMARY FUNCTION

To make any type of sand cores to be used in dry or green sand foundry molds.

TOOLS AND EQUIPMENT

Core boxes, patterns, pneumatic rammers, and miscellaneous tradesman's hand tools, including hammers, mallets, lifters, slicks, spoons, trowels, shovels, etc.

MATERIALS

Used: Core sands, bonding materials, paste, wire, steel rods, vent wax, mold wash, graphite, chills, sea coal, etc.
Produced: Sand cores.

SOURCE OF SUPERVISION

Foreman or immediate supervisor.
Performs work with a minimum of direction.

DIRECTION EXERCISED

Works alone or directs helpers and other workmen as required.

WORKING PROCEDURE

Receives prints, sketches, and instructions for the job.
Interprets blue prints or sketches as required for making and assembling cores.
Plans working procedure and material and equipment requirements.
Prepares proper sand mixture. Assembles and clamps core boxes or sweep patterns.
Places adequate reinforcing wires and rods. Fills core box with sand and packs with hand or pneumatic rammers, making sure that core is adequately vented to carry off gases and that chills of various types are accurately placed. Removes core from core box, patches any breaks, and applies core wash.
Transports or directs movement of core to core oven drying buggy. After cores have been thoroughly dried, assembles and pastes sand core sections together to form completed core. Fills in cracks and seams with silica paste and applies graphite facing to entire surface of core.
Performs work requiring a thorough knowledge of core making practice, including the physical properties of various sand mixtures, various methods of reinforcing, the adequate venting of cores, and the skillful use of various types of tools and equipment of the trade.

FIGURE 71. SPECIMEN EXAMPLE OF JOB DESCRIPTION AND CLASSIFICATION. (Represents an Actual Case in Fact.)

JOB CLASSIFICATION

Job Title (Plant)   CORE MAKER   File Code   HAX 0011   CWSB

Factor	Reason for Classification	Code	Classi-fication
Pre-Employment Training	Requires mentality to learn to: Read core charts. Visualize core construction and plan work details.	C	1.0
Employment Training and Experience	Requires experience on this and related work of from 37 to 48 months of continuous progress to become proficient.	H	3.2
Mental Skill	Reason through problems and work details using considerable judgment in making cores.	D	2.2
Manual Skill	Exercise considerable dexterity with trowel and finishing tools to finish simple and complex cores.	D	1.5
Responsibility for Material	Close attention for a majority of turn to produce properly constructed and finished cores. Poor coremaking will result in loss of casting. Break or destroy cores by careless handling—poor workmanship. Cost to remake cores—labor and material. Estimated cost: $100 or under.	D	1.1
Responsibility for Tools and Equipment	Some attention and care required to prevent damage to air powered rammers and core drying ovens. Damage core boxes by careless handling.	B LO	.2
Responsibility for Operations	Perform an individual processing operation.	C	1.0
Responsibility for Safety of Others	Works in such a manner that injury to others due to carelessness or negligence is very remote.	A	Base
Mental Effort	Moderate mental application to prepare sand, ram sand manually or with powered rammer, place chills and reinforcing, jolt and draw cores, patch and finish cores.	C	1.0
Physical Effort	Moderate physical exertion to shovel and ram sand; lift and carry heavy cores and core boxes, place reinforcing pieces. Plan work, read core charts, inspect cores.	C	.8
Surroundings	Inside, dirty, dusty, not uniformly heated.	B	.4
Hazard	Exposed to slight bruises, cuts, scratches. Handle moderate weight material manually.	A	Base
	Job Class 12 Total		12.4

FIGURE 71. (*Concluded.*)

It was pointed out in Chapter 3 that the Weighted-in-Points plan does not always use the predetermined degree definitions for rating a new job. When the new job is one of a "family" it is safe and time-saving to interpolate its characteristics among those of previous rated jobs in its family. Figures 63–70 from the N.M.T.A. provide a sample of such a family of jobs, namely, vertical boring mill jobs.

Page No.	673
File Code	EB 0710 Q-14

Department	FINISHING & SHIPPING
Sub Division	BAR & STRIP MILLS
Job Title (Std.)	SHEARMAN
Job Title (Plant)	STOCK SHEARMAN

JOB DESCRIPTION

PRIMARY FUNCTION
To shear to ordered length piles of Merchant Mill recut or stock.

TOOLS AND EQUIPMENT
Stock shear, roll entry line, hooks, or pry bars, delivery table, wrenches, tape, hand tools, etc.

MATERIALS
Various sections of Merchant Mill material up to 3¼" rounds and squares.

SOURCE OF SUPERVISION
Stock shear foreman is directed in cutting procedure by checker.

DIRECTION EXERCISED
None.

WORKING PROCEDURE
Secures cutting information as to cutting from checker and tags.
Sets bar stop and tapes for length.
Operates controls on roller line to position material at shear. May use hook or pry bar to position manually.
Operates foot pedal to shear.
Checks length and adjusts to stop if necessary.
Length tolerance ⅛" over and under.
Places tags on completed pile.
Shears test pieces.
Changes shear knives and adjusts.

FIGURE 72. SPECIMEN EXAMPLE OF JOB DESCRIPTION AND CLASSIFICATION. (Represents an Actual Case in Fact.)

JOB CLASSIFICATION

Job Title (Plant)　STOCK SHEARMAN　　　File Code　EB 0710 Q-14

Factor	Reason for Classification	Code	Classification
Pre-Employment Training	Requires mentality to learn to: Exercise judgment in setting up and operating stock shear.	B	.3
Employment Training and Experience	Requires experience on this and related work of from 7 to 12 months of continuous progress to become proficient.	C	.8
Mental Skill	Exercise judgment in setting up and operating shear to shear materials within the required tolerance.	C	1.6
Manual Skill	Uses hand tools to change shear blades and to make minor adjustments.	B	.5
Responsibility for Material	Requires close attention for part of turn. May cut material too short. Checker would detect and hold loss down. Estimated cost: 100 T. @ 5% (45–15) × 5 = $150.	C	1.2
Responsibility for Tools and Equipment	Moderate attention and care required. Damage shear and shear knife by improper adjustment.	C MED.	.7
Responsibility for Operations	Responsible for maintaining production of shearing on stock shear.	C	1.0
Responsibility for Safety of Others	Exercise care and attention in operating shear—material is handled manually by Helpers.	B	.4
Mental Effort	Moderate mental or visual application in setting stop and controlling movement of material into shear. Changes and adjusts knives.	C	1.0
Physical Effort	Moderate physical exertion required. Assisting in pulling material into position. Use bars, wrenches, and hand tools.	C	.8
Surroundings	Inside finishing department building. Dirty—noisy.	A	Base
Hazard	Accident hazard moderate. Exposed to fractures—mashed fingers, etc., handling material manually.	B	.4

Job Class　　9　　　　Total　　　　　　8.7

FIGURE 72. (*Concluded.*)

Example of Rating for Weighted-in-Points Above Base. The Basic Steel case already discussed gives no weighting to the first degrees, merely uses the word "base." Other degrees have weighted points in small numbers (one digit, one decimal place). Reference to these is by code letters A, B, C, etc. The original specimen jobs were ranked one characteristic at a time and assigned these values by the "characteristic comparison" technique, but subsequent rating for nonspecimen jobs is done by the other technique, namely, by matching description subdivisions with predetermined degree definitions. Since these definitions have been tailor-fitted to the steel industry and will not fit any other industry we have given only one set by way of a sample (see Chapter 6). For the complete set of these predetermined degree definitions see the CIO booklet, *Inequities Program—Agreements Between Carnegie-Illinois Steel Corporation and the United Steelworkers of America.* Thus we have a situation where the techniques are used in inverse order from the way they are used in the Kress-Cole plans. Ingeniously the total of the degree values for any one job has been planned to constitute labor grade. By the courtesy of Mr. William Jacko, member, Wage Division, U.S. of A., we present five of their job descriptions, all for specimen jobs and ranging from Grade 18 to Grade 9 (see Figures 68 to 72). At the bottom of each description is the reminder, "The above statement reflects the general details considered necessary to describe the principal functions of the job identified, and shall not be construed as a detailed description of all the work requirements that may be inherent in the job."

9

CLASSIFYING THE JOBS

At some point in any procedure having to do with the human factor, the ability to obtain results on a scientific basis ceases, and the judgment of a competent, unprejudiced group must be pooled to arrive at the final result. It is recognized that this result will be subject to all the errors of human judgment. The only way to reduce the number of such errors is to obtain as many opinions as is consistent with the progress in the work.

—SAMUEL L. H. BURK

Classification Is a Check on Evaluation. We select the above quotation for this chapter because we believe that both analysis and judgment should come in whenever job relationships are considered. In the first place we must not be confused by the kind or field of activity, such as construction, accounting, clerical, etc. It is the level and scope of activity which should determine the relativity of job worth. In the second place we should not attempt to set up many gradations with fine distinctions. An eminent psychologist has said:

Increased reliability in job evaluation calls for a drastic reduction in the number of points assigned to each factor. Limiting the number of points, it is true, will tend to promote a clustering of final scores and to restrict the number of groups or grades of jobs. However, the final results will tend to be more exact, because they are the outcome of a logical approach based upon the recognition that the results of any summation cannot possibly be more accurate than the most inaccurate measurement taken and used in the formula.[1]

In the third place we advocate that the original assignment of points to a job should not unalterably determine its relative worth. Of course the pooled judgment can and should be applied at the time the degree measurements are made but we think it should be tentative at that stage and that further use of pooled judgment should be used as a check at the time of classification.

[1] Morris S. Viteles, "A Psychologist Looks at Job Evaluation," *A.M.A. Personnel,* XVII, No. 3.

Tendency Toward Fewer Classes. Early practice in the factory used too many gradations. The International Harvester Company in 1919 put its 400 time-paid jobs into 18 grades. The American Rolling Mill Company and Atlantic Refinery used the same number but the latter extended above hourly paid jobs. An unnamed company classified 500 jobs into 15 grades. A case reported by E. J. Benge in 1932 cited:

> 9,800 hourly paid employees.
> 757 distinct jobs.
> 70 different rates of pay ($.415 to $.975).

reduced by evaluation to

> 294 distinct jobs.
> 14 different rates of pay.
> Even in 1952 one study of hourly rates came up with thirteen levels of pay.
> There are at least two reasons for preferring fewer grades. First, the rate differentials are larger and that in turn sets the grades apart more distinctly and lessens expectation of frequent upgrading. Second, there is greater chance of finding two or more key jobs for each grade.

Usually the point range for classes of hourly paid jobs is kept constant and at first thought there seems little need for doing otherwise, but one of our highest authorities, S. L. H. Burk, has given arithmetic increases to a succession of such ranges, probably because he extends his structure to include jobs of high worth. His lowest grade (1) has a range of about ten points and his highest grade (18) has a range of nearly thirty-five points. Such increases are definitely needed in the money rate ranges to allow for greater variation in job content. There may also be greater job worth variation for similar jobs as the worth ascends. We recognize that phenomenon in jobs which can be expanded and even created by their occupants. For hourly paid jobs this has not been generally recognized, but variation can be used to correct lapovers and provide more room for merit increases in the higher grades. Since the trend is toward fewer job grades there is likely to be a trend toward this variation in point range; there will be more room for it (see Chapter 11).

Certain consultants are still using as many as seventeen classes for hourly paid jobs and Basic Steel has a possibility of thirty-two, but the influence of the National War Labor Board, which favored eleven brackets for mechanical work, and of the CIO, which insisted on ten grades, is now showing results. By way of sampling: The Westinghouse Electric and Manufacturing Company has ten grades for men's jobs and five grades for women's and boys' jobs, the latter lapping over to leave a total of twelve rate grades. The American Machine and Foundry Company has ten grades. The Farrel-Birmingham Company has nine grades, the Goodyear Tire and Rubber Company has six grades and the Worthington Pump and Machinery Company, Wellsville plant, has only five grades. We think ten to twelve grades are optimum for hourly paid jobs. Determination of labor grades is merely a matter of convenience. Varying increments between grade midpoints of from ten to twenty-five cents is the usual practice at present.

Government Action Has Spurred Classification. The Fair Labor Standards Act of 1938 made it necessary to classify borderline jobs on the basis of service levels so that an accurate distinction could be made between executive and operative positions. Then the National War Labor Board directed many companies to classify jobs, and it used the terms *classification* and *evaluation* without distinction. In short, the federal government exerted considerable influence in extending systematic classification.

Start With a Broad Frame. It is logical and probably helpful to start with a broad classification of all work from top to bottom. Two such classifications are harmonized as follows:

The Westinghouse Electric and Manufacturing Company [2]		The Philadelphia Electric Company [3]
Policy Administrative Top Executive Management Creative		General Management Dept. Associate Management Major Supervision or Highly Technical Service
Interpretive Shop Skilled Management Unskilled		Highly Skilled Service or Minor Supervision Skilled Service Semiskilled Service Slightly Skilled Service Primary

Mr. Hopwood's scheme, at the right, is not so simple as we have indicated because he recognizes wide lapovers. We present this in full (Figure 73) because it demonstrates how complex such matters actually are and because it carries a caution against arbitrariness in

[2] W. G. Marshall, *Developing a Supplementary Compensation Program*, A.M.A. Personnel Series No. 30.
[3] J. O. Hopwood, *A.M.A. Personnel*, XI, No. 4.

fixing demarkations. There must, however, be definite demarkations.

Key Jobs for Bench Marks. Classification for any single department would be of itself simple but it must be set up to be in harmony with the classifications of other departments. This problem might be approached by setting up independent classifications for all departments, leaving the harmonizing to be done afterwards, but we think it sounder practice to select several jobs in each department, at least one of which is clearly equivalent to one in another depart-

GRADES AND SUB-GRADES

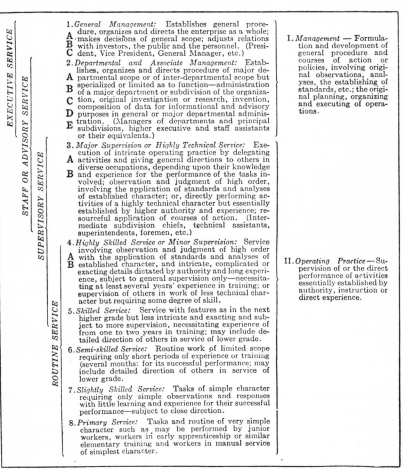

1. *General Management:* Establishes general procedure, organizes and directs the enterprise as a whole; A makes decisions of general scope; adjusts relations B with investors, the public and the personnel. (President, Vice President, General Manager, etc.)

2. *Departmental and Associate Management:* Establishes, organizes and directs procedure of major de- A partmental scope or of inter-departmental scope but specialized or limited as to function—administration B of a major department or subdivision of the organiza- C tion, original investigation or research, invention, composition of data for informational and advisory D purposes in general or major departmental adminis- E tration. (Managers of departments and principal subdivisions, higher executive and staff assistants or their equivalents.)

3. *Major Supervision or Highly Technical Service:* Execution of intricate operating practice by delegating A activities and giving general directions to others in diverse occupations, depending upon their knowledge B and experience for the performance of the tasks involved; observation and judgment of high order, involving the application of standards and analyses of established character; or, directly performing activities of a highly technical character but essentially established by higher authority and experience; resourceful application of courses of action. (Intermediate subdivision chiefs, technical assistants, superintendents, foremen, etc.)

4. *Highly Skilled Service or Minor Supervision:* Service involving observation and judgment of high order A with the application of standards and analyses of B established character, and intricate, complicated or exacting details dictated by authority and long experience, subject to general supervision only—necessitating at least several years' experience in training; or supervision of others in work of less technical character but requiring some degree of skill.

5. *Skilled Service:* Service with features as in the next higher grade but less intricate and exacting and subject to more supervision, necessitating experience of from one to two years in training; may include detailed direction of others in service of lower grade.

6. *Semi-skilled Service:* Routine work of limited scope requiring only short periods of experience or training (several months: for its successful performance; may include detailed direction of others in service of lower grade.

7. *Slightly Skilled Service:* Tasks of simple character requiring only simple observations and responses with little learning and experience for their successful performance—subject to close direction.

8. *Primary Service:* Tasks and routine of very simple character such as may be performed by junior workers, workers in early apprenticeship or similar elementary training and workers in manual service of simplest character.

I. *Management* — Formulation and development of general procedure and courses of action or policies, involving original observations, analyses, the establishing of standards, etc.; the original planning, organizing and executing of operations.

II. *Operating Practice* — Supervision of or the direct performance of activities essentially established by authority, instruction or direct experience.

EXECUTIVE SERVICE
STAFF OR ADVISORY SERVICE
SUPERVISORY SERVICE
ROUTINE SERVICE

FIGURE 73. CLASSIFICATION SCHEME FOR GRADING POSITIONS. (J. O. Hopwood, *Salaries, Wages and Labor Relations.* The Ronald Press Co., 1945, p. 47.)

ment, and so on. By this means a skeleton of jobs can be found which will set a single classification for the whole plant. Such select jobs are generally called specimen or *key jobs*. Considerations for selecting a key job are: (*a*) One which has escaped the specializing effects of tool or method refinement, but this need not rule out a widely standardized machine; (*b*) one which is stable as to content and rating and preferably has been proved satisfactory as a bench mark, by previous use as such; (*c*) one which has a fair number of operatives with no handicaps to free competition in the labor market; (*d*) as a series of key jobs, ones which represent all the grades of job worth.

Classification Work Sheet. Any selection of key jobs should be studied with particular care, that is, the descriptions and degree weightings must be so well accepted that no serious question can be raised regarding them later on. As an aid to checking the relationship of these bench marks a classification work sheet such as Figure 74 is needed. Since this is only a work sheet, a special form may be avoided. In fact, we used a regular Gantt Progress Chart for this illustration. It is particularly helpful if the total points for successive jobs happen to show fairly regular intervals, allowing these values to be taken as representative of their classes. Note that the maximum potential of 100 points facilitates the process of comparison.

Typical Key Jobs. Naturally the jobs that qualify for key jobs vary by industries although there are a few which can usually be found in all industries, for instance, toolmaker's job and sweeper's job. Certainly some of them must be common to the various industries in one locality. The importance of this will be treated in a later chapter. The National War Labor Board descriptions for which it recorded brackets of "sound and tested rates" were much used to guide classification work but E. N. Hay estimates that these published job descriptions "cover considerably less than 5 per cent of all jobs that a large company may have." The trouble here is identification. The National War Labor Board descriptions used terms such as "large and expensive assemblies," "medium-size work," "small-size work," "fairly close tolerances," "fairly complicated circuits," and many others which are indefinite and subject to a great deal of pulling and hauling.[4]

Job Descriptions for Job Foundries, published jointly in 1938 by the Division of Standards and Research, U. S. Department of Labor,

[4] See *Conversion of Electrical Manufacturing Industry Basic Job Descriptions to "Dictionary of Occupational Titles" Job Definitions and Code Numbers,* prepared by NEMA with the War Manpower Commission, June, 1943.

JOB NO.	NAME	Experience	Education	Initiative Ingenuity	Mental Visual	Physical	Product or Process	Work or Safety of Others	Hazardous	Disagreeable	Total Points	Labor Grade
1	Pattern Maker, a	20	16	16	12	6	3	2		4	83	10
15	Layout, a	15	16	16	12	6		1	2	6	77	9
31	Lathe, Engine, a	15	12	16	9	6	3	2	4	4	71	8
47	Floor Molder, o	15	4	8	9	9	3	4	6	8	66	7
75	Lathe, Turret, b (Warner and Swasey)	10	12	12	9	6	2	1	4	4	60	6
104	Car Loader, b	5	8	8	6	9	3	2	6	8	55	5
128	Power Saw	5	8	8	6	9	2	2	4	6	50	4
160	Cupola Charger	5	4	4	3	12	1	4	4	8	45	3
172	Painter Repair	5	4	4	6	6	1	1	4	8	39	2
175	Sweeper	5		4	3	9	1	2	2	8	34	1

FIGURE 74. CLASSIFICATION WORK SHEET

, and the U. S. Employment Service, have the same shortcoming. The *Wage Administration Manual for Ungraded Civilian Jobs in the Services of Supply,* published in 1942 by the Civilian Personnel Division, U. S. Army, provides a much better set of descriptions. In fact, they were described and ranked by Weed, Burk, and Balderston. We submit these for 44 key jobs, together with a 20-rung ladder diagram (Figure 75). They are preceded by three definitions which fix the usage of the terms *supervision* and *direction.*

LIST OF KEY JOBS

U. S. Army, Service of Supply

Immediate Supervision: Supervisor watches and follows the actual doing of the work in order that the workers may know what to do at any step in the operation which deviates from the routine, and in order that the correct routine may be followed efficiently in accordance with routine and/or detailed instructions. Gives attention to one worker, or group of workers, in one place for a large part of the worker's time.

General Supervision: Supervisor watches the actual doing of the work in order that the workers perform efficiently in accordance with instructions received. Divides attention among several workers or groups of workers so that no one worker is watched during the greater part of his working period.

Direction: Supervisor directs and confers with subordinates who are charged with carrying on actual operations, employing records and reports in order to be certain that employees are operating within limits of predetermined policies and programs. May make "spot" checks of employees at work and may confer frequently with them in order to determine need for making changes in instructions to complete effectively the work program.

DESCRIPTIONS OF KEY JOBS

1. Janitor: Under immediate supervision, keeps area assigned to him in clean and orderly condition. Sweeps, scrubs, mops, waxes and polishes floors. Dusts office furniture. Opens and closes windows. Empties waste baskets. Washes windows. Cleans light globes and Venetian blinds. Moves office furniture. Washes walls and glass partitions. Cleans and cares for toilets and rest rooms. Makes minor repairs to windows or occasionally to doors, such as replacing screws, catches, and latches.

2. Laborer Common: Under immediate supervision, performs wide variety of simple tasks, involving muscular rather than mental effort. (Usually works as member of group, so that every laborer receives close attention from supervisor, including instructions as to what to do, when to do it, and how to do it.) Does work of a generally preparatory nature, such as digging, hauling materials, and heavy lifting to facilitate efforts of more skilled workers. Also acts as rough helper to skilled workers, holding material in

place, fetching tools, and generally performing the unskilled, heavy tasks requiring minimum mental exertion. Is not expected to show initiative, think for himself, or assume responsibility. Uses only rough tools, such as shovels, picks, crowbars, jacks, ropes, and similar articles designed for crude work.

3. Labor Skilled: Under immediate supervision, performs simple tasks, principally involving muscular effort. Does work of a generally preparatory nature, such as hauling materials, heavy lifting, and holding material in place while journeyman works on it. Knows nomenclature of one or more trades to which he may be assigned, and is familiar with location of tools and materials so that minimum instruction is required. Gains this knowledge through repetitive experience while assigned to a particular trade or shop. Uses only rough tools of the trade and is not expected to perform any but the simplest preparatory operations.

4. Labor Pusher: Under general supervision, performs work of laborer, but at same time acts as leader of small group of from 6 to 8 laborers. Performs all manual work done by laborers. Transmits orders from foreman to laborers, and acts as working foreman. Uses some initiative, thinks for himself, and exercises minor degree of authority over laborers, subject to constant check from foreman. (Purpose of this position is to insure close supervision over laborers, by providing a sort of sub-foreman to direct and watch every six or eight men, when total labor gang is too large for one foreman to supervise closely.)

5. Ironer Flat Pieces: Under general supervision, operates any one of various types of flat piece ironers and general apparel presses for ironing flat articles. Operates hand iron to do touch-up work on flat pieces or nearly flat garments such as nurses' uniforms.

6. Elevator Operator Freight: Under general supervision, transports materials, equipment, and employees between floors of an industrial or commercial establishment by manipulating control levers or other starting or stopping devices to regulate movements of an elevator cab. Opens and closes safety gate and door at each floor where a stop is made. Assists employees to load and unload freight.

7. Packer: Under immediate supervision, packs non-fragile materials after they have been assembled previously by others. Selects proper size box, counts and places contents and excelsior in box, nails or straps covers on boxes, makes shipping tickets, and stencils directions on boxes. Is not required to transport boxes after packing.

8. Operator Tractor Inside: Under immediate supervision, operates electrically or gasoline powered tractor to tow smaller trucks within a building. Is expected to know building locations and routes. Does not load or unload trailers but is expected to couple or uncouple trailers.

9. Operator Nailing Machine: Under immediate supervision, makes boxes by feeding shooks into machine, holding them in place and operating machine to nail shooks into boxes. Oils machine but does not repair.

10. Helper Trades: (May be helper in any one of several trades: such as carpenter, plumber, painter, steamfitter, electrician, or sheet metal worker). Under immediate supervision, assists journeyman in particular trade by fetch-

Grade	Job
	LADDER DIAGRAM
1	Charwoman Janitor
2	Ironer, Flat Pieces Painter or Sprayer, Productive Laborer, Common Elevator Operator, Freight
3	Operator Tractor—Inside Laborer, Skilled
4	Operator Nailing Machine Packer
5	Laborer, Pusher Helper Carpenter Helper Machinist
6	
7	Jr. Electrician Jr. Painter Jr. Cement Finisher
8	Jr. Blacksmith Jr. Steamfitter—Plumber Jr. Carpenter Fireman, Boiler
9	Truck Driver
10	Jr. Welder
11	Cement Finisher Painter

FIGURE 75. LADDER DIAGRAM

Grade	Job
	LADDER DIAGRAM (*Continued*)
12	Carpenter, Construction Carpenter, Shop Roofer
13	Blacksmith Sr. Painter
14	Sheetmetal Worker Steamfitter—Plumber Machinist, Maintenance
15	Bricklayer Welder Electrician Auto Mechanic
16	Sr. Steamfitter—Plumber Sr. Sheetmetal Worker Automatic Screw Machine—Set-up Man
17	Sr. Carpenter Sr. Electrician Operating Engineer
18	Principal Carpenter Sr. Auto Mechanic
19	Machinist, All Around
20	Tool, Die, or Gauge Maker

FIGURE 75. (*Concluded.*)

ing tools, holding material in place so that work may be done, doing rough preliminary work, and generally performing the heavy, unskilled labor peculiar to that trade. Does work requiring some initiative and intelligence, and is required to learn repetitive operations at least, thus being distinguished from laborer. Does not require previous experience, however, to begin work as helper. Uses tools of the trade, but only for rough preliminary work.

11. Helper Machinist: Under immediate supervision, assists machinist in the performance of his regular work, but does more routine parts of

machinist's work. May work on lathes, milling machines, and drill presses. Some bench work. Uses no measuring instruments. Does not set up machines.

12. Painter or Sprayer, Productive: Under immediate supervision, performs simple brush or spray operations, or repetitive spraying of products on conveyor. Does hand or conveyor dipping in japans or enamels, etc.

13. Jr. Painter: Under immediate supervision, performs rough painting work only. Applies prime coat to flat surfaces such as walls and fences. May apply finish coats only in cases where appearance is a secondary consideration to protection. Under some circumstances may brush-coat machinery and other objects. Works only with and under supervision of journeyman or senior, except for very occasional assignments where he is given specific instructions to perform a very rough assignment such as priming coats by himself. May work inside or outside on ladders, scaffolds, and wherever regular painter works. Assists painter in all operations but does not do any real finish work.

14. Painter: Under general supervision, performs painting duties incident to maintenance and repair of buildings and equipment. Does both brush and spray painting. Mixes own paints when necessary. Paints buildings, inside and outside. Paints or stains or sprays furniture and equipment, including machinery. May paint signs, either free-hand or by stencil. In some localities may be called upon for glazing work.

15. Sr. Painter: Under direction, paints exterior and interior of buildings, furniture and metal material. Work performed is of highest grade, such as finish work on hardwood, furniture, and striping. Supervises work of painters, junior painters, and helpers on jobs requiring more than one individual. In absence of foreman painter, acts in that capacity. Mixes paint and matches colors. May paint signs either freehand or by stencil. Uses both brush and spray guns. Supervises and participates in rigging and moving of rigging. In some localities does glazing work.

16. Jr. Cement Finisher: Under immediate supervision, hand tamps and finishes surface of concrete and cement work poured by others. Applies grout and smooths on vertical surfaces to obtain smooth finish. Smooths flat surfaces with screed and float. Observes pouring by laborers and signifies whether mixture is satisfactory or not.

17. Cement Finisher: Under general supervision, performs cement finishing work on structures of a plant. Floats and finishes horizontal surfaces by hand, such as floors and walks. Applies grout and patches and smooths vertical surfaces by hand. May assist in rodding or hand tamping concrete in forms to insure homogeneity. Works only upon concrete and cement already mixed and placed by others. May supervise one or two laborer assistants on large jobs but generally works alone. Observes consistency of concrete as it is poured and indicates to foreman of concrete gang whether or not the mixture is satisfactory. Suggests wetter or dryer mix to foreman as needed to achieve best results, but exercises no supervision over concrete gang.

18. Jr. Electrician: Under immediate supervision, performs minor electrical work. Performs some of the duties of an electrician, including installation of new equipment and maintenance and repair work, but receives much closer supervision and works only on the simpler tasks. Usually works in a group, but may occasionally work alone on such things as lighting circuits and on smaller motors of less than 1 H.P. Does no radio or telephone work. Seldom works with voltages beyond those found in regular lighting circuits: 110 to 220. Does no rewiring of motors. Makes no diagnoses. Corrects trouble if of simple nature after it has been located by supervisor.

19. Electrician: Under general supervision, performs general electrical work, including installation of new equipment and maintenance and repair work. Installs new wiring, working from blueprints or other diagrams. Installs motors, generators, or lighting fixtures. Works on usual problems only, and does not do work of highly complicated nature. Repairs and maintains wiring and fixtures. Rewinds motors. Usually performs this type of work after preliminary diagnosis of trouble by foreman electrician, but can make simple diagnoses himself. Works with high voltages, 2,300 volts and up, but seldom encounters anything over 4,400 volts. Does no radio or telephone work. Usually supervises helper or laborers where volume of work warrants added help.

20. Sr. Electrician: Under direction, performs more difficult electrical work, including installation of new equipment and maintenance and repair work. Supervises lower grades of electricians, and helpers on jobs requiring more than one individual. In absence of foreman electrician, acts in that capacity. Diagnoses trouble and, if difficulty is reasonably simple, assigns actual repair work to electrician or junior electrician after explaining what is to be done. In cases of major repair on work involving great difficulty, performs work himself. Works alone on more intricate work such as laboratory equipment or special motors. Works on transformers and primary lines carrying high voltages; 2,300 volts up. Does no radio or telephone work, but may rewind motors. Works from sketches, blueprints, or diagrams. In absence of foreman electrician, lays out work and interprets same to other workers. In absence of foreman electrician, prepares estimates on work to be done as necessary.

21. Jr. Blacksmith: Under immediate supervision, performs the simpler blacksmith duties. Forges small, simpler parts alone, such as putting bends in small, flat pieces. Occasionally forges larger pieces of rough nature. Performs regular duties of helper, such as carrying material, swinging sledge, operating shears, or benders. Duties of this job differ from those of helper job to the extent that junior blacksmith uses all tools and actually fabricates some parts, while helper does not. Does acetylene cutting in connection with dismantling operations, and may occasionally do acetylene welding under close supervision of blacksmith. Does not turn out finished parts without close inspection from blacksmith.

22. Blacksmith: Under general supervision, performs forging operations to repair and make metal parts. Forges metal for machine parts. Makes star drills and chisels. Forge welds broken parts and repairs and tempers

concrete drills, picks, or shovels. Fabricates iron fences, gates, and railings and installs. Substitutes for foreman but does not do planning or layout work. Is seldom required to read blueprints.

23. Jr. Steamfitter-Plumber: Under immediate supervision, performs the simpler tasks involved in the installation, maintenance and repair of pipeline systems, gas, water, waste and drain pipes and other connections throughout the post including steam distribution systems. Usually works under close inspection, assisting on such jobs as removing piping from tunnels, replacing gaskets, repacking expansion joints, repairing leaks in steam lines, repairing or renewing traps, cutting threads and bending pipe. On individual assignment, may repair leaking faucets or clogged drain pipe, repair minor leaks, renew gaskets, etc., subject to immediate or complete inspection.

24. Steamfitter-Plumber: Under general supervision, repairs, maintains and installs gas, water, waste and steam distribution systems on post. Works on both high and low pressure steam systems. Installs, maintains and repairs lines and pumps, valves, dials, gauges, and other apparatus. Cuts, threads, and bends pipe or supervises performance of such activities. Fits and solders joints, installs fixtures, and does general plumbing work. May work in group under supervision or may, upon occasion, perform routine tasks himself. In latter case supervises laborers or helpers.

25. Sr. Steamfitter-Plumber: Under direction, performs most difficult steamfitting and plumbing work. Lays out work and prepares estimates and bills of material. Inspects material received. Supervises journeymen, juniors, helpers, and laborers where work requires. Works from plans and sketches and interprets same to subordinates.

26. Jr. Carpenter: Under immediate supervision, works in group of several employees and performs simple carpentry work. Uses all carpentry tools but is limited to simple and rough work such as concrete forms, scaffolds, flooring, roof sheeting, or nailing on construction work. In shop, works as member of group, repairing doors, sash, performing simple operations as nailing. Operates power machinery very infrequently and only on simplest work such as sawing lumber to lengths. Works under supervision of carpenter or senior carpenter except for very occasional minor assignments involving a minimum degree of skill, such as nailing back loose boards and simple repairs.

27. Carpenter Construction: Under general supervision, performs general carpentry work in connection with maintenance, repairs, additions, and minor new construction. Usually works with carpenter foreman or senior carpenter, but may occasionally do minor jobs without supervision. May also supervise laborers or carpenter helpers on rough preliminary work. Erects new structures, additions or makes repairs to existing structures, including framing, building forms for concrete, hanging doors and sash, exterior and interior trim, siding and insulation. May be required to do roofing, glazing, and some sheet metal work, such as placing gutters and down-spouts.

28. Carpenter Shop: Under general supervision, performs all shop carpentry work incident to maintenance and repairs, using carpenter's tools and woodworking machinery. Cuts, saws, joins, nails, glues, assembles lumber

and allied materials, both in the repair of broken objects and the construction of needed new equipment. Runs power saws, planers, as well as uses hand tools and sandpaper. May construct simple articles of furniture, such as desks, tables, as well as screens, sash, and trim, but is not a fine cabinet-maker. May crate furniture and other objects, building crates to fit particular piece. Seldom works outside shop.

29. Sr. Carpenter: Under direction, performs the more highly skilled carpentry operations. May work either in the shop or in field. Usually exercises supervision over other carpenters, carpenter helpers and laborers. On building maintenance and repair, acts as supervisor in absence of carpenter foreman. Personally does the more intricate finish work himself such as cabinet-making.

30. Principal Carpenter: Under direction, supervises group of approximately thirty carpenters and several laborers engaged in building cabinets, desks, and tables, making molding and millwork, repairing doors, sashes, or trailers. Assigns, coordinates and follows up work of group, lays out work, answers questions of subordinates and sees that safety precautions are taken.

31. Fireman Boiler: Under general supervision, tends 2500 H.P. boilers rated 75,000# per hour usually generating steam at 200# pressures. Regulates manual controls to feed pulverized coal to fire boxes. Observes operation of automatic water feed. Regulates drafts. Remains on firing platform at all times due to fact that pulverized coal may fail to ignite. Adjusts oil feed with coal feed when necessary to insure ignition and prevent blow backs. Takes coal samples while on day shift. When extra fireman is on duty, assists operating engineer in making repairs.

32. Operating Engineer: Under general supervision, supervises, assigns work to junior operating engineers and laborers. Makes frequent tours to see that temperatures, pressures, and combustion are regulated properly and that equipment is in proper running order. Treats water by adding chemicals, according to instructions of chief operating engineer. Maintains boiler log.

33. Truck Driver: Under general supervision, operates motor trucks such as the following: 1½ ton cargo, 5 ton dump, tractor trailer (1½ ton tractor-3 ton pay load), ¾ ton utility truck, 10 ton cargo trucks. Operates within plant, throughout city and occasionally between cities. Performs drivers maintenance. Helps load and unload trucks and is assisted by helper when on short hauls.

34. Welder: Under general supervision, performs welding operations, using electric or acetylene equipment according to needs of work. Works on material from ⅛ inch to 1½ inches. Selects type of welding rod to be used. Works both in shop and field. Welds on flat work, as well as some vertical and overhead. Does not weld pipe or pressure vessels. Generally works on tractor wheels, machine parts or gates.

35. Roofer: Under general supervision, performs roofing work incident to industrial or commercial establishment. Lays roofing-asphalt, tin, shingles, etc., depending upon type of construction. Repairs leaks in roof. Installs and repairs flashing. Assembles and erects sky-lights, ventilators or gutters.

Under supervision, erects and dismantles scaffolding. Usually works in gang if size of force permits, but may work by himself on smaller jobs.

36. Sheet Metal Worker: Under general supervision, maintains, and repairs sheet metal work. May supervise helpers or laborers as work requires their services. Cuts, bends, and fits sheet metal to sizes and shapes required for new or maintenance work, using shears, benders, and other sheet metal working tools. May supervise helper in some of these operations. Makes layouts from blueprints of pieces needed. Installs or repairs down-spouts, gutters, metal sheathing, stacks, heater and ventilation ducts.

37. Sr. Sheet Metal Worker: Under direction, performs the more intricate sheet metal work. Makes calculations as to size and type of installation, and repairing of down-spouts, gutters, metal sheathing, stacks, heater and ventilation ducts. Performs the more intricate operations in connection with this work himself. In absence of foreman, acts in that capacity.

38. Bricklayer: Under general supervision, performs any work with brick, hollow tile, concrete, cement finish and plastering. Points up brick. Makes all necessary construction or repair work with bricks. Responsible for work of helper.

39. Automatic Screw Machine-Setup Man: Under general supervision, sets up Brown and Sharpe automatic screw machines #0. Must be able to read blueprints. Obtain proper tools and cams. Must adjust tools and machine for correct speeds and feeds until pieces are being produced according to specifications. Occasionally may lay out cams; however, most cams are purchased from the outside.

40. Auto Mechanic: Under general supervision, diagnoses motor trouble, examines rings, pistons. Makes major repairs and overhauls motor. Times motors. Determines whether brake linings should be replaced. Lubricates autos. May cut and weld (acetylene).

41. Sr. Auto Mechanic: Under supervision, supervises three to five auto mechanics and helpers. Diagnoses motor trouble, examines rings and pistons. Makes major repairs and overhauls motor. Times motors. Determines whether brake linings should be replaced. Acts for foreman auto mechanic in his absence. Keeps record of work performed, parts and material. Makes inspection of repaired equipment.

42. Machinist Maintenance: Under general supervision, installs and maintains ordinary engine lathes, milling machines, or radial drills. Lays out and performs difficult machining operations on replacement parts. Diagnoses and remedies trouble, tears down and reassembles machines. Performs skilled fitting of bearings, spindles, scraping of ways.

43. Machinist All-Around: Under general supervision, sets up and operates various types of machines such as lathes, milling machines, boring mills, or grinders, and performs progressive machining operations for any equipment with tolerances up to $\pm.0025$ inch. Fits and assembles where necessary. Does work of highly diversified nature. Does maintenance work as required.

44. Tool, Die or Gauge Maker: Under direction, plans and constructs highly intricate tools, dies, fixtures, gauges to extremely close tolerances.

Involves considerable development work, highly skilled fitting, timing and adjusting. Constructs tools where no design is available, selects allowance, devises mechanism details; e.g., multistation progressive and deep drawing dies, complex indexing fixtures, sub-press dies for parts of delicate outline, optical gauges.

———

Comparison Technique the Better Guide to Classification. Job analysts who use the technique of predetermined degree definitions have not made much use of key jobs as a guide to classification. Usually they apply the degree measures to key jobs before going on to other jobs but they depend largely on the degree measures to give the point weightings and let the classification follow automatically. At best this procedure will conform to the key jobs throughout a plant but there is a danger that the interdepartment relativity will be less consistent than the intradepartment relativity. Left to subordinates this system can become too mechanistic. E. J. Benge and others who use the characteristic comparison technique are safer here, because they depend wholly on the key job relativity to measure the relativity of other jobs. We see merit in both techniques and find it difficult to choose between them. Perhaps we are trying to keep our cake and eat it too but we feel that for a few bench mark jobs a company could afford to use the comparison technique as an over-all check, even if it intends to use the degree definitions for the original evaluating. In short, we would take considerable pains with the classification and would check it on bench mark jobs regardless of individual job measurement, but as Paul M. Edwards says, "It should be pointed out that promiscuous tampering with broad relationships in existing wage structures is dangerous. The modifications advocated should be confined to relatively small changes in the rank order of individual jobs or small groups of jobs."

Method of Paired Comparisons. This term is given by psychology investigators to the method of successively comparing each unit in a series with every other unit in the series, thereby increasing the validity of appraisal, or for classifying jobs, increasing the consistency of the classification. In the case of key jobs this would mean comparing job 1 with all the other key jobs successively, appraising its worth relative to job 2, job 3, etc. The process would then be repeated for job 2 relative to job 1, job 3, etc. Nothing more than a plus or minus need be used for scoring, one or the other at each comparison to indicate more or less worth. At completion the plus signs for each job are counted to constitute its score. The whole series of key jobs can then be arranged in the order of scores. Of course this should be done by several analysts independently. It seems like a lot of foolishness, but investigators who have had experience in this sort of thing, specifically Dr. Viteles, claim that "the reliability and validity of the judgments obtained in this manner are so far superior to those obtained in the ordinary manner [of ranking] as to more than compensate for the extra time and effort involved." The characteristic comparison practitioners have come close to this standard of validity not by going around the circle with each whole job but by comparing one major characteristic of a key job with the like characteristic of all other key jobs and then another characteristic, etc.

Ranking by Characteristics. S. L. H. Burk in his excellent "A Case History in Salary and Wage Administration" [4] gives a picture of his treatment of key jobs as follows:

The new committee of 10 people, composed of five job analysts and five operating representatives, was given copies of the specifications for the 15 key jobs selected. The entire committee was requested to study the job specifications and to raise any questions in connection with job content, responsibilities, and requirements which would be necessary for a complete understanding of the key jobs. The first committee meeting was devoted entirely to an explanation of the method to be used and a thorough discussion of the 15 key jobs.

At the conclusion of the first meeting the members of the committee were given a key job ranking sheet, on which they were asked to rank all the key jobs for each of the five critical factors—mental effort, skill, physical effort, responsibility, and working conditions. The jobs were ranked in such a way that the job requiring the least mental effort, skill, physical effort, or responsibility was placed as No. 1 on the scale, and the job with the highest amount was listed as No. 15 on the scale. In the case of working conditions, the job with the most agreeable conditions was ranked No. 1 on the scale, and the job with the least favorable conditions was ranked No. 15. Each member of the committee, at the expiration of about 10 days' time, returned his ranking sheets, and after approximately another 10-day interval was asked to rerank the 15 jobs. When the results of this reranking had been turned over to the chief job analyst, the committee was asked to rank the jobs for a third time.

When each of the 10 members of the committee had ranked the 15 key jobs three times in each of the five critical factors, 30 ranking estimates had been secured, from which an average estimated rank for each job in each critical factor was computed. Analyses of the results of this ranking were sent to all members of the committee, and at a subsequent meeting the averages for each factor were discussed by the entire committee. After very lengthy discussion, the average ranks of a few of the key jobs were changed by majority vote of the committee, and final agreement was secured.

[4] *A.M.A. Personnel*, XV, No. 3.

Series of Jobs as a Standard Comparison Scale. The General Electric Company, which combined the characteristic comparison technique with a weighted point method, calls its master list of jobs a "key list of jobs," not a list of key jobs. Perhaps this is because Mr. Weed selected

. . . jobs having the highest rating in each characteristic and other jobs having the lowest rating in each characteristic. Jobs in between these are selected until finally a key list of some fifty jobs is developed. In selecting the additional jobs, it is essential that only one characteristic should be considered at a time and the rating for this characteristic should be on the basis of known jobs. It is also necessary that the work of preparing this key list should be done with extreme care and should have the benefit and support of supervisors.

Nevertheless inspection indicates that the jobs so selected fulfill the specifications we have made for key jobs; certainly they are used in the same way. Because the General Electric key lists are segregated by characteristics and thereby make a most interesting study we reproduce all six lists and a summary of the 35 jobs involved (Figures 76 to 82, inclusive). Such listing can also be used advan-

---

Mentality is the prerequisite mental development necessary to factory training for the normal development of skill and knowledge required for the job. It is a complement of skill and should be so considered on assigning points.

JOB	POINTS
Diemaker, 1st, combination dies	100
	95
Toolmaker, 1st, complic. large jigs	90
Boring mill, 1st 16' stator frames	85
Machinist, maint. 1st diagnose	80
	75
Lathe, engine, 1st, intricate	70
Tinsmith, maint. 1st, layout	65
Lathe, turr. mfg. compl. arm. spiders	60
Diemaker, 4th, plain shear dies	55
Lathe, engine, 2nd turn for grind	50
Punch press, over 200 T, irregular	45
Spray, loco. finish large surfaces	40
Auto. screw mach., no set up	35
Lathe, engine 3rd roughing of stk	30
Milling mach. to fractional dimen	25
Truck, shop electric	20
	15
Chip large castings, air hammer	10
Labor, inside, bar stock	5
Sweeper, sweep & remove chips	0

FIGURE 76. MENTALITY—MENTAL POWER—INTELLIGENCE

tageously to test the composition of jobs. If skill and effort are high in the same job it may be desirable to revamp, that is, make two jobs to allow the skilled operator to spend less time on mere physical effort. The war encouraged this to make suitable jobs for women but it ought to be done anyway on the principle of keeping each individual at his highest level as much as practicable. The same purpose can be furthered by care in scheduling jobs for skilled individuals.

Putting Jobs into Classes. With key jobs for all departments satisfactorily related it is fairly simple to fix the desired number of classes and as other jobs are rated to put each into its appropriate class. By the characteristic comparison technique each job is fitted successively into each scale and finally by summation finds its classification. The Monard V. Hayes & Associates' comparison scale for a candy factory (Figure 83) will indicate one way of doing this. Figure 84, from S. L. H. Burk, further illustrates the give and take which is necessary to keep within the chosen number of classes. By the predetermined degree definitions technique used in connection with weighted point methods the classification, as we have said, is automatic after degrees are determined.

Skill has been authoritatively defined as "Trade knowledge and the ability to apply it." The relative degree of skill required for dissimilar jobs and occupations can best be evaluated on the basis of length of training necessary for an individual of given mentality to be able to perform the work.

JOB	POINTS
	400
	380
Diemaker, 1st, combination dies...............................	360
Patternmaker, wood, difficult..................................	340
Toolmaker, 1st, complicated jigs...............................	320
Patternmaker, metal, difficult.................................	300
Boring mill, 1st 16′ stator frames.............................	280
Patternmaker, metal, ordinary	260
Planer, 7′ & over, fab. frames................................	240
Auto. screw mach., 1st, die work & S.U.......................	220
Assemb. floor, 1st, align, large appara........................	200
Planer under 7′, motor frames.................................	180
Drill, radial, 1st, complicated, to L/O........................	160
Drill, sensitive, 1st, complicated to L/O......................	140
Weld, arc, gas, large mach. strength..........................	120
Weld, arc, gas, repet. ref. cab................................	100
Auto screw mach., no setup....................................	80
Truck, shop electric	60
Weld, resistance & spot.......................................	40
Laborer, inside bar stock	20
Sweeper, sweep & remove chips	0

FIGURE 77. SKILL

The degree of responsibility involved in a job depends upon the hazard of error and its probable cost. The use of expensive materials or equipment of itself does not necessarily involve a high degree of responsibility unless a slight mistake will involve a serious loss. The subfactors to be considered therefore are: chance of error, value of materials or equipment, extent to which they could be damaged by temporary carelessness.

JOB	POINTS
	100
	95
	90
	85
	80
	75
Boring mill, 1st, 16′ stator frames.............................	70
	65
Diemaker, 1st, combination dies	60
Machinist, maint., 1st, diagnose correct........................	55
Toolmaker, 1st, comp. large jigs...............................	50
Patternmaker, metal, ordinary.................................	45
Assem. floor, 1st, align, large appara........................	40
Assem. bench, 1st, fit, scrape, align..........................	35
Auto. screw mach. & S.U. die head............................	30
Weld, arc, gas, large, mach. strength	25
Truck driver, shop electric	20
Weld, arc, gas, high rep. ref. cab.............................	15
Auto. screw mach. operator, no S.U...........................	10
Weld, resistance & spot......................................	5
Sweeper, sweep & remove chips...............................	0

FIGURE 78. RESPONSIBILITY

Application is the degree and continuity of applied effort called for on the job. When repetitiveness of the work is sufficient to form motion habit, very little concentration of mental application is required. The degree and continuity of direct thought necessary in directing or performing motions on mental planning each should be in the process.

JOB	POINTS
	50
	45
Diemaker, 1st, combination dies...............................	40
Planer 7′ & over fab. frames..................................	35
Weld, arc, gas, large mach. strength...........................	30
Grind, precision, 1st, gas, eng. cranks	25
Drill, radial, 1st, comp. to layout.............................	20
Weld, resistance & spot.......................................	15
Laborer, inside..	10
Sweeper, sweep & remove chips................................	5
Assem. conveyor, simple short cycle...........................	0

FIGURE 79. MENTAL APPLICATION

Application is the degree and continuity of applied effort called for on the job. The subfactors to be considered are: physical exertion called for on the job (pulling, pushing, lifting, etc.); the degree of continuity of such effort.

JOB	POINTS
Chip, large castings air hammer.................................	50
	45
Labor, inside	40
Sweeper, sweep & remove chips.................................	35
Assem. floor, 1st, align appara.	30
Weld, resistance or spot.......................................	25
Auto. screw mach., all grades..................................	20
Lathe turret, all grades..	15
Lathe, eng, all grades	10
Craneman, 30 to 200 Ton single hook..........................	5
Gateman, no patrol, direct visitors.............................	0

FIGURE 80. PHYSICAL APPLICATION

In evaluating working conditions it should be kept in mind that the Company is a good place to work and that the low-rated job, such as a sweeper, is not undesirable for the type of individual normally engaged in that class of work, except where he may be exposed to unusual hazards. The subfactors to be considered in the evaluation of working conditions are: hazards to health or clothing, hazard of injury, exposure to disagreeable conditions (fumes, heat, cold, etc.).

JOB	POINTS
Sand blast, room castings......................................	100
	95
	90
	85
	80
	75
	70
	65
	60
Weld, arc, gas, large mach. strength...........................	55
	50
	45
Spray loco. fin. large surfaces.................................	40
Chip, large castings, air hammer...............................	35
Weld, arc, gas, high, sep. ref. cab.............................	30
Electrician, maint., lead. man..................................	25
Labor, foundry, remove scraps, etc.............................	20
Machinist, all grades..	10
Lathe, eng., all grades..	5
Weld, resistance & spot..	0

FIGURE 81. WORKING CONDITIONS

Total variable points on thirty-five selected jobs covering the entire point range are as follows:

JOB	M	S	R	MA	PA	WC	Total
Sweeper, sweep, remove chips......	0	0	0	0	35	0	435
Laborer, inside	5	30	5	10	40	0	490
Spray paint, supply parts..........	20	45	0	10	20	15	510
Gateman, directs visitors..........	35	60	25	20	15	10	565
Truck driver, shop, elec..........	20	60	20	20	20	0	540
Screw mach. auto., no setup......	35	80	10	20	20	5	570
Grind, large cast. portable........	10	80	10	10	40	30	580
Chip, large cast. air hammer......	10	80	15	10	50	30	595
Punch press 80–150 arm. P........	35	80	25	20	30	15	605
Weld, arc, gas, repet. ref. cab......	35	100	15	20	20	25	615
Drill, sensitive, coml. layout......	40	140	20	20	20	0	640
Sand. blast. room. castings.......	10	60	15	10	50	100	645
Crane. 200 T. double hook........	35	120	70	30	10	0	665
Drill, rad., compl. L/O............	50	160	25	20	20	5	680
Weld, arc, gas, large, mech. strg....	50	120	25	30	40	55	720
Screw mach. bar. mic. & S.U......	60	200	30	30	20	5	745
Milling machine, ordinary, index...	60	220	30	30	10	5	755
Lathe, turret, irreg. complic........	60	220	30	30	15	5	760
Screw mach. auto. die head & S.U...	60	220	30	30	20	5	765
Assem. bench, 1st, fit, scrape, etc..	60	220	35	30	20	0	765
Assem. floor, 1st, align, large......	60	200	40	30	30	5	765
Grind, precision, 1st, gas, eng. cr....	60	220	40	25	20	5	770
Carpenter, 1st, finish work........	60	220	25	30	25	20	770
Lathe, eng. 1st, intricate..........	70	240	30	30	10	5	785
Sheet metal, 1st, L/O develop......	65	240	30	30	25	15	805
Plumber & steamfitter, 1st........	60	240	40	25	30	25	820
Planer 7' & over fab. frames.......	70	240	60	35	10	10	825
Mach. oper. jig borer toolroom....	80	280	50	40	10	0	860
Electrician, 1st, leading man......	80	260	60	30	25	20	875
Machinist, 1st, diagnose..........	80	280	55	30	30	10	885
Bor. mill, 1st, 16' stator frame....	85	280	70	40	10	10	890
Patternmaker, metal, difficult......	90	300	50	30	20	0	890
Toolmaker, 1st, compl. jigs........	90	320	50	40	20	0	920
Patternmaker, wood, difficult......	100	340	60	40	20	5	965
Diemaker, 1st, comb. dies.........	100	360	60	40	20	0	980

NOTE: On a maximum evaluation of 1,000 points for the highest theoretical job, the bottom job is given 400 points and all other jobs are given the same 400 points as foundation. (*Job Evaluation*, by D. W. Weed, A. M. A. Production Series No. 111.) At the time these weightings were adopted, 1932, most wage rates ranged between $.40 and $1 per hour and 10 points made a convenient amount to use per $.01. This recognized that at least 40 per cent of all requirements are a normal body plus sanity and perhaps the ability to converse satisfactorily in an acceptable language.

FIGURE 82. JOB EVALUATION SUMMARY

KEY JOB SCALE

	MENTAL EFFORT	SKILL	PHYSICAL EFFORT	RESPONSIBILITY	WORKING CONDITIONS	
26						26
25		Mechanic		Mechanic		25
24						24
23	Mechanic					23
22						22
21						21
20		Caramel M. Op.	Trucker	Cook		20
19				Caramel M. Op.		19
18			Supply Boy	Candy Bar Op.		18
17	Order Filler					17
16		Cook		Order Filler		16
15	Cook	Order Filler		Candy Feeder		15
14	Caramel M. Op.	Candy Bar Op.				14
13			Order Filler			13
12	Candy Bar Op.	Candy Feeder	Cook	Trucker	Order Filler	12
11	Candy Feeder			Supply Boy		11
10					Cook	10
9			Mechanic		Mechanic	9
8	Trucker	Trucker	Caramel M. Op.		Caramel M. Op.	8
7	Supply Boy		Candy Bar Op.		Candy Bar Op.	7
6		Supply Boy	Candy Feeder		Trucker	6
5					Supply Boy	5
4					Candy Feeder	4
3						3
2						2
1						1

FIGURE 83. KEY JOB SCALE A MEASURING SCALE FOR ALL JOBS.
(Monard V. Hayes & Associates.)

Framework for Classification Is Arbitrary. NEMA and N.M.T.A. use the same point allotment and until recently both put No. 1 on the top grade, but in 1953 NEMA put No. 1 on the bottom grade. The Cole version keeps No. 1 for the top grade and has virtually the same degree definitions as NEMA but Cole divides the points into 10 grades while the NEMA has 12. If point values run from, say, 118 to 381 and you want N grades (12) you merely take the difference (263), subtract $N - 1$ to allow 1 point clearances ($263 - 11 = 252$), and divide by N ($252 \div 12 = 21$). This

JOB	Mental Effort	Skill	Phys. Effort	Responsibility	Work. Cond.	Total Points	Base Class
Toolmaker Leaderman (Working gang-pusher) (Daywork)	27	37	16	22	5	107	106
Gyroscope & Marine Instrument Repairman (Daywork)	28	34	17	19	7	105	106
First Operator—Pipe Still Battery (Shift work)	24	24	16	24	14	102	103
Ethyl Blending Plant Operator (Daywork)	19	21	21	22	21	104	103
Toolmaker, Machine Shop (Daywork)	24	34	19	17	5	99	100
Bricklayer, 1st Class, Outside Plant (Daywork)	17	28	30	14	11	100	100
Flying Squad. Man (Comb. pipefitter, bollermaker, rigger, welder) (Daywork)	23	20	27	14	10	94	94
Shop Machinist, All-Around (Daywork)	21	29	24	15	5	94	94
Pipefitter, 1st Class, Outside Plant (Daywork)	17	22	27	15	10	91	91
Operator, Pipe Stills, Stabilization Plant (Shift work)	22	19	16	19	15	91	91
Operator, Sodium Plumbite Plant (Shift work)	17	16	20	16	17	86	85
Automobile Painter—Finisher, Striper & Spray (Night work)	16	24	25	12	9	86	85
Asst. Engineer, Electrical Power House (Shift work)	14	19	19	17	9	78	79
Tool Checker & Tester (Daywork)	28	11	19	15	6	79	79
Ship Loader, Wharves (Shift work)	4	8	33	10	16	71	70
Tester, Viscosity (Daywork)	18	20	15	11	6	70	70
Boilermaker's Helper, Outside Plant (Daywork)	6	7	33	5	10	61	61
Sample Room Attendant, Research Dept. (Daywork)	14	10	23	9	6	62	61
Common (Heavy) Labor, Outside Plant (Daywork)	3	3	37	3	9	55	55
Induced Draft Engine Tender, Boiler House (Daywork)	6	8	23	12	7	56	55
Janitor, Pipe Still Battery & Pump House (Daywork)	4	3	30	4	9	50	49*
Stencil-Cutter & Shipping-Tank Gauger (Daywork)	8	6	19	8	6	47	49*

*Jobs totaling 50 points and under placed in minimum-rate class

FIGURE 84. EXAMPLES OF DETAILED RATING AND GRADING OF PLANT HOURLY RATED POSITIONS. (*A.M.A. Personnel,* XV, No. 3.)

gives 21 points for worth variation in each of the 12 grades and the limits for the grades will be as follows under NEMA Score Range.

N.M.T.A. Grade	Score Range	NEMA Grade	Cole Grade	Score Range
—	Up to 139	1⎫		
—	140 – 161	2⎬	10	Up to 177
10	162 – 183	3⎫		
9	184 – 205	4⎬	9	178 – 201
8	206 – 227	5	8	202 – 225
7	228 – 249	6	7	226 – 249
6	250 – 271	7	6	250 – 273
5	272 – 293	8	5	274 – 297
4	294 – 315	9	4	298 – 321
3	316 – 337	10	3	322 – 345
2	338 – 359	11	2	346 – 369
1	360 – 381	12	1	370 – —

Some NEMA members set aside a separate set of grade numbers for "Women's and Boys' Jobs" running from 25 to 21 and paralleling regular numbers 12 to 8! We are not convinced that the "Women's or Boys' Grades" should have such separation and we would prefer to reverse N.M.T.A. grades. It is more likely that a new job may exceed the present maximum value than that any will ever come below the present minimum. If grade 1 is assigned to the job of least worth it will cause no trouble to add a grade 13 for a job of greater worth when needed. With point ranges established the jobs are sorted according to their point values (Figure 85). The a, b, c, etc., indicate subdivisions for the general titles. For classification of foundry jobs see Figure 37.

Increasing Worth Ranges in Classification. It is not necessary to use a constant worth range for classification. For positions of highest worth it is definitely preferable to lay out worth classes with increasing ranges. When all jobs are included in a single structure it is therefore logical to arrange a consistent variation into the hourly paid classes. The question is important because it has a considerable effect on the whole rate structure; in fact, we postpone further treatment of the subject in order to show its whole involvement (see Chapter 11).

Class Description-Specification. Tentative classes,[5] more commonly called grades, can be set at this time. Where practicable, natural cleavages may be followed but other considerations must not be ignored. The main thing is to show the dividing lines distinctly in the class descriptions. As in the case of job descriptions,

---

[5] Some reserve the term *class* to designate the levels within a family of kindred jobs as shown in Figure 85. We see little need for this and prefer to stick entirely to one or the other term for both kinds of designation.

Former Grade Numbers

OCCUPATIONS - MEN	1	2	3	4	5	6	7	8	9	10
Tool and Die Maker	a	b	c	d						
Tool Room Machine Operator		a	b		c					
Machinist - Production		a	b	c						
Machinist - Service		a	b	c						
Millwright - Service		a	b	c						
Electrician - Service		a	b	c						
Pipe Fitter - Service			b		c					
Autom.Screw Mach. Operator		a	b		c					
Boring Mill Operator		a		b		c				
Layout Man		a		b		c				
Carpenter - Service			a	b		c				
Lathe Operator (Engine)			a		b		c			
Lathe Operator (Turret)			a		b		c			
Milling Machine Operator			a		b		c			
Planer			a		b		c			
Sheet Metal Worker			a		b		c			
Welder (Arc or Gas)			a		b		c			
Assembler,Adjuster,Wireman				a	b		c	d	e	
Grinder				a	b			c		
Painter - Service				a	b					
Craneman				a		b				
Painter (Apparatus, Metal)				a		b	c			
Drill Press Oper. (Radial)				a		b	c			
Polisher				a		b	c			
Winder					a		b		c	
Punch Press Set-up Man					x					
Truck Driver					x					
Punch Press Operator						a	b	c	d	
Drill Press Op. (Sensitive)						a		b	c	
Packer, Crater							a	b		
Plater							x			
Welder (Spot or Resistance)							a	b		
Stock or Toolkeeper							x			
Helper (Trades)								x		
Platers' Helper, Pickler								x		
Truck Operator								x		
Watchman								x		
Stock Selector									x	
Common Laborer									x	
Elevator Operator										x
Janitor, Sweeper										x

OCCUPATIONS - WOMEN & BOYS	21	22	23	24	25	
Assembler & Adjuster	a	b	c	d	e	
Inspector or Checker	a	b	c	d	e	
Winder	a		b	c		
Welder			x			
Punch Press Operator				a	b	
Drill Press Operator					a	b
Insulator				x		
Packer					a	b
Matron				x		
Labor - Unskilled						x

FIGURE 85. OCCUPATIONS CLASSIFIED BY LABOR GRADES. (*NEMA Industrial Relations Bulletin*, No. 43.)

the class descriptions become specifications when they are completed. These cannot be as narrowly specific as the job description-specifications upon which they are based, but they must embrace the similar essentials and exclude the dissimilarities of the jobs involved. If the doing of this gives trouble a recheck must be made. In fact, the writeup of a class is itself a check on all that has been done up to this stage. A proper classification, well described, will be very useful both in hiring and in classifying the employees as well as in classifying any new jobs.

Classification a Last Chance to Do Justice. We now revert to our original contention that the determination of the class in which a job belongs may transcend in importance the sacredness of standard procedure. It is a last chance to render justice. If the employees express a lack of confidence in the results of standard procedure we think it behooves management to listen. If management cannot convince the employees concerned it is far wiser to make the system bend a little than to save the system and lose the confidence. Doubtless such a situation should not arise, but in arbitrating we have seen it arise and threaten to destroy a whole evaluation program. After all, no job evaluation is above human judgment and the judgment of the employees, despite subjectivity, may at times be closer to truth than a mechanistic determination. As much as we admire systematic evaluation, in case of emergency we would put it second to honest conciliation. We substantiate our position with a quotation which refers to characteristics rather than to classification, but an error of human judgment regarding worth of characteristics will affect classification and may be first exposed by classification. When we finally classify we deal with net effects and we should treat net effects with reasonableness.

The determination of the relative importance of these characteristics involves a broad visualization of the conditions applicable to the organization under consideration and the greatest care must be exercised not to allow a narrow consideration of individual cases or minor variations to influence the minds of those engaged in the evaluation.[6]

Checking Measurements. To check the correctness of degree measuring the N.M.T.A. takes the following steps: [7]

   a) Sort all job rating sheets by labor grades.
   b) Sort all sheets within each labor grade in order of decreasing point value.

[6] W. W. Finlay, "Comparative Valuation of Occupations in Industry," *N.A.C.A. Bulletin,* XIX, No. 3.
[7] *NMTA Industrial Relations Policies and Procedures,* Bulletin No. 3, Part II.

JOB RATING SUMMARY BY LABOR GRADES

PRODUCTIVE JOBS – MACHINE SHOP

OCC CODE NO.	OCCUPATION	CLASS	LABOR GRADE	TOTAL POINTS	EDUCATION DEG	EDUCATION PTS	EXPERIENCE DEG	EXPERIENCE PTS	INITIATIVE AND INGENUITY DEG	INITIATIVE AND INGENUITY PTS	PHYSICAL DEMAND DEG	PHYSICAL DEMAND PTS	MENTAL-VISUAL DEG	MENTAL-VISUAL PTS	EQUIP OR PROCESS DEG	EQUIP OR PROCESS PTS	MATERIAL OR PRODUCT DEG	MATERIAL OR PRODUCT PTS	SAFETY OF OTHERS DEG	SAFETY OF OTHERS PTS	WORK OF OTHERS DEG	WORK OF OTHERS PTS	WORKING CONDITIONS DEG	WORKING CONDITIONS PTS	HAZARDS DEG	HAZARDS PTS
104	Lay-Out Man	A	2	347	4	56	5	110	4	56	2	20	4	20	2	10	4	20	3	15	1	5	2	20	3	15
55	Boring Bar-Horizontal	A		343	3	42	5	110	4	56	3	30	4	20	3	15	3	15	3	15	1	5	2	20	3	15
45	Assembler-Group Leader	A		341	3	42	4	88	4	56	3	30	4	20	2	10	2	10	3	15	5	25	3	30	3	15
85	Inspector-Mechanical	B	3	335	4	56	4	88	4	56	2	20	4	20	3	15	3	15	3	15	3	15	2	20	3	15
122	Set-Up Man-Welding	A		331	3	42	4	88	4	56	3	30	4	20	3	15	2	10	3	15	3	15	3	30	3	15
125	Sheet Metal Worker	A		331	4	56	4	88	4	56	3	30	3	15	3	15	2	10	3	15	1	5	4	40	3	15
103	Lay-Out Man	A		327	4	56	5	110	4	56	2	20	4	20	2	10	2	10	2	10	1	5	2	20	2	10
76	Grinder-External	A		326	3	42	4	88	4	56	3	30	4	20	3	15	2	10	3	15	1	5	3	30	3	15
78	Grinder-Internal	A		326	3	42	4	88	4	56	3	30	4	20	3	15	2	10	3	15	1	5	3	30	3	15
97	Lathe Operator-Turret	A		326	3	42	4	88	4	56	3	30	4	20	4	20	2	10	3	15	1	5	3	30	3	15
116	Planer Operator	A		326	3	42	4	88	4	56	3	30	4	20	3	15	3	15	3	15	1	5	2	20	3	15
58	Boring Mill Operator	A		321	3	42	4	88	4	56	3	30	4	20	4	20	3	15	3	15	1	5	2	20	3	15
91	Lathe Operator-Engine	A		321	3	42	4	88	4	56	3	30	4	20	3	15	3	15	3	15	1	5	2	20	3	15
90	Lathe Operator-Engine	A		316	3	42	4	88	4	56	3	30	4	20	3	15	2	10	3	15	1	5	2	20	3	15
96	Lathe Operator-Turret	A		316	3	42	4	88	4	56	3	30	4	20	3	15	2	10	3	15	1	5	2	20	3	15
108	Milling Machine Operator	A		316	3	42	4	88	4	56	3	30	4	20	3	15	2	10	3	15	1	5	2	20	3	15
109	Milling Machine Operator	A		316	3	42	4	88	4	56	3	30	4	20	3	15	2	10	3	15	1	5	2	20	3	15
130	Welder-Arc	A	4	314	3	42	3	66	4	56	3	30	3	15	2	10	4	20	3	15	1	5	4	40	3	15
56	Boring Bar-Horizontal	B		307	3	42	4	88	3	42	3	30	4	20	3	15	3	15	3	15	1	5	2	20	3	15
105	Lay-Out Man	B		306	4	56	4	88	3	42	2	20	4	20	2	10	3	15	3	15	1	5	2	20	3	15
83	Heat Treater	–		305	3	42	3	66	3	42	3	30	3	15	4	20	3	15	3	15	1	5	4	40	3	15
67	Drill Press Operator-Radial	A		302	3	42	4	88	3	42	4	40	4	20	3	15	2	10	3	15	1	5	2	20	3	15
113	Miller – Worm Thread	–		300	3	42	3	66	3	42	4	40	4	20	3	15	3	15	3	15	1	5	3	30	3	15
110	Milling Machine Operator	B		299	3	42	3	66	3	42	3	30	4	20	3	15	3	15	3	15	1	5	2	20	3	15
120	Punch Press-Set-Up Man	B		296	2	28	3	66	3	42	3	30	3	15	3	15	2	10	4	20	3	15	4	40	3	15
126	Sheet Metal Worker	B		295	3	42	3	66	3	42	3	30	3	15	3	15	2	10	3	15	1	5	4	40	3	15
86	Inspector-Mechanical	C		294	4	56	3	66	3	42	2	20	3	15	3	15	3	15	3	15	3	15	2	20	3	15

FIGURE 86. JOB RATING SUMMARY BY LABOR GRADES. (N.M.T.A. and *Factory Management and Maintenance*, CXVII. No. 10.)

    c) Tabulate all ratings on a job rating summary form (Figure 86) in order of decreasing labor grades and point values.

    d) After this tabulation is completed, all jobs should be compared for each factor. For example, considering education, it should be determined if all jobs rated fourth degree on education have the same educational requirements, then if all rated third degree have the same requirements, and continue to first degree in the same manner. The same procedure should then be followed for each of the other ten factors.

In cases where inconsistencies are found, it is necessary to make the correction on the job rating substantiating data sheet as well as on the summary sheet. In making the correction on the substantiating data sheet, the write-up must be changed to conform with the change in degree. For example, if the original write-up shows fourth degree initiative and ingenuity factor and the review indicates that it should be third degree on this factor, the write-up should be changed to agree with the third degree definition in the manual.

Relationship Between Evaluation and Existing Rates. After all jobs have been rated and reviewed to the satisfaction of management, the next step is to get a picture of existing wage differentials. To record the wage data, the National Metal Trades Association has prepared a simple record card (Figure 87). In using this card the following procedure is recommended:

    a) One such card should be made up for each occupation and the employees classified by occupation. For example, if a card was made out for Engine Lathe Operator—Class C, labor grade 8, points 215, all employees working on this occupation should be listed on this card by clock number and name.

    b) In the column headed "Day or Base Rate" opposite each employee's name, the base rate or day rate should be recorded.

    c) In the column headed "Average Hourly Earnings," the incentive earnings should be recorded. It is recommended that a representative period be selected, preferably one month, and the average hourly earnings for each employee computed for this period.

    d) The period selected should be recorded in the space provided above the columns containing rates and average hourly earnings.

    e) A study of the rates on each card will usually disclose considerable difference in rates or earnings of individuals in each job. When these differences are found, it is recommended that the employee classification be checked to be sure all are classified correctly and are doing the same type of work.

With these cards filled in for all key jobs a company is ready to furnish the data needed in the survey.

JOB CLASSIFICATION RECORD

CODE NO.

JOB NAME				CLASS		DEPT.									LABOR GRADE		TOTAL POINTS	

			NAME		RATE RANGE						RATE RANGE				
					PERIOD						PERIOD				
DATE ASSGD.	MACH. NO.	MAN NO.			Employe Rating		Day or Base Rate	Av. Hrly Earnings			Employe Rating		Day or Base Rate	Av. Hrly Earnings

Figure 87. Job Classification Record. (N.M.T.A. *Industrial Relations Policies and Procedures*, Bulletin No. 3, Part II.)

10

LOCALITY SURVEYS—SETTING THE GENERAL WAGE LEVEL

A survey must be based upon carefully drawn descriptions of the work performed and not simply upon job titles or designations.
—D. W. WEED

The Problem Widens. Final classification is as far as any one management can go alone in this program. Figure 88 shows a plan for rate structure, but notice the rate scale is in percentage. From there on it is important to have data which will give an adequate sample of prevailing practice in the whole locality as to wage differentials. A wage differential may be defined as the difference in *general* or average hourly wage level between any two countries, territories, industries, crafts, or plants under comparison; also the difference in hourly *base* rates between any two adjacent labor grades in the same rate structure or between different shifts or sexes for the same job; also (between any two job holders) *total* rates of pay on the same job and shift. Obviously one of the major purposes of systematic evaluation is to attain and to maintain correct wage levels. To achieve this ultimate objective comparisons are needed periodically. Since this need for intercompany data is mutual most industrial neighborhoods have developed some system of periodic exchange. The company identities may be hidden behind A B C designations but the key is eventually known to all directly interested. Wage rates are not as secret as they used to be and perhaps it is just as well. Only a low-pay company has anything to worry about and if there is a union its officers will know all about the low rates and will provide plenty of publicity regarding them. It seems that every local union has an intercompany survey of its own, plus local color. Square managements do not like subnormal rates any better than unions do. More than once in arbitration we have heard managers tell union leaders to go out and organize the employees of the low-pay competitors.

236

Intercompany Standardization of Titles. At the time of installing job evaluation it is desirable to compare job descriptions as a guide to the revision of job titles. In fact, it is a good idea to prepare for this by collecting existing job description forms at the time of

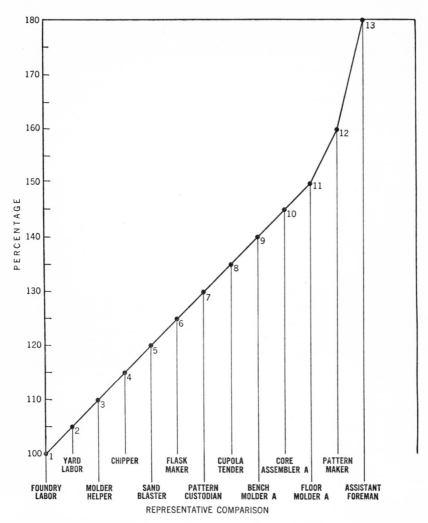

FIGURE 88. BASE WAGES IN PERCENTAGE. (National Founders' Association.)

designing your own form. It is not necessary to have these forms identical but it may make subsequent comparisons easier if the forms are similarly arranged as to certain essentials. With all job descriptions in order someone familiar with a group of jobs should visit the plants whose managers have agreed to exchange data, compare descriptions, check variations or omissions by observing actual operations, and finally note how the other companies have titled the jobs. Companies do not always conform on job titles after making the comparisons but there is little excuse not to do that. In fact, there is some advantage in conforming to the *Dictionary of Occupational Titles* [1] if you can make sure the dictionary description is really the job in question. Sometimes job titles are clarified in the process of negotiation between a union and a management. Preferably they should be settled in advance. The trend is to use fewer words and more letters or numbers, such as assembler a, b, c, carpenter 1, 2, 3, etc. Personally we prefer one adjective apiece, such as machinist-production, machinist-service, etc. You can still use the a, b, c, or 1, 2, 3 for the several levels of the same kind of work, or better yet use the grade numbers and thereby obviate any trouble from the insertion of a new job in a family. When differences in function need to be recognized as well as differences in level of worth, it is an excellent idea to use letters for the former and numbers for the latter.[2] Of course the No. 1 level for one "family" will not line up with the No. 1 of another family, that is, these numbers used to break down an occupation are not necessarily the same as the job class or labor grade numbers. There is no reason why the labor grade numbers should not be made to do double duty except that for any one family of jobs there may be skips, as 1, 3, 5, 7. When all job titles are revised to give simple identification, if practicable standardized throughout the survey group, it will be possible to exchange data by routine. It is not safe to attempt anything of this sort by telephone or by mail until key job descriptions and titles have been personally checked.

Routine Surveys. The forms to be used for locality surveys should be designed to call forth just what is wanted. Only day shift, hourly rates, exclusive of overtime or incentive payment, should be reported, unless incentive earnings can be averaged over a month and so explained. The data when summarized must show quickly and accurately the level of wages paid in the local labor market. Data on jobs which are not common among several companies are utterly useless. Hence the first essential is to determine which company key jobs are truly intercompany key jobs. If the individual companies have several key jobs for each job class, it should be

[1] Occupation Analysis Section, Bureau of Employment Security, Social Security Board.

[2] See J. O. Hopwood, *Salaries, Wages and Labor Relations* (New York: The Ronald Press Co., 1945).

possible to find at least one key per class which is common among the companies. The titles of these intercompany key jobs can be printed on the form or typed on each time. It is not satisfactory to use only job numbers as in the case of our illustration, Figure 89. Separation of the rates, to show the number of employees receiving each, is commendable. This "work sheet" is an assembly of two company reports on a single job, No. 7. In practice there should be reports from ten or more companies, each showing data for at least ten or as many key jobs as there are job classes. After the original survey a smaller number of companies may be sufficient, if that is satisfactory to the union.

WAGE SURVEY WORKSHEET

Data Collected

Locality___DALLAS_____   From_10/3—_ to_10/12—

Job = 7					Company Code __A____						Summary
No. of Employees	3	4	5	1							Total: 13
Hourly Rates	1.20	1.30	1.40	1.60							Co. Av.: 1.34
Remarks: _____											

Job = 7					Company Code___B_____						Summary
No. of Employees	2	3	1	1	1						Total: 8
Hourly Rates	1.24	1.28	1.30	1.36	1.38						Co. Av.: 1.29
Remarks: _____											

FIGURE 89. WAGE SURVEY WORK SHEET. (U. S. Army *Supply Services Manual.*)

Determining the Prevailing Key Job Rate. Some surveys show only maximum, minimum, and average rates but there are often exceptional figures at either end of the distribution. These may mean new or long-term employees and should be so explained, but it is not easy to make a form that will assure that kind of filling out. Many managements are content to deal in average rates, company averages, and altogether a locality average, all weighted as to number of employees. Of course an average does approach the conception of "prevailing," but a management should not be content with any average which is badly affected by extreme exceptions. Erratic items should be eliminated before averaging or some other basis should be used. A choice of range, modal, or between near minimum and near maximum, according to policy, is much more satisfactory if not more defensible. The point is this—complete inclusion of erratic items may or may not give an average which truly reflects the prevailing rate. There is likely to be some cancellation of extremes but a management ought to know whether or not that is the case, and it ought to be satisfied with nothing less than reasonable accuracy. A few managements go to the trouble of making a distribution curve for each class rate (Figure 90). With this kind of picture it is possible to select modal spreads of various widths, thereby allowing a choice of prevailing limits for a range of rates. This is important because when you get a single prevailing rate you still have to decide where it is to go in your range and how big a range is necessary (see Chapter 11).

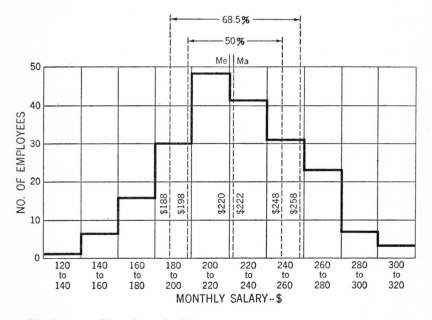

The Summary Sheet shows for 384 persons:

    Salary: Max. $312   Min. $138   Average $220 (1 company omitted)
    Service: Years 11.0   Years 2.0   Years 6.5

Detailed data were secured for 207 persons. The distribution of these 207 persons is shown graphically above.

The arithmetic average (Ma on the graph) for the 207 persons was $222 while the median (Me on the graph) was $220, which means that half received less than $220 and half more.

The concentration of the salaries of the 207 persons about the $222 average is shown also on the graph. Of these, 50 per cent received between $198 and $248, while 68.5 per cent received between $188 and $258. The average length of service of the 50 per cent was about 8.5 years.

FIGURE 90. DISTRIBUTION OF RATES, STENOGRAPHER—WOMEN
(A. L. Kress, A. M. A., *Office Management Series*, No. 84)

WAGE SURVEY RECAP

Locality ____ Dallas ____

Wage Board Established by letter of ____ September 25, 19 — ____

Data Collected From 10/3— to 10/17—

Job #	Title		A	B	C	D	E	F	G	J	K	S	Total Empls	Locality Av. Rate
							Company Codes							
6	Elevator Operator, Freight	Empls	6	1	2		4	2					15	
		Co. Av.	1.20	1.30	1.40		1.37	1.31						1.29
7	Packer	Empls	13		15	6							34	
		Co. Av.	1.33		1.45	1.40								1.39
12	Painter or Sprayer, Productive	Empls	10		5			4					19	
		Co. Av.	1.30		1.36			1.40						1.33
44	Tool, Die or Gauge Maker	Empls		14		2	20	28	3	10	8	4	89	
		Co. Av.		2.28		2.40	2.36	2.42	2.30	2.48	2.28	3.44		2.37

FIGURE 91a. WAGE SURVEY RECAP. (U. S. Army *Supply Services Manual.*)

Recapitulation Should Retain Significance of Data. Going back to the Army Supply Service type of survey, the data collected for each key job are summarized on a wage survey recapitulation sheet (Figure 91*a*) which carries instructions on the reverse side (Figure 91*b*). Unfortunately this example includes only four key jobs and three of these are scantily represented. The greater the inclusion of companies, large and small, the greater will be the reliability. Note also that the spread for the tool-, die-, or gauge-maker's job extends from $2.27 to $3.44, the latter average coming from only four employees of a single company. One would like to know if there were any other employees approaching that high figure, as might well be, where 20 and 28 employee rates are averaged. In short we insist that it is important to sort the rates into four or six levels for all companies separately and to retain that segrega-

---

INSTRUCTIONS: Enter for each job, under the appropriate Company Code headings, the total number of employees and the company average rate copied from the Wage Survey Work Sheets. Under "Total Employees," enter for each job the total of the entries in the "Employees" blocks for all companies for that job. To compute "Locality Average Rate," multiply each rate by the number of employees at that rate, total the results, and divide by "Total Employees." Omit from this recap any data concerning incentives reported on the work sheets. If additional "Company" blocks are needed, use the next set of lines, putting ditto marks in the "Job" and "Title" spaces and recording the appropriate company code letters in the corners of the "Employees" blocks.

FIGURE 91*b*. INSTRUCTIONS FOR WAGE SURVEY RECAP

tion to the end. It is not fair to let a majority of low rates absorb such high rates and call $2.37 the prevailing rate. The reverse would be equally misleading. It would be much better to leave the data in the form of the work sheets, one per key job, all companies carrying the selected rate ranges from these direct to the scatter diagram upon which each management compares its existing rates with proposed rates. Figure 92 shows a recapitulation or wage survey summary, as the National Metal Trades Association calls it. It is but one of several sheets covering the entire survey. For each job title there are two horizontal lines, (D) for day rates, and (I) for incentive rates, also twenty-nine vertical columns with narrow rate range headings. Here one can see whether or not the high and low items cancel and how far the weighted average varies from the mode.

Instructions

1. Report data for the payroll period ending nearest to (date).

2. Report actual hourly rates for all operations based on a 40 hour work week, excluding overtime and shift premium.

3. Report separately for each job, the earnings and the number of day work employees and of incentive employees.

4. Enter total number of employees in each job classification in the proper place.

5. Report all employees in the job description where they fit. Note that the job title * used in this report sometimes will be different from the job name used in a particular plant.

6. Read through all job descriptions before filling in the form in order to avoid possible inclusion of some workers in the wrong classification.

7. Where there are several classes of a key job (such as assemblers, drill press operators, etc.) decide carefully into which class or classes each of your affected jobs belongs. In this connection the indicated labor grade should be of assistance.

Job Description	Labor Grade	Day or Inc.	75 to 80	80 to 85	85 to 90	90 to 95	95 to 1.00	1.00 to 1.05	1.05 to 1.10	1.10 to 1.15	1.15 to 1.20	1.20 to 1.25	1.25 to 1.30	1.30 to 1.35	1.35 to 1.40	1.40 to 1.45	1.45 to 1.50	1.50 to 1.55	1.55 to 1.60	1.60 to 1.65	1.65 to 1.70	1.70 to 1.75	1.75 to 1.80	1.80 to 1.85	1.85 to 1.90	1.90 to 1.95	1.95 to 2.00	2.00 to 2.05	2.05 to 2.10	2.10 to 2.15	2.15 over	Total No. Empls

HOURLY EARNINGS (CENTS PER HOUR)

Job Description	Labor Grade	Day or Inc.
Assembler, Adjuster	9	D
Automatic Screw Machine Operator	5	D/I
Automatic Screw Machine Set-Up Man	3	D/I
Carpenter	3	D/I
Craneman	8	D/I
Drill Press Operator (Sensitive)	9	D/I
Electrician	2	D/I
Helper (Trades)	9	D/I
Inspector, Tester	9	D/I
Janitress	10	D/I
Machinist (Maintenance)	2	D/I
Plater	6	D/I
Punch Press Set-Up Man	5	D/I
Stockkeeper	7	D/I
Tool, Die, Gauge Maker	1	D/I
Trucker—Electric	9	D/I

FIGURE 92. SAMPLE SURVEY SCHEDULE FOR COLLECTING AREA WAGE DATA.
(National Electrical Manufacturers Association.)

* Under each job title the job description should appear. For job descriptions of the job titles used in this schedule see sample job rating specification sheets.

In order to make these data as complete as possible, a group of questions covering fringe benefits is given below. We would appreciate your answers to these questions.

VACATION POLICY: Years of
Service—   ½   1   2   3   5   10   15   25
Weeks of
Vacation—   __ __ __ __ __ __ __ __

PAID HOLIDAY POLICY: Check holidays paid for though not worked.

__ New Year's	__ Columbus Day
__ Lincoln's Birthday	__ Armistice Day
__ Washington's Birthday	__ Election Day
__ Good Friday	__ Thanksgiving Day
__ Memorial Day	__ Christmas Day
__ Fourth of July	__ Other (Specify)
__ Labor Day	

SPECIAL BENEFIT PLANS: Check financing method of your employee plans.

	Company Finances	Employee Finances	Both Contribute
Group Life Insurance	—	—	—
Hospitalization Insurance	—	—	—
Medical and Surgical Insurance	—	—	—
Accident and Health Insurance	—	—	—
Annuity	—	—	—
Profit Sharing Plan	—	—	—
Other (specify)	—	—	—

WAGE ACTIONS: Effective date of last general increase or decrease _____
Amount of last adjustment   _____

JOB EVALUATION PROGRAM: Please check the job evaluation program for each type of employee.

	Clerical	Manual	Supervisory & Administrative
Ranking	—	—	—
Point	—	—	—
Classification	—	—	—
Factor	—	—	—
None	—	—	—

JURY DUTY: How is the employee compensated?   Full Pay + jurors' fees.
Full Pay − jurors' fees.
No pay from company.

MILITARY SERVICE POLICY: 1. Please attach policy covering Selective Service Act of 1948.
2. Please complete table below for reserves.

	No pay in addition to vacation	Pay for __ weeks + vacation	Company pay − service pay for __	No pay
Must take training				
During vacation	—	—	—	—
__ Weeks + vacation	—	—	—	—
Leaves of absence	—	—	—	—

FIGURE 92. (*Concluded.*)

Fringe Benefits Must Be Considered. In the last decade most companies have gone in for all kinds of "social wages" or fringe benefits and sometimes the unions will take less in base rates because of them. Hence the extent to which the companies are committed must be considered along with the levels of base rates. The following illustrates the way such information is gathered.

Intercompany Scale for Job Content. Under the leadership of the American Type Founders Association, a scale contrived in 1946 and 1947 solely to aid the wage survey was developed for use among some forty-five machine companies around Elizabeth, N. J. It had been found that no two managements talked exactly the same language when it came to job content. So after several conferences it was decided to create a series of common denominators to cover the essential occupational categories. First a job content scale was devised for productive jobs common to the various plants. Eleven characteristics (A to K), and four degrees for each were used. The degrees are: (1) Negligible, (2) Simple, (3) Average, and (4) Complex. Each of these was defined in exact but broad enough terms to have application throughout the class of work involved.[3] Several scales were found necessary, Scale I for productive jobs, Scale II for service jobs, and so on. Point values were then worked out by pooled judgment, providing such a range as 36 to 44 points as total for the highest ranking category, in this case that of a first-class tool- and diemaker's job. The next category, that containing the second-class tool- and diemaker's job, was given a range of 26 to 35 points, and so on down to laborer, 7 to 12. Thus typical total values were derived for the specimen jobs and allotments of the points were worked out for all the degree subdivisions. Brief job descriptions were then prepared to bring out the degrees and a form was designed which provided space for recording and scoring by each reporting company. At first the descriptions and scores were tried out in a single plant where the shop superintendent reviewed each as to job content and degree credits. When a job showed multiple duties it was eliminated as a specimen job. Eventually the list included 33 job titles and 78 categories. This seemed quite an order, but with experience it was found that the liaison could go through the complete report with a local representative in from 2 to 3½ hours. After attaining proper classification the rates actually paid could be reported in routine fashion (see Figures 93 and 94).

[3] Benj. McClancy, *Mill and Factory*, July, 1948, and W. R. Hanawalt, *Personnel*, XXIV, No. 5.

Occupation Description

Tool- and Diemaker 1st
Plans and constructs; repairs and maintains a wide variety of highly intricate tools, dies, fixtures, instruments and standard gauges, operating all types of machine tools on work requiring exceptionally close tolerances. Involves considerable development, highly skilled fitting, timing, and adjusting. Makes complex layouts.

Tool- and Diemaker 2nd
Plans, constructs, repairs, and maintains a limited variety of tools, dies, fixtures, instruments, and gauges operating all types of machine tools on work requiring very close tolerances. Involves development work, skilled fitting, timing, and adjusting.

Job Content — Tool- and Diemaker 1st

A	B	C	D	E	F	G	H	I	J	K	Total	Limits
4	4	3	4	4	4	2	4	3	4	5	41	36–44
4	4	3	4	4	4	2	4	3	4	5	41	

Structural Rate Range   min. 1.62   max. 1.87

Is there incentive applied to this job?   YES ___   NO ✓

If yes, what is the average percentage of earning over base rate?   ___ %

Job Content — Tool- and Diemaker 2nd

A	B	C	D	E	F	G	H	I	J	K	Total	Limits
3	3	3	3	3	3	2	3	2	4	4	33	26–35
3	3	3	4	3	3	2	3	2	4	4	34	

Structural Rate Range   min. 1.39   max. 1.61

Is there incentive applied to this job?   YES ___   NO ✓

If yes, what is the average percentage of earning over base rate?   ___ %

Actual hourly base rates for Piecework and Daywork Employees

	Daywork		Piecework	
	Actual Rate	No. of Employees	Actual Rate	No. of Employees
1st	1.67	2	1.80	4
	1.70	1	1.85	10
	1.72	3	1.87	2
	1.75	1		
	1.77	1		
2nd	1.40	1		
	1.44	3		
	1.46	5		
	1.50	2		
	1.55	1		
	1.57	1		
	1.60	4		

FIGURE 93. BASIC INFORMATION PROVIDED BY COMPANY. (American Type Founders Association.)

246

Plans and constructs; repairs and maintains a wide variety of highly intricate tools, dies, fixtures, instruments and standard gauges, operating all types of machine tools on work requiring exceptionally close tolerances. Involves considerable development, highly skilled fitting, timing, and adjusting. Makes complex layouts.

Co. Code No.	Structural Rates			Actual Base Rate Jobs Without Incentive				Actual Base Rate Jobs With Incentive					Total Earnings With Incentive				
	Minimum	Maximum	Single	No. Employees	Minimum	Average	Maximum	No. Employees	Minimum	Average	Maximum	% Incentive	No. Employees	Minimum	Average	Maximum	% Incentive
2	1.535	1.735		8	1.635	1.679	1.735										
11	1.600	1.850		18	1.650	1.822	1.850										
13	1.440	2.000		9	1.480	1.680	2.000										
16				9	1.750	1.817	1.900										
20	1.815	2.035		5	1.815	1.936	2.035										
23	1.405	1.685		8	1.485	1.594	1.685										
25	1.600	1.840	1.750					14	1.600	1.724	1.800	10	14	1.760	1.758	1.980	10
27				23	1.750	1.750	1.750										
29	1.425	1.625		78	1.475	1.581	1.625										
30	1.650	1.750		2	1.650	1.700	1.750										
33			1.815	1	1.815	1.815	1.815										
37	1.590	1.740		2	1.640	1.690	1.740										
38	1.520	1.770		26	1.560	1.710	1.770										
39	1.650	1.750		14	1.700	1.797	1.855										
42	1.530	1.890		1	1.890	1.890	1.890										
45	1.480	1.700		1	1.590	1.590	1.590										
16 Cos.	1.336	1.735		205	1.475	1.633	2.035		14	1.600	1.724	1.800		14	1.760	1.758	1.980
Final rates for Each Job Middle 50%					1.59–1.76				1.62–1.80					1.78–1.98			

FIGURE 94.   Work Sheets for Final Rates for Each Job.   (American Type Founders Association.)

247

During the period of checking the plan job loci for each plant were plotted between average points assigned and average hourly rates paid. The line of central tendency was found by the semi-average method. This indicated the line of wage policy for each company. Two additional lines were drawn parallel, one above and one below, providing a band of normal job loci. From this exceptional points became conspicuous and such items were investigated. By this means each occupational locus which was not properly reported, or did not conform to policy, came under the limelight, but most loci were within the narrow band and indicated that the point allotments and the degree definitions were conforming closely to established policy. In a few cases the pattern shown by charting was not orderly and in consequence complete reviews of those reports were made so that the causes of disorder were discovered and mostly eliminated. In any case items that were outside the band could be eliminated from further consideration, so that the middle 50 per cent of the remaining rates for an occupation could be narrowed and made reliable for intercompany comparison.

Liberal Policy Allows Simplification. A company that is always willing to match the highest rates can approach this matter somewhat differently. For instance, the Procter & Gamble Company of Cincinnati merely selects nine main groups of jobs as follows: (a) stationary engineers, (b) firemen, (c) maintenance mechanics, (d) apprentice mechanics, (e) semiskilled, (f) unskilled, (g) female production, (h) male weekly paid, and (i) female weekly paid. Every six months, ten or twelve comparable manufacturing companies in the community are surveyed as to their rates for the nine job groups. The average base rate per job group for each of these employees is determined and the five highest averages per job group are combined into an interplant average. This interplant average is accepted as the community composite for each group. These rates are then compared with the average base rates paid in similar groups at the P & G plant. If any P & G rate is below the composite rate, the P & G rate is automatically made to match the composite. One employee, appointed by the union, is entitled to sit with the representatives of the employer during the compilation of the survey data but it is agreed that all such information shall be strictly confidential and that no record of the figures shall be taken. Results of the work may be furnished the union if it so requests and of course the adjusted base rates are subject to readjustment through bargaining.

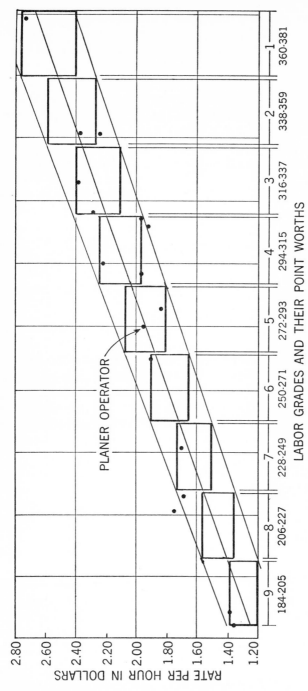

FIGURE 95. AVERAGE HOURLY RATES AND JOB RATING POINTS. EQUAL WORTH
RANGES AND ±7½ PER CENT RANGES. (Farrel-Birmingham Company.)

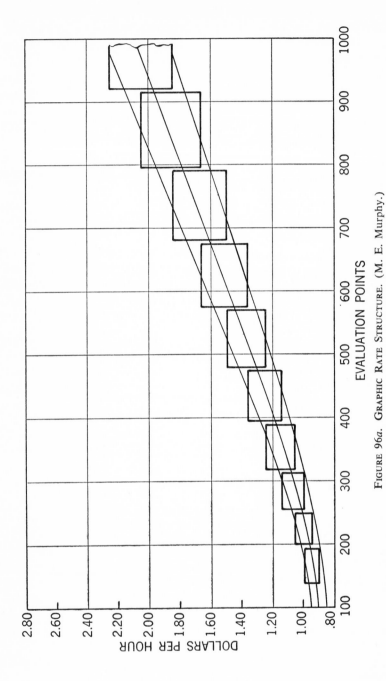

FIGURE 96a. GRAPHIC RATE STRUCTURE. (M. E. Murphy.)

Determining the General Wage Level. In the foregoing paragraphs we have urged the study of exceptional rates, high and low, as a natural means of determining the limits for rate ranges. If this is not practicable then locality averages for the labor grades must be used to set a single line of loci and some percentage of variation from these loci used to set the limits for rate ranges. The percentage need not be wholly arbitrary. Experience has shown conclusively that 10 per cent, or at most 12 per cent, above and below the loci of weighted averages for a community is ample variance to embrace all the hourly rates which are "sound and tested," i.e., stabilized rates. The whole series of such *brackets* will compose *the general wage level* of the community. There are geographical or regional differentials in a country as large as the United States but they have been decreasing. For instance, the North-South differential for the aluminum industry was reduced in July, 1952, from seven cents to four cents per hour.[4] The data can be handled in tabular form but there are many reasons to use a graphic form in addition. Some individuals are good at visualizing the significance of tabulated data but most of us are aided by graphs which are unmistakably visual. In Figure 95 we show a determination of general wage level by

Point Range	Wage Range
140– 195	.90–1.00
200– 250	.94–1.06
255– 315	1.00–1.14
320– 390	1.06–1.24
395– 475	1.14–1.36
480– 570	1.24–1.50
575– 675	1.36–1.66
680– 790	1.50–1.84
795– 915	1.66–2.04
920–1,050	1.84–2.26

FIGURE 96b. TABULAR RATE STRUCTURE

using a straight average trend line and two straight limit lines ±7½ per cent from it. Another case, not shown, has ±$.18 normal limit lines and ±10 per cent maximum limit lines. The former are parallel to the trend line. In Figures 96a and 96b we show a determination of the general wage level by using the modal spreads direct. This particular rate structure was designed to replace one

[4] N. J. Samuels, "Patterns of Wage Variations in the U. S. 1951–1952," *Personnel*, XXIX, No. 2. Also the B. L. S. *Community Wage Survey Bulletins for 40 Major Labor Markets.*

that had 33 job classes all laid out between parallel straight lines. This change is a great improvement.

Establishing the Line. The trend line means the line plotted on job worths and average job rates in the locality. Each point on it should represent the requirements of work qualification and prevailing compensation. If we are going to consider all "out-of-line" rates as erroneous we must take every precaution to set the trend line correctly. It is customary and necessary to set end rates by bargaining. It is also common practice, but not necessary, to draw a straight line between these end points and establish that straight line as the average trend line against which all other rates are judged. It is granted that a straight trend line is simple to establish and seemingly logical, in lieu of any criteria for lines of other shapes, but are there really any criteria for the straight line? There are none worthy of being called principles. Unions, if smart, know that a straight line overpays all intermediate jobs when the end jobs are staked correctly. Hence they concentrate on elevating these two rates, particularly the top one, and are content. Managements suspect that some geometric curve would be more correct but few managements have the slightest idea as to what geometric curve should be used; the rest consider a straight line practical, and are also content if they can hold the top point down to competition level. As a matter of fact, a straight line, as the chord of a curve, does approximate the curve ever closer as the scale of items lessens. In other words, when hourly paid jobs alone are under consideration there will not be much curvature anyway. Conversely as supervision jobs, and still higher jobs, are brought into a single structure, the natural curvature will be extended and accelerated, preventing any one chord from being a close approximation (see end of Chapter 14). Even here a reasonable approximation can be secured by using three straight lines as in Figure 88.

Criteria for an Accelerating Line. Observation of work and earning collectively, or by individual careers, should give everyone sufficient evidence as to the actuality of acceleration. Reasoning alone should account for this on the grounds that as increasing degrees of responsibility, education, and other factors are demanded, the supply of competent candidates decreases rapidly, thereby bidding up the compensation. But there is one psychological law which covers the phenomenon, namely, *Weber's Law of Discrimination,* which states that when sensations or responses are in arithmetic relationship, the corresponding stimuli form a geometric series. Even this is not exactly quantitative because there are many "geometric series." Doubtless there are also many different series in application, evolved to meet practical requirements, and almost none of these is predetermined according to any mathematical curve. All we can expect at present, therefore, is recognition of the accelerating principle and persistent experimentation. Negatively we can discard straight lines except as acknowledged approximations which, as we have already said, may be as close, if used in multiple, as an empiric curve. Until further research is done we will have to be satisfied with trial and error. Some recommend making the measures themselves "geometric." Others would get an accelerating curve by aid of semilog paper. Still others suggest using the preferred number series.[5] In this state of affairs we would rely on key jobs carefully described and personally checked. It may be that adherence to key jobs will sometimes result in irregular curves rather than exponential curves, but pushing a few exceptions nearer the average trend is less highhanded than pushing over a whole trend line.

Substantiation of Accelerating Trend Lines. W. H. Frater, Director, Work and Wage Analysis Section, General Motors, says, "your normal wage curve is not a straight line, unless your point distribution is on a geometrical basis." So far very few point allotments for degree measurement have been made on a geometrical basis but revision in that direction offers one solution worthy of consideration. In fact, it is interesting to plot the behavior of point allotments by characteristics. The National Founders' Association did that and found that the point values of characteristics coming from arithmetically predetermined degree allotments gave entirely different kinds of curves when plotted on ordinary scales of key jobs for abscissa and point values for ordinate. The curves for schooling, versatility, and responsibility showed the geometric tendency particularly at the right. Job knowledge gave practically a straight line and working conditions decelerated in value as might have been expected. The composite of these seven curves gave approximately a straight line for the lower ten job classes and then turned up perceptibly (Figure 88) for the two highest classes. The General Electric Company curves are similar.

A. W. Bass, writing back in 1936,[6] says, "theoretically, any wage structure should embody the mathematics of a geometric progression." He advocates the use of semilog grids on which an exponen-

---

[5] See the present author's *Wage Incentive Methods*, The Ronald Press Co., 1953, Appendix A and Chapter 15, "Accelerating Premium Plans." Also E. N. Hay, *Personnel*, XXII, No. 6, pp. 372–73.

[6] *The Iron Age*, CXXXVIII, No. 11.

tial series is represented by a straight line and again depends on the position of the two end points. This is, however, for determining the point allotment range, that is, maximum and minimum limits for each job class (see Chapter 6). It secures the exponential spread of values for each class so that jobs evaluated within these ranges will give exponential progression in a series of total worths. With this exponential progression inserted in some of the measuring scales the final building of the rate structure can be done on a plane coordinate grid and a straight trend line used without violating Weber's law.

The Scatter Diagram. A diagram with point values on the abscissa and rates in cents per hour on the ordinate between which jobs can be represented is called a scatter diagram. Such a diagram can be made as soon as the total point values of all jobs are ascertained. Undoubtedly every evaluating committee is anxious to see what this looks like for its plant and so it is generally made before the locality survey is made (see Chapter 1). As it is a picture of overall worth as well as one of rate relationships it may have value in connection with classification. But the rate relationships, shown by the vertical spread, and consequently any trend or limit lines, are of little use until the old rate scale is replaced by the new one based on bargaining and, by way of preparing for that, a locality survey. With the survey summary in hand, tentative decisions can be made as to the correct rates, ranges, or single averages for the key jobs and from these the new rate scale can temporarily be staked as a basis for bargaining. Figure 97, called by A. L. Kress a correlation of average rates and points, has a straight "line of average relationship" which is determined by averaging the averages after the prevailing rates are determined. Note that all jobs are identified by code numbers so that their titles and descriptions may readily be checked. We do not know which of these were the intercompany key jobs but doubtless some of them did not fall exactly on the line of average relationships. This might still be so if the theoretically correct curve were known. Always there must be some compromise and readjustment.

Lower End of Line a Problem. Academically any geometric trend line for worth-rate relationship should start at the origin, that is, have no (x) or (y) intercept. In practice such a postulate is upset by the fact that one or more characteristics for the jobs of least worth would not be zero. For instance, there is some intelligence and learning time for any job, and both effort and working conditions are likely to have some value for the lowest jobs. Consistent

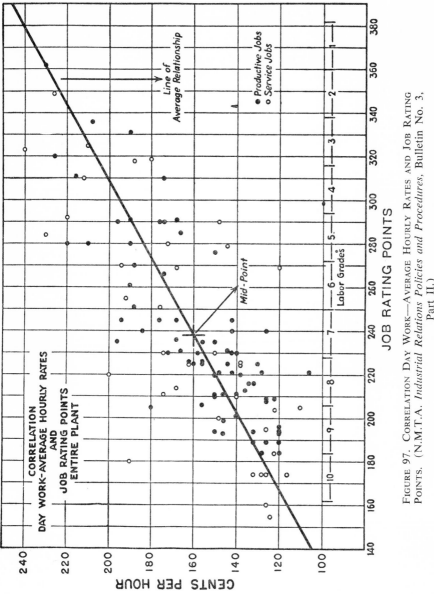

FIGURE 97. CORRELATION DAY WORK—AVERAGE HOURLY RATES AND JOB RATING POINTS. (N.M.T.A. *Industrial Relations Policies and Procedures*, Bulletin No. 3, Part II.)

evaluation of such jobs would still result in very low wage rates but most American employers have long been accustomed to pay more than the calculated worth for their lowest jobs. In our time the subsistence needs of human beings have been legally protected by law so that every employer must have a minimum starting wage. The federal minimum is now $.75 per hour. This suggests that points must be added to actual evaluated worths to the extent that these jobs will rate at or above the legal minimum. It is, however, better to leave the worths as they come and put the doctoring all on

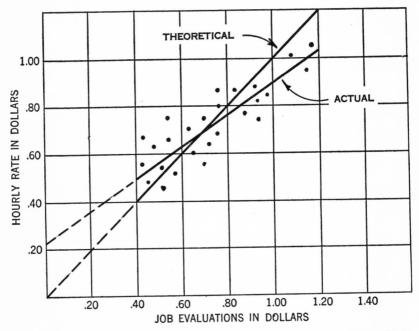

FIGURE 98. ACTUAL TREND LINE AT VARIANCE WITH THEORETICAL LINE. (E. J. Benge and The National Foreman's Institute.)

the rates. In the case of a straight trend line the requirement may be met by lowering its slope, i.e., raising the left end, by elevating the whole line, or by curving it at the lower end. Those who insist on a straight line usually lower the slope (Figure 98). The Industrial Management Society uses considerable curvature at the lower end and carries some curvature far up the line.[7] If survey-checked key job locations are followed regardless of line contour the problem is solved. We think that is the correct answer but we do not think any data in this connection so reliable that they might not be sub-

[7] See their *Attribute Handbook*.

jected to a reasonable amount of smoothing out if that is done bilaterally (see Chapter 11, Figure 102).

Example of Market Comparison Study.

The industrial relations department, with the cooperation of the job analysis staff, selected 30 or 40 anchor jobs, and prepared a questionnaire con-

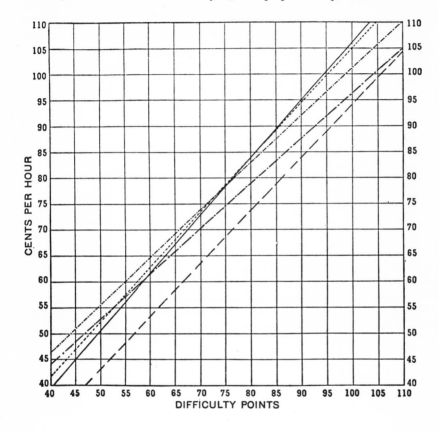

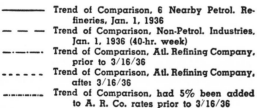

Trend of Comparison, 6 Nearby Petrol. Refineries, Jan. 1, 1936

Trend of Comparison, Non-Petrol. Industries, Jan. 1, 1936 (40-hr. week)

Trend of Comparison, Atl. Refining Company, prior to 3/16/36

Trend of Comparison, Atl. Refining Company, after 3/16/36

Trend of Comparison, had 5% been added to A. R. Co. rates prior to 3/16/36

FIGURE 99. COMPARISONS OF ATLANTIC REFINING COMPANY RATES WITH OUTSIDE COMPANY RATES PAID FOR JOBS OF COMPARABLE DIFFICULTY. (Samuel L. H. Burk, "A Case History in Salary and Wage Administration," A.M.A. *Personnel,* XV, No. 3.)

taining condensed job descriptions of the anchor jobs. These jobs were believed to be common either to the petroleum industry or industry in general around Philadelphia, or both. The questionnaires were mailed to executives in other companies. They were asked to study the job descriptions and determine whether or not similar jobs existed in their organizations and to note outstanding points of difference. Two weeks after the questionnaires were mailed, representatives of the job analysis and industrial relations departments called upon each of the individuals to whom the inquiries had been sent, and discussed each job that appeared similar to the jobs described in the questionnaire. For purposes of this initial study, only those jobs which were similar or contained very minor differences were finally used in the computation of the average market rate, although in subsequent studies it has been possible to rate major differences on the basis of our mathematical evaluation scale, so that a larger sample can be secured for comparative purposes.

In addition to the rate paid for similar jobs, all information in connection with hours of work, number of hours per week, privileges granted, vacations, sickness pay, etc., was secured in order that outstanding differences in these respects could be properly weighted. Actually, it was necessary to eliminate rates from the comparison when such differences made it impossible to arrive at a reasonably correct mathematical rating. Such factors as number of hours a week could of course be equated, but matters having to do with sickness allowance, vacation privileges, differences in performance, etc., could not be accurately measured.[8] (See Figure 99.)

The Pivot Point. When a straight line is calculated by Least Squares, there is a "pivot point" where a line representing the weighted average of job worths intersects with a line representing the weighted average of the money rates. Any rotation of the trend line about this point will leave the payroll constant. Thus the pivot point can be used as an anchor for bargaining. Actually any highly populated point on the trend line can be so used as an approximation, but it should be either the one defined above or one nearer the left end. Kress calls this the Mid-point. See Figure 97.

---

[8] Samuel L. H. Burk, "A Case History in Salary and Wage Administration," AMA *Personnel,* XV, No. 3.

11

BUILDING THE RATE STRUCTURE

> A job takes its position in the wage structure, on the stairs or ladder, not because a man, a woman, or a boy does it; it takes its place in the wage structure because of the basic requirements of the job itself.
>
> —A. L. KRESS

The Framework of a Rate Structure. Several problems concerning rate structure have been anticipated in previous chapters. It will, therefore, be unnecesary to treat them fully here. For instance, the formation of job grades is described in Chapter 9, and with classification fixed you have the independent or abscissa scale settled, at least tentatively. The dependent or ordinate scale, which is one of money rates, is only partly covered in Chapter 10, and remains, therefore, the problem for this chapter. Majority practice at present works from a straight trend line outward. If geometric progression is already in the degree measures this procedure is above criticism, but if geometric progression is left to be achieved at this last stage then it may be better to work from limit points, ignoring or leaving the trend line to depend on the accepted limits. If the job loci show a fairly narrow and regular dispersion it is reasonably safe to set a straight trend line by inspection. This is probably the general practice anyway because the correct statistical method is cumbersome. Most data in this field are, however, neither narrowly nor regularly dispersed and we again stress the importance of the trend line as the final arbiter of very important conclusions. In the interest of an incontestable gauge for these important conclusions, everybody's earnings, we recommend the method of least squares as the only way to find the exact straight trend line.

Finding a Straight Trend by the Method of Least Squares. We leave it to the statisticians to explain the theory of least squares by which the correct straight trend line may be calculated. We merely quote Frederick C. Mills,[1]

[1] F. C. Mills, *Statistical Methods.*

Where the measurements or observations relate to functions of a number of unknown quantities the most probable values are those for which the sum of the squares of the residuals is a minimum. The residuals are the differences between the computed and the actual values of the dependent variable.

The two formulas involved derive from the analytical geometry formula for any straight line.

$$y = mx + b$$

y = Value of the ordinate
x = Value of the abscissa
m = Slope of the line, altitude divided by base
b = Intercept of line on ordinate when $x = 0$

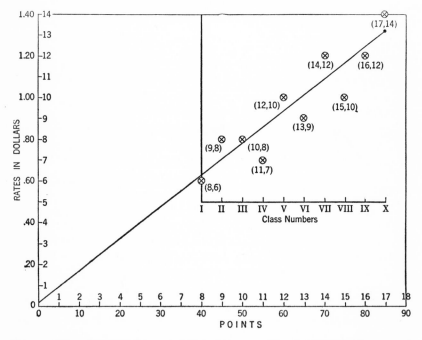

FIGURE 100*a*. ASSUMED LOCI FOR TEN JOBS AND TREND LINE BY METHOD OF LEAST SQUARES

For purposes of demonstration we have assumed the loci of ten hypothetical jobs, one for each class with worths varying from 40 points up to 85 points. In practice the money rates would have been derived from a locality survey (see Figure 100*a*). Note that full scales to the origin are used. The lower left corner can be eliminated later as indicated. To avoid unnecessary digits we suggest that simple abstract scales be used temporarily as we have done here. Start by tabulating the (x, y) values as in Figure 100b, then compute the xy and x^2 values, all of which must be added. See last line Σ for summation.

		$y = m$	$x + b$	xy	x^2
Job	1	$6 = m$	$8 + b$	48	64
	2	$8 = m$	$9 + b$	72	81
	3	$8 = m$	$10 + b$	80	100
	4	$7 = m$	$11 + b$	77	121
	5	$10 = m$	$12 + b$	120	144
$n = 10$	6	$9 = m$	$13 + b$	117	169
	7	$12 = m$	$14 + b$	168	196
	8	$10 = m$	$15 + b$	150	225
	9	$12 = m$	$16 + b$	192	256
	10	$14 = m$	$17 + b$	238	289
	Σ	$96 = m$	$125 + 10b$	1,262	1,645

FIGURE 100b. CALCULATIONS BY METHOD OF LEAST SQUARES

Further calculations speak for themselves as follows:

[The two formulas needed are (I) and (II).]

$$\Sigma xy = m\Sigma x^2 + b\Sigma x \quad\text{(I)}$$
$$1{,}262 = m\ 1645 + b\ 125 \quad\text{(1)}$$
$$\Sigma y = m\Sigma x + nb \quad\text{(II)}$$
$$96 = m\ 125 + 10b \quad\text{(2)}$$

Multiplying (2) by 12½ to equalize b,

$$1{,}200 = 1562.5m + 125b \quad\text{(2a)}$$
$$1{,}262 = 1645m + 125b \quad\text{(1)}$$

Subtracting (2a) from (1),

$$62 = 82.5m \quad\text{(3)}$$
$$m = .757 \quad\text{(3a)}$$

Substituting (3a) in (1),

$$125b = 16.73$$
$$b = .134 \quad\text{(the } y \text{ intercept)}$$

Trend line equation

$$y = .757\ x + .134 \quad\text{(4)}$$

For any value of x, say 17, substitute in (4) from which $y = 13$. Similarly $x = 0$, $y = .134$.

Draw straight line between points $(0, .134)$ and $(17, 13)$. In our illustration the slope m comes out .757 and the intercept b is .134, so that the equation for the trend line may be written $y = .757x + .134$ and by substituting in that any x value the corresponding y value appears. We can now locate the straight line from the intercept point $(0, .134)$ to the highest point $(17, 13)$. As a check on calculations we use Figure 100c in which a set of y_t values are calculated from the trend line formula to correspond to the x values. Differences, r, are made by subtracting y_t values from y_j values. These are added algebraically. The sum should be zero. Finally the r values are squared and added. These are the "residuals" and their sum is the least possible attainable from the given data.

Loci of Jobs		Ordinates for x Intervals on Trend Line	Residuals Plus and Minus r		Residuals Squared r^2
x	y_j	y_t	$+$	$-$	
8	6	6.19	.19		.04
9	8	6.95		1.05	1.10
10	8	7.70		.30	.09
11	7	8.46	1.46		2.13
12	10	9.22		.78	.61
13	9	9.97	.97		.94
14	12	10.73		1.27	1.61
15	10	11.51	1.51		2.28
16	12	.27	.27		.07
17	14	13.00		1.00	1.00
Σ			4.40	-4.40	9.87

y_j = Ordinate values of the job loci from the ground line, $x = 0$.
y_t = Ordinate values of same from the trend line formula
r = Residuals or differences between y_j and y_t

FIGURE 100c. PROOF OF METHOD OF LEAST SQUARES

Use of Limit Lines. A trend line shows the loci of averages, which means roughly that half of the jobs will lie below and half above it. Few managements aim to relocate all the jobs right on this line. Even if the unaccountable variations were all eliminated there would still be variations due to length of service and other man-merit differences which are justly accounted for. These should fall between reasonable limits, which are usually found to be about ±12 per cent or not more than ±15 per cent for high-skilled jobs. For low-skilled jobs it can be ± 4 per cent. It is therefore permissible and helpful to add lines indicating such sectors. Figure 101 illustrates this practice applied to an actual set of job loci. This kind of graph makes a good framework for the further construction of a rate structure, that is, the rate ranges can now be related vertically to the limits while the job worth classes fix the relation of "class-rate boxes" to the horizontal scale. Some managements keep both limit lines at, say, ±10 per cent from the trend line while others use a

±$0.12. We prefer to reduce the percentages as the job classes descend. This convergence reduces an undesirable amount of rate range lapover at the left of the chart. Another way of setting the limit lines is to proportion their magnitudes so that the minimum rates are always a certain percentage, say 75 per cent, of the maximum rates. This method seems just but it involves excessive lapovers at the left of the structure (see Figure 116a).

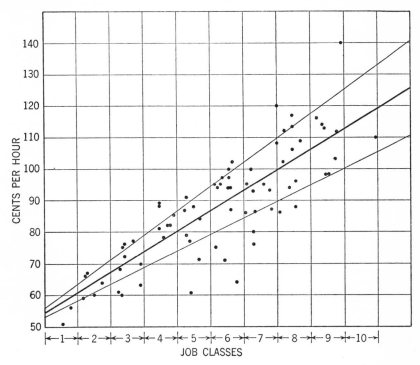

FIGURE 101. AVERAGE OF PREVIOUS HOURLY EARNINGS AND JOB RATING POINTS SHOWING TREND WITH TWO LIMIT LINES. (The job loci from National Metal Trades Association.)

Fixing Line by Inspection Allows Adherence to Pattern. Some companies start with a trend line but shun the statistical method. They do so, not because the statistical method is cumbersome, but because they find that the straight trend line is not their true trend line. Among these companies there are two approaches in use, one taking only intercompany key jobs and one taking averages of all jobs within their own plants. The first approach has the advantage of directness and can at once use a money rate scale in harmony with the locality survey while the second approach will give a tentative money rate scale which must be checked and perhaps altered if it is to conform to the locality survey figures. Nevertheless this latter approach, the use of averages, may be preferred by a company which has been paying above the prevailing rates. It brings all jobs into the picture and relies less on interpolation for nonkey jobs. A union may want this practice in order to retain a rate pattern that it has previously influenced. The American Rolling Mill Company first averages the rates by classes for each plant, and plots an actual irregular curve for each. It then averages the rates by classes for all plants and plots that irregular curve (see curve A, Figure 102). This curve is now smoothed out by inspection (curve

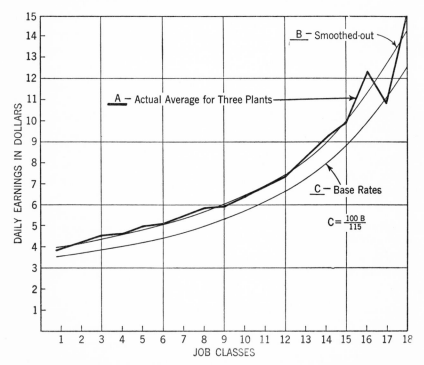

FIGURE 102. JOB CLASS-RATE CURVES FOR THE AMERICAN ROLLING MILL COM-
PANY, SHOWING TREND LINE AND ONE −15 PER CENT LIMIT LINE

B), and the resulting empiric geometric curve is adopted as the line of prevailing rates. To secure a range for money rates the company next plots another curve 15 per cent below the original smoothout. This curve C is established as the line of base rates. Thus the company may hire at rates below curve C and have more than the 15 per cent range for increases as new operators become seasoned.

The General Motors Corporation finds the trend line but uses a dozen trusted key job loci to set two limit lines.

Working from Limit Lines Inward. As we hinted in the previous chapter it is possible to take limits directly from the locality survey data (see Chapter 10, Figure 90). It may even seem desirable to predetermine two limit lines before or even without ascertaining a trend line. This is likely to occur when jobs of very high worth are to be included with those of lower worth because there would be need for more than one segment of trend line. In fact, when higher supervisory jobs are included there is no room for doubt about geometric progression. Not even two straight diverging limit lines, which provide room for increasing the absolute rate ranges, are satisfactory. The divergence would have to be very great and at the right end the lower limits would be much too low. For these reasons many companies have declined to apply systematic evaluation to their higher jobs. Others have devised entirely separate systems for the two categories. Almost alone, at least in publication, is the case of the Philadelphia Electric Company (Figure 103). The figures given are fictitious but the inclusion of departmental and associate management jobs is real enough. No average trend line is used. We do not criticize that omission but when we calculate mid-loci we notice that the variance begins with ±35 per cent and decreases to ±16⅔ per cent at the top of skilled service, then declines to ±11½ per cent at the top of highly skilled or minor supervision, etc., ending at ±15½ per cent for the last grade shown. Perhaps it is the fictitious figures but ±12 per cent should be more than ample at the bottom. Ever widening spreads are usually needed as you ascend to the highest levels.

Practical Circumstances Produce a Variety of Job Loci Arrangements. One should not infer that limit lines are applied inexorably. They are needed as guide lines but for practical reasons are not carried into the final structure. For instance, if ranges are used, both for job worth and for money rates, each two-way range would be set up as a rectangle. This keeps the top, intermediate, and bottom money rates on constant levels for any one range of worths. If the oblique limit lines were used as boundaries the money rate range would have a varying floor and a varying ceiling, either of which is obviously impractical. In Figure 104 (A, B, C, D, E, and F) we conventionalize some of the arrangements that are developed by special conditions in practice. These graphs are restricted to the lowest five job classes and the abscissa scale is made relatively small to get all six graphs on a single page. The

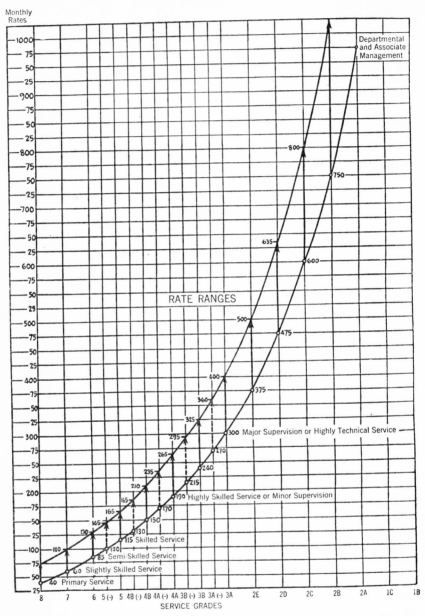

FIGURE 103. RATE GRADATION OF MINIMUM AND MAXIMUM RATES BY SERVICE
GRADES. (A.M.A. *Management Series* No. 55.)

"pinpoints" of graph A represent the best structure attainable when a union wins the right to negotiate for each job. A single rate for each class is fairly common practice for hourly paid jobs. Graph B is the arrangement which frequently occurs when a union succeeds in blocking any use of money rate ranges. Either of these arrangements may happen when seniority is carried to the extreme. Graph C is the rare case of combining no worth range with wide money rate ranges. It invites strong union pressure to raise the lower rates. Graph D represents the practice of progression on a time basis. Some companies have applied this arrangement to the new hires of all classes of hourly paid jobs but we think it should be applicable only to apprentice jobs. Unless end rates alone are used, favoritism, or the suspicion of it, is bound to develop. Graph E illustrates the use of rectangles for two-way ranges. Note that there is a one-point gap laterally to preclude the question to which group a job belongs. Boxes without money lapover necessitate very low money range to prevent impractical stacking as to rate location. Note that in Graph E this is already manifested in the first five job classes. In Graph F a starting lapover of $.04 brings much more practical locations for the end boxes. If floor rates are fixed irregularly the use of constant ranges will give irregular ceilings.

Practical Arrangements of Trend and Limit Lines. In Figure 105 A, B, C, D, E, and F we present six arrangements of these lines to illustrate what can and what cannot be obtained by purposeful selection. Superficial critics may conclude that any selection of lines, choice of arrangement, and the like, will sell out the natural results of job evaluation. Well, it does end any illusion of a single mathematical solution but one can hardly expect such a simple solution if he has taken all the complexities into consideration. Building a rate structure is like assembling equipment in a submarine. Either the over-all dimensions must be set to include all the subassemblies or else the latter must be adjusted to fit the former. Certainly all interference must be overcome so that ceilings and floors will be suited to what they are to house, or vice versa. Graphs A and B show the differences between constant money limits and constant percentage limits. Graphs C and D illustrate varying percentage limits, one with a straight trend line and one with a logarithmic trend line. Graphs E and F suggest a way to favor the lower worth jobs if that should be desired. We will show subsequently that the arrangement of graphs A and B have the fault of excessive rate lapovers for the lower worth classes and conversely graphs C and D have the fault of excessive rate lapovers for the

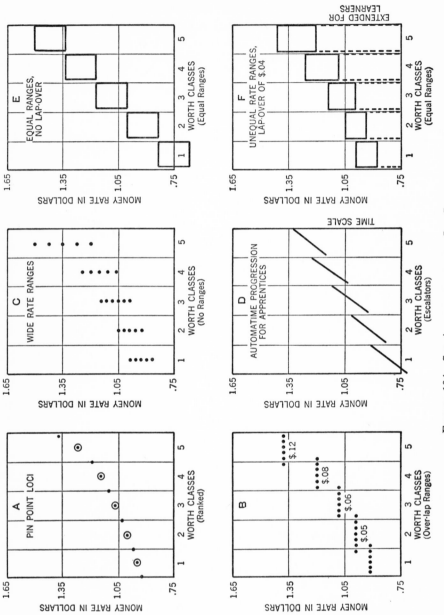

FIGURE 104. SIX ARRANGEMENTS OF JOB LOCI

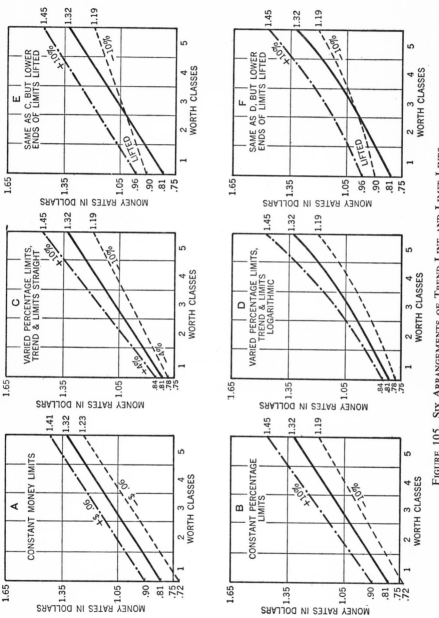

FIGURE 105. SIX ARRANGEMENTS OF TREND LINE AND LIMIT LINES

higher worth classes. Graphs E and F avoid both of these faults and are therefore worthy of serious consideration for that reason alone.

Rate Structure for all Skilled Jobs. Wherever skill is high it is customary to hire novices or untried operatives at a rate considerably below the average. Figures 106 and 107 illustrate the use of automatic time increases to build up from low hiring rates to the regular rate structure. In Figure 106 progression within each grade would be scheduled by abscissa subdivisions, but they are not shown.

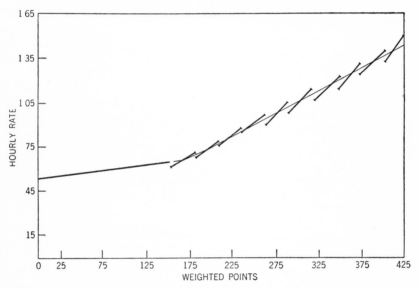

FIGURE 106. AUTOMATIC TIME PROGRESSIONS FOR SEMISKILLED JOBS (from hiring rates to prevailing rates). (Western Electric Company, Inc.)

In Figure 107 these intragrade schedules are shown as ordinates. The latter may be recognized by imagining a minimum limit line through the loci marked with zeros. At these points qualified operatives are hired. From there on they too progress according to time periods as indicated by the numbers (months) within the chart. The scale of months for the "learners" is along the right ordinate and has the maximum of 33. The topmost two steps are not on the automatic basis because they lie above the average trend line, not shown. A line along the 9-month points would be the maximum limit line. Note that there is a pronounced acceleration in this series of ceiling loci. There is also some acceleration in the floor (0) loci starting from Class No. 8.

Two Kinds of Rate Progression. The use of automatic time progressions as described above is definite, does not depend on favor, and is in no sense a pretext for hiring below the limits for qualified craftsmen. Most employers believe, however, that their use is justified only between hiring rate and base rate; that wherever individual variance of input can effect substantial variance of output, rate pro-

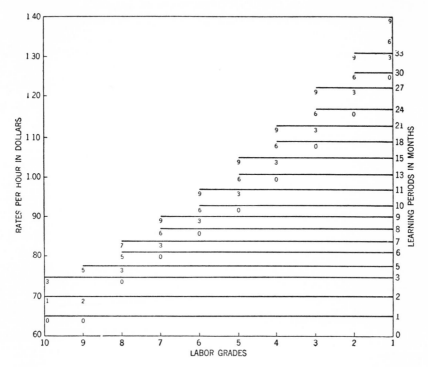

FIGURE 107. AUTOMATIC TIME PROGRESSION FOR BEGINNERS AND QUALIFIED OPERATORS (from hiring rates to maximum rates).

Numbers within chart represent the number of months for qualified operators, i.e., zeros show levels at which they are hired. (Data from Agreement of February 6, 1943, between the Curtiss-Wright Corporation, Propeller Division, and Aircraft Lodge No. 703, International Association of Machinists, AF of L.)

gression above mid-line should not be determined solely by the lapse of time. The National War Labor Board, after some seesawing, came to the same conclusion in 1945. It ordered the use of automatic time progressions from hiring rates to qualified rates (mid-line) and merit progressions between qualified rates to maximum rates "subject to appeal through the established grievance procedure." This did not please the extremists of either side, but it gave each side the part it wanted most and conformed to what the students of wage rate structure had contended for all the time as a matter of sound principle. In fact, there are two principles and no conflict. First, the lower sector of the rate structure exists primarily as a recognition that the employer has the right to hire below base rate because he cannot be sure that the new employee is really qualified. A trial over some reasonable time [2] will prove whether or not the new employee is qualified. Retention at the end of this trial period is acknowledgment of his qualification. In other words, this is a matter of time. Second, the upper sector of the structure exists as a recognition that the employee may perform better than the qualifying requirement and if he does so he is worth more than the base rate, that is, he is entitled to an individual- or man-differential in proportion to his degree of excellence regardless of how soon it is evidenced.

Base Rates for Incentive-Paid Jobs. Jobs for which tasks have been developed as a gauge for measuring productive efficiency should have base rates set in exactly the same manner as going rates are set for the other jobs. Special guarantee rates may be different from the regular going rates (see Chapter 5). Rates in terms of productivity or efficiency are a different matter. These rates per piece, per standard hour, per "B," etc., all depend on the tasks which are not comparable between plants but should be consistent within any one plant. Because this kind of rate setting requires continuous adjustment we leave its treatment to the next chapter.

More Grades, Smaller Differentials. A larger number of job grades provides for more frequent promotion, but unions may object to the smaller differentials. If there is no objection to extra grades and to considerable lapover in the money rates it is possible to make a consistent structure by laying out a background of horizontal lines spaced as follows: the first three at $.06 intervals, the next seven at $.08 intervals, the next five at $.10 intervals, and the last three at $.12 intervals. On this background 16 job grades of equal worth range can be set up, using each successive horizontal level as the base of each successive rate range. If each of these ranges spreads upward over three of the intervals each grade will extend one interval higher than the preceding grade and the top of each box will be on the level of the bottom of the third grade farther along. This causes a four-grade rate lapover but always provides

---

[2] The National War Labor Board's second directive to Maxson said: "four months for unskilled jobs, six months for semiskilled jobs, and eight months for skilled jobs." (See Figure 120.)

one full step per grade above the top of the preceding grade. With clearances of one cent the lapover could be reduced to three grades. There is some acceleration in pay along the floors and considerable acceleration along the ceilings because of the increase in the magnitudes of the pre-arranged horizontals. This also provides four standardized rates A, B, C, and D (3 ingrades) within each box— the horizontal lines can be used for keeping the ingrade rates in harmonious relationship throughout the whole structure. Figure 108 illustrates this ingenious arrangement.

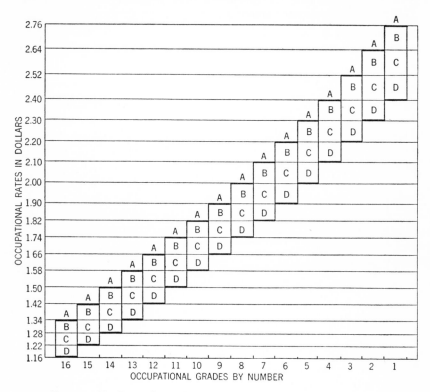

FIGURE 108. FOUR GRADE LAPOVER. (American Seating Company.)

The Problem of Money Range Lapover. Some lapping over of money ranges is desirable primarily for merit rating but also for flexibility. An operative is frequently hired for a job which he or she has held elsewhere and must be given a "man-differential" on top of the base rate (see Chapter 13). Furthermore, it is impossible to keep some jobs going all the time and so an employee must be temporarily transferred to some job other than his regular one.

When this is carried beyond any one class it raises complications as to money rate if there is no lapover of money ranges. Of course the width of worth ranges, or number of job classes, also is involved and it is apparent that the fewer the grades are, the wider will be their worth ranges, which makes for some flexibility without any lapover. Excessive lapover of wage ranges is likely to bring disorder and injustice; it will tend to defeat the main purposes of job evaluation. So each management must work out some policy on how far to overlap. No doubt many rate structures are built without predetermin-

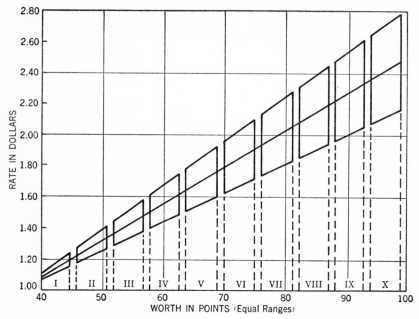

FIGURE 109. THEORETICAL FLOOR AND CEILING FOR MONEY RATES

ing any specific policy on this matter and we see no objection to experimenting with the purpose of finding a practical policy; in fact we recommend just that. The experimenting is best done by means of graphs and tables; always use both. The National War Labor Board of World War II approved of a 20 per cent spread throughout the structure for shop jobs and 33⅓ per cent for office jobs. The Wage Stabilization Board allowed variations from 15 to 35 per cent provided they averaged around 25 per cent.

Straight Lines and Equal Worth Ranges. Figure 109 continues with the data shown in Figure 101. First the limit lines are broken into ten parts by drawing vertical lines from the divisions of worth or job classes shown in the abscissa. We do this to show the imprac-

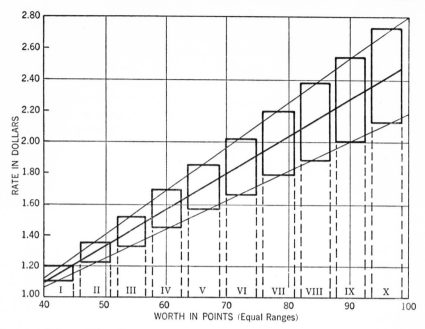

FIGURE 110a. COMPROMISE FLOOR AND CEILING FOR MONEY RATES

Classes		Dollar Rates		
No.	5-Point Range	Floor Differentials	Range Limits	Ceiling Differentials
10	94–99		2.12–2.73	
9	88–93	.12	2.00–2.56	.17
8	82–87	.12	1.88–2.39	.17
7	76–81	.12	1.76–2.22	.17
6	70–75	.11	1.65–2.05	.17
5	64–69	.11	1.54–1.88	.17
4	58–63	.11	1.43–1.71	.17
3	52–57	.11	1.32–1.54	.17
2	46–51	.11	1.21–1.37	.17
1	40–45	.11	1.10–1.20	.17

FIGURE 110b. DATA FROM FIGURE 110a

ticality of using the limit lines themselves for floors and ceilings. To get floors and ceilings which will be practical we use Figure 110. By the way, contrast the lapovers here with those in Figure 116. Here we take the money values of the mid-locations of the class ceilings from Figure 109 and draw horizontals, thereby changing the worth-rate boxes into rectangles of varying height. The increasing variation in money-rate range as we pass to higher job classification is according to facts; but, facts or no facts, the amount of lapover becomes excessive for the higher job grades. We tabulate the determinations found in Figure 110a and get Figure 110b. From this tabulation we observe that the differentials between the range floors would be constant ($2.12 — $1.10) ÷ 9 = $.11⅓ but we made the upper three $.12 to use up the thirds and leave the others at an even $.11. The differentials between the range ceilings are even ($2.73 — $1.20) ÷ 9 = $.17. We can now set up Figures 111a and 111b. Here we hold the floors just above the hiring line a constant $.12 differential, and by tabulation we improve the ceiling

Classes		Dollar Rates		
No.	5-Point Range	Floor Differentials	Range Limits	Ceiling Differentials
10	94–99		2.20–2.73	
9	88–93	.12	2.08–2.48	.25
8	82–87	.12	1.96–2.26	.22
7	76–81	.12	1.84–2.06	.20
6	70–75	.12	1.72–1.88	.18
5	64–69	.12	1.60–1.76	.12
4	58–63	.12	1.48–1.64	.12
3	52–57	.12	1.36–1.52	.12
2	46–51	.12	1.24–1.40	.12
1	40–45	.12	1.12–1.32	.08

FIGURE 111a. DATA FOR FIGURE 111b

differentials: (1) to increase the money range for grade 1 which by virtue of the converging limits is too limited. The lifting of this roof is in the interests of humanity because some of grade 1 job holders will be in need of all they can rightfully earn. (2) to lessen the lapovers of the high grades. We have accomplished the latter by reducing the total range of all but the first two grades. It is not necessary to carry this as far as we have done but we have incidentally achieved an arithmetic progression for the ceiling differentials, grades 6 to 10, and we consider that the next best thing to a real geometric progression in the trend line. The National War Labor Board came to much the same conclusion, it would seem, by approving such bracket adjustments.

Straight Lines and Increasing Worth Ranges. The concept on which increasing worth ranges are justified is none too well estab-

lished for hourly paid jobs and it may be difficult to get employees
to believe in it but it has practical advantages as well as practical
disadvantages. To bring these out we have made Figure 112a, using
the same scales, same limit lines, and the same number of grades,
10, but the latter differently located, of course. In general, we have
aimed to keep ceiling mid-points on the upper limit line and all the
floors above the lower limit line. The former aim is sacrificed at
the lower end of the structure in the interest of helping the lowest
job holders as we did in the previous case. The latter aim is also

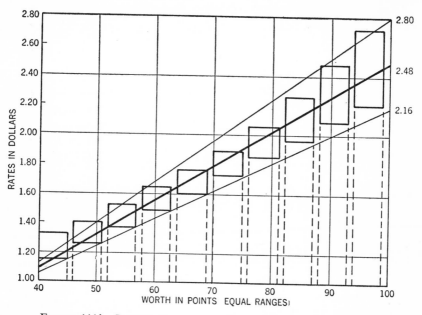

FIGURE 111b. REVISED FLOORS AND CEILINGS FOR MONEY RATES

slightly sacrificed in the upper four grades to get a better consistency
in the differentials (see Figure 112b). These extra aims are fulfilled
with less deviation from the limit lines than in the previous case but
the lapovers are not so ideal. Note that for any class n, the $n-1$
ceiling is frequently above the $n+1$ floor. This happens only once
in the previous case and could be avoided there by raising the floor
of grade 10. The main reason for increasing the worth ranges is
that they are necessary for the highest jobs and if the latter are ever
to be added it is more consistent to carry the concept through. If
there is no objection to crowding the lower grades it is a desirable
practice. The structure shown in Figures 112a and 112b is recommended for companies whose policy is to provide increases through

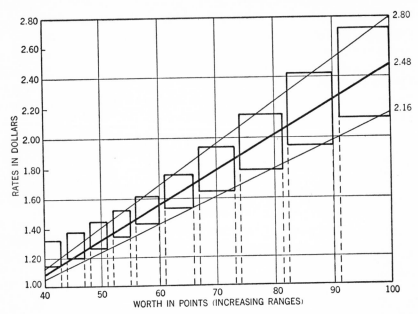

FIGURE 112*a*. REVISED FLOORS AND CEILINGS FOR MONEY RATES, WORTH RANGES ALSO REVISED

Classes		Dollar Rates			
No.	Point Range	Floor Differentials	Range Limits	Ceiling Differentials	Difference Between Differentials
10	91–100		2.12–2.73		
9	82– 90	.18	1.94–2.42	.30	12
8	74– 81	.16	1.78–2.16	.26	10
7	67– 73	.14	1.64–1.94	.22	8
6	61– 66	.12	1.52–1.76	.18	6
5	56– 60	.10	1.42–1.62	.14	4
4	52– 55	.08	1.34–1.52	.10	2
3	48– 51	.08	1.26–1.44	.08	0
2	44– 47	.06	1.20–1.38	.06	0
1	40– 43	.06	1.14–1.32	.06	0

FIGURE 112*b*. DATA FROM FIGURE 112*a*—WORTH RANGES INCREASING FROM THREE POINTS TO NINE POINTS

merit rating. The one shown in Figures 116a and 116b is recommended for companies whose policy is to have no merit rating. Note that the ceiling line is approximately parallel to the trend line.

Comparison of Arithmetic and Geometric Progressions. Besides the choice between constant and variable worth ranges we have a choice between arithmetic and geometric progressions. In Figure 113 we have taken the end values of the trend line already used in Figure 101 and drawn a straight line between these loci on semilogarithmic coordinates, which gives logarithmic rate values and will show as an accelerating curve if transferred to plain coordinates.

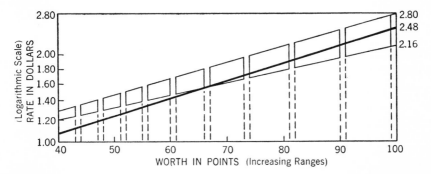

FIGURE 113. TOP AVERAGE AND LOGARITHMIC TREND, LIMITS CONVERGING FROM ±12 PER CENT HIGHS

As previously explained, we alter the lower loci in favor of the lower class jobs, in this instance from $1.08 to $1.24. Similarly we converge two limit lines from the ± 12 per cent at the right, viz., $2.80 and $2.16 to $1.28 and $1.20 respectively. Next we lay out the worth ranges as shown in Figure 113 and complete the point-money boxes. We have not tabulated the money rates from this chart because there is obviously excessive lapover, but in Figure 114a we transfer the trend line and limit lines to plain coordinates and fit new boxes within the limits. Here we can see that both the worth range variation and the logarithmic progression reduce the lapover to ideal proportions. This is repeated statistically in Figure 114b. For a total money range of $1.24 to $2.50 this arrangement is hard to beat. To meet other ranges the vertical scale can be altered. In Figures 115a and 115b we use a doctored trend line, $1.24 to $2.48, and retain the limits of ± 12 per cent variation throughout. To illustrate the effects of these limit lines we have laid out constant worth ranges [3] and then changed to the varying

[3] See also Farrel-Birmingham structure in Chapter 10.

worth ranges of foregoing charts in Figures 116*a* and 116*b*. In these we have kept the same trend and limit lines as in Figures 115*a* and 115*b* to allow comparison. Note that the logarithmic progression of itself does not avoid excessive lapover for the lower job grades. When it is desired to contain the box corners wholly within

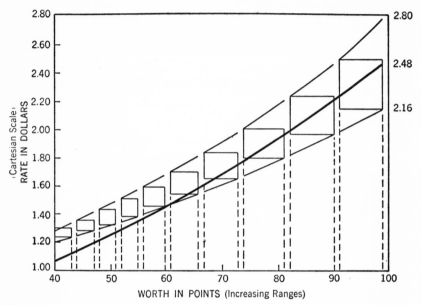

FIGURE 114*a*. TRANSFER TO PLAIN COORDINATES, BOXES LEVELED WITHIN LIMITS

Classes		Dollar Rates			
No.	Point Range	Floor Differentials	Range Limits	Ceiling Differentials	Difference Between Differentials
10	91–100		2.14–2.50		
9	82– 90	.18	1.96–2.24	.26	8
8	74– 81	.16	1.80–2.00	.24	8
7	67– 73	.16	1.64–1.84	.16	8
6	61– 66	.10	1.54–1.70	.14	4
5	56– 60	.08	1.46–1.58	.12	4
4	52– 55	.08	1.38–1.50	.08	0
3	48– 51	.06	1.32–1.42	.08	2
2	44– 47	.04	1.28–1.36	.06	2
1	40– 43	.04	1.24–1.30	.06	2

FIGURE 114*b*. DATA FROM FIGURE 114*a*

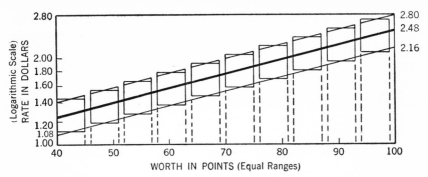

FIGURE 115a. EQUAL WORTH GRADES AND LOGARITHMIC TREND, LIMITS ±12 PER CENT THROUGHOUT

the limit lines, shift the minimum line to the right for the range of one half a grade so that it will pass through the lower right corners of the grade boxes; and shift the maximum line to the left for one half a grade so that it will pass through the upper left corners. This study conclusively favors the combination of three things, namely, the use of expanding worth ranges, with limit lines of varying percentages and the latter lines elevated slightly at the lower end (see Chapter 10, Figures 96a and 96b).

Preferred Numbers. Geometric progression can also be achieved by using the formula for "preferred numbers" which has long been used for machine tool speeds and other matters needing accelerat-

Classes		Dollar Rates			
No.	5-Point Range	Floor Differentials	Range Limits	Ceiling Differentials	Difference Between Differentials
10	94–99		2.08–2.70		
9	88–93	.14	1.94–2.52	.18	4
8	82–87	.14	1.80–2.36	.16	2
7	76–81	.12	1.68–2.20	.16	4
6	70–75	.12	1.56–2.04	.16	4
5	64–69	.10	1.46–1.90	.14	4
4	58–63	.10	1.36–1.78	.12	2
3	52–57	.10	1.26–1.66	.12	2
2	46–51	.08	1.18–1.54	.12	4
1	40–45	.06	1.12–1.44	.10	4

FIGURE 115b. DATA FROM FIGURE 115a

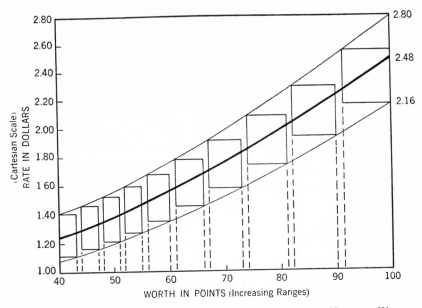

FIGURE 116*a*. TRANSFER TO PLAIN COORDINATES, BUT WITH VARYING WORTH GRADES

Classes		Dollar Rates			
No.	Point Range	Floor Differentials	Range Limits	Ceiling Differentials	Difference Between Differentials
10	91–100		2.16–2.52		
9	82– 90	.24	1.92–2.28	.26	2
8	74– 81	.18	1.74–2.08	.20	2
7	67– 73	.16	1.58–1.90	.18	2
6	61– 66	.14	1.44–1.78	.12	2
5	56– 60	.10	1.34–1.68	.10	0
4	52– 55	.08	1.26–1.60	.08	0
3	48– 51	.04	1.22–1.52	.08	4
2	44– 47	.06	1.16–1.46	.06	0
1	40– 43	.08	1.08–1.40	.06	—2

FIGURE 116*b*. DATA FROM FIGURE 116*a*

ing rates of progression.[4] Values resulting from the formula progress by a constant percentage. Hence their logarithms step up by a constant value. The formula is:

[4] The late Carl G. Barth used this formula as early as 1904 for machine-hour rates.

$$f = \sqrt[N]{\frac{Z}{A}}$$

in which f = The factor or rate of progression
Z = The last item in the series
A = The first item in the series
N = The complete number of steps or number
of items minus one
n = The number of each successive step

Applying the formula to hourly rates it is necessary to calculate the lowest and highest rates desired and to choose the number of steps desired. This means that the key job rates for the two end classes, as in the case of a straight line, can be used to set the whole series. Rates for each, as per locality survey, are averaged, or better than average rates are selected, and substituted in the formula for A and Z respectively.[5] N and n are fixed when you decide the number of job classes. Successive items are built up from the one lower by multiplying that by the factor f^n, viz.: A, fA, f^2A, f^3A, . . . f^nA or Z, or by multiplying each successive item by the factor.

Use of Standard Series. As a short cut it is convenient to look up series of preferred numbers already prepared,[6] four of which are shown in Figure 120. Each series is circular, that is, you can start anywhere as indicated and finish from the top, of course changing the decimal places to suit either hourly or salaried rates. Note that you can get ten items from the twenty series running from $.80 to $2.24. These steps are 12 per cent apart. For weekly salaries you might start at $30.00 and come all the way back to it, $300.00 in 39 steps, or less by regular skipping. These steps are 6 per cent apart.[7] We believe that such rates are truly to be preferred over arbitrary and irregular progressions, but it is better to use the formula for a permanent setup so that you will be free to select any kind of limits and any number of steps. For other techniques of smoothing out limit lines see J. P. Guilford, *Psychometric Methods.*

Ranges. Similar series for floor and ceiling limits may be worked out by setting the range for the bottom grade, say, $\pm$ 10 per cent from the median. For salaried jobs it is necessary, however, to

---

[5] A log-log slide rule makes it easy to find any N^{th} root. This should be done first for the mid-line, then for the two limit lines.

[6] See John Gaillard's article in *Mechanical Engineering,* November, 1942.

[7] The thirty series would give 31 items, each successive one about 8 per cent higher than its predecessor.

5-Series (60% steps)	10-Series (25% steps)	20-Series (12% steps)	40-Series (6% steps)
10.0	10.0	10.0	10.0
			10.6
		11.2	11.2
			11.8
	12.5	12.5	12.5
			13.2
		14.0	14.0
			15.0
16.0	16.0	16.0	16.0
			17.0
		18.0	18.0
			19.0
	20.0	20.0	20.0
			21.2
		22.4	22.4

Finish

			23.6
25.0	25.0	25.0	25.0
			26.5
		28.0	28.0
			30.0
	31.5	31.5	31.5
			33.5
		35.5	35.5
			37.5
40.0	40.0	40.0	40.0
			42.5
		45.0	45.0
			47.5
	50.0	50.0	50.0
			53.0
		56.0	56.0
			60.0
63.0	63.0	63.0	63.0
			67.0
		71.0	71.0
			75.0

Start

	80.0	80.0	80.0
			85.0
		90.0	90.0
			95.0

FIGURE 117. FOUR PREFERRED NUMBERS SERIES.

Note: At end of Chapter 14 a curve for the thirty series is compared with a semilog curve extending through the same limits.

allow greater ranges. Before evaluation these ranges run all the way from 20 per cent to 50 per cent and the former figure is not usually considered enough for high salaries. The extent of lapover should be one of the considerations. Thirty per cent at the most should give satisfactory results. The National War Labor Board accepted 33⅓ per cent; as much as 40 per cent is definitely undesirable because it lessens control. For a complete series of, say, twenty classes we suggest setting the first and last items at $\pm$ 5 per cent and $\pm$ 15 per cent respectively, and then reapplying the formula separately to each of the three sets of $\dfrac{Z}{A}$. This accommodates the need for increasing money ranges and is more practical than working from each of the grade rates in the median series. That technique can, however, be managed easily if a constant proportion is to be used, such as $\pm$ 10 per cent, by multiplying the mid-values by $\sqrt{1.20}$ for the ceiling items and by dividing the mid-values by $\sqrt{1.20}$ for the floor items. Thus each grade ceiling value will be 120 per cent of its respective floor value.

Application of Principles. We illustrate these techniques with a brief study of five sample rate structures, all for the Kress type of plan, 12 grades, and points from 118 to 381. The first two samples, Figures 118a and 119a, use constant worth ranges of 21 points and straight trend-limit lines, but one case keeps the money spread constant at 20 per cent ($\sqrt{1.20} = 1.097$) while the other varies the money spread from 10 per cent ($\sqrt{1.10} = 1.05$) at the left to 25 per cent ($\sqrt{1.25} = 1.12$) at the right. This change provides more latitude for payment to the higher grades, but leaves the two lowest grades without the needed lapover. That can, however, be remedied by arbitrarily lifting the ceilings of those two grades.

Figure 120a retains the constant worth range and the varying money spread, but derives the trend-limit lines by aid of the semilog grid, not shown. Mid-grade values by this technique fall a few cents below those derived by the preferred numbers formula but, of course, come to the same amounts at the end grades. We have, therefore, shown this sample structure, with three grades left off at each end, and enlarged to allow portrayal of time-progression ingrades. Notice that the first grade left in is considered to be near the bottom of semi-skilled work and is given only four ingrades—one per month for four months. The next three grades are provided ingrades for five-, six-, and seven-month progressions respectively. This is appropriate for semiskilled to fairly highly skilled jobs. The last two grades are provided with eight ingrades, which allows eight monthly progres-

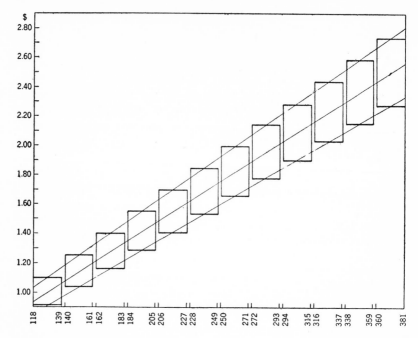

FIGURE 118*a*. SAMPLE RATE STRUCTURE. CONSTANT WORTH RANGE OF TWENTY-ONE POINTS. STRAIGHT TREND AND LIMIT LINES. CONSTANT 20 PER CENT MONEY SPREAD.

Grade Nos.		Floor Differ-entials	Job Pricing in Dollars			
Previous	Present		Floor Limits	Trend-Base (Qualified)	Ceiling Limits	Ceiling Differ-entials
1	12		2.28	2.50	2.74	
2	11	13	2.15	2.36	2.59	15
3	10	13	2.02	2.22	2.44	15
4	9	13	1.89	2.08	2.29	15
5	8	13	1.76	1.94	2.14	15
6	7	13	1.63	1.81	1.99	15
7	6	12	1.51	1.67	1.84	15
8	5	12	1.39	1.54	1.69	15
9	4	12	1.27	1.40	1.54	15
10	3	12	1.15	1.27	1.39	15
11	2	12	1.03	1.13	1.24	15
12	1	12	.91	1.00	1.10	14

FIGURE 118*b*. DATA FOR SAMPLE RATE STRUCTURE. CONSTANT WORTH RANGE. STRAIGHT LINES FOR TREND AND LIMITS. CONSTANT 20 PER CENT MONEY SPREAD ($\sqrt{1.20} = 1.097$).

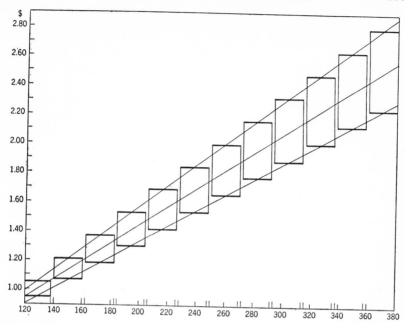

FIGURE 119a. SAMPLE RATE STRUCTURE. CONSTANT WORTH RANGE OF TWENTY-ONE POINTS. STRAIGHT LINES FOR TREND AND LIMIT LINES. LOWER END 10 PER CENT MONEY SPREAD. UPPER END 25 PER CENT MONEY SPREAD.

Grade Nos.		Floor Differentials	Job Pricing in Dollars				Differentials Between Dif. a Constant .04
Previous	Present		Floor Limits	Trend-Base (Qualified)	Ceiling Limits	Ceiling Differentials	
1	12		2.23	2.50	2.77		
2	11	.11	2.12	2.37	2.62	.15	
3	10	.11	2.01	2.24	2.47	.15	
4	9	.11	1.90	2.11	2.32	.15	
5	8	.11	1.79	1.98	2.17	.15	
6	7	.12	1.67	1.84	2.01	.16	
7	6	.12	1.55	1.70	1.85	.16	
8	5	.12	1.43	1.56	1.69	.16	
9	4	.12	1.31	1.42	1.53	.16	
10	3	.12	1.19	1.28	1.37	.16	
11	2	.12	1.07	1.14	1.21	.16	
12	1	.12	.95	1.00	1.05	.16	

FIGURE 119b. DATA FOR SAMPLE RATE STRUCTURE. CONSTANT WORTH RANGE. STRAIGHT LINES FOR TREND AND LIMITS. LOWER END 10 PER CENT MONEY SPREAD ($\sqrt{1.10} = 1.05$). UPPER END 25 PER CENT MONEY SPREAD ($\sqrt{1.25} = 1.12$).

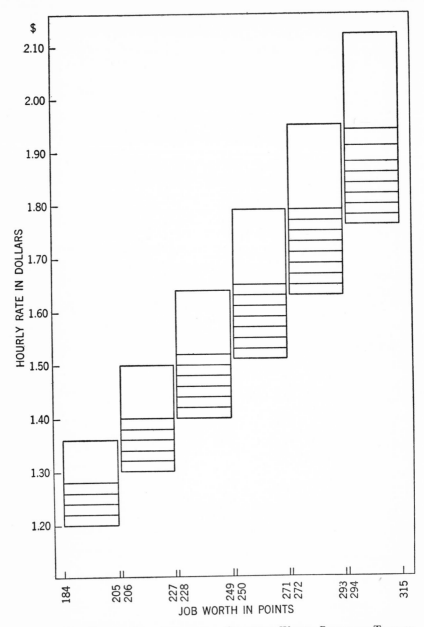

FIGURE 120a. SAMPLE RATE STRUCTURE. CONSTANT WORTH RANGE OF TWENTY-ONE POINTS. SEMILOG ACCELERATION FOR TREND AND LIMITS. LOWER END 10 PER CENT MONEY SPREAD. UPPER END 25 PER CENT MONEY SPREAD. LOWER HALVES DIVIDED INTO APPROPRIATE INGRADES FOR AUTOMATIC TIME PROGRESSION.

| Grade Nos. | | Floor Differentials | Job Pricing in Dollars | | | | Dif. Between Differentials |
Previous	Present		Floor Limits	Trend-Base (Qualified)	Ceiling Limits	Ceiling Differentials	
1	12		2.23	2.50	2.77		
2	11	16	2.07	2.31	2.55	22	6
3	10	16	1.91	2.12	2.33	22	6
4	9	15	1.76	1.94	2.12	21	6
5	8	13	1.63	1.79	1.95	17	4
6	7	12	1.51	1.65	1.79	16	4
7	6	11	1.40	1.52	1.64	15	4
8	5	10	1.30	1.40	1.50	14	4
9	4	10	1.20	1.28	1.36	14	4
10	3	9	1.11	1.18	1.25	11	2
11	2	8	1.03	1.09	1.15	10	2
12	1	8	.95	1.00	1.05	10	2

Note: The graph from these data drops off three grades on each end because they are so closely like the following case. The six grades that are charted are enlarged to allow the portrayal of ingrades for automatic time progressions.

FIGURE 120b. DATA FOR SAMPLE RATE STRUCTURE. CONSTANT WORTH RANGE. SEMILOG ACCELERATION FOR TREND AND LIMITS. LOWER END 10 PER CENT MONEY SPREAD ($\sqrt{1.10} = 1.05$). UPPER END 25 PER CENT MONEY SPREAD ($\sqrt{1.25} = 1.12$). ADJUSTED TO GIVE EQUAL PLUS AND MINUS VALUES FROM MID-LINE.

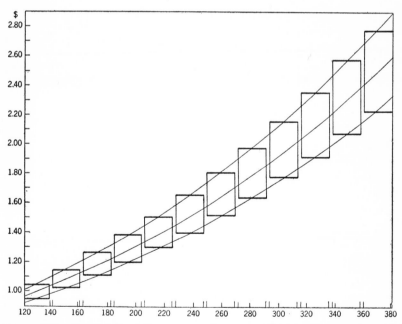

FIGURE 121a. SAMPLE RATE STRUCTURE. CONSTANT WORTH RANGE OF TWENTY-ONE POINTS. PREFERRED NUMBERS FOR TREND AND LIMIT LINES. LOWER END 10 PER CENT MONEY SPREAD. UPPER END 25 PER CENT MONEY SPREAD.

Grade Nos.		Floor Differ- entials	Job Pricing in Dollars			
Previous	Present		Floor Limits	Trend- Base (Qualified)	Ceiling Limits	Ceiling Differ- entials
1	12		2.23	2.50	2.77	
2	11	.16	2.08	2.30	2.58	.22
3	10	.16	1.92	2.12	2.36	.22
4	9	.14	1.78	1.95	2.16	.20
5	8	.14	1.64	1.79	1.98	.18
6	7	.12	1.52	1.65	1.81	.17
7	6	.12	1.40	1.51	1.66	.15
8	5	.10	1.30	1.39	1.51	.15
9	4	.10	1.20	1.28	1.39	.12
10	3	.09	1.11	1.18	1.27	.12
11	2	.08	1.03	1.09	1.15	.12
12	1	.08	.95	1.00	1.05	.10

FIGURE 121b. DATA FOR SAMPLE RATE STRUCTURE. CONSTANT WORTH RANGE. PREFERRED NUMBERS FOR TRENDS AND LIMITS. LOWER END 10 PER CENT MONEY SPREAD ($\sqrt{1.10} = 1.05$). UPPER END 25 PER CENT MONEY SPREAD ($\sqrt{1.25} = 1.12$)

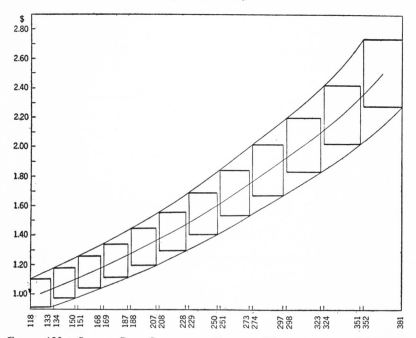

FIGURE 122a. SAMPLE RATE STRUCTURE. VARIABLE WORTH RANGE. FIRST THREE QUARTERS OF GRADES ARITHMETIC INCREASES OF ONE; LAST QUARTER OF GRADES ARITHMETIC INCREASES OF TWO. SEMILOG ACCELERATION FOR TRENDS AND LIMIT LINES. CONSTANT 20 PER CENT MONEY SPREAD ($\sqrt{1.20} = 1.097$).

Grade Nos.		Floor Differ-entials	Job Pricing in Dollars				Dif. Between Differ-entials
			Floor Limits	Trend-Base (Qualified)	Ceiling Limits	Ceiling Differ-entials	
Previous	Present						
1	12		2.28	2.50	2.74		
2	11	25	2.03	2.25	2.41	33	8
3	10	20	1.83	2.04	2.17	24	4
4	9	16	1.67	1.85	1.98	19	3
5	8	14	1.53	1.68	1.81	17	3
6	7	13	1.40	1.54	1.66	15	2
7	6	11	1.29	1.43	1.53	13	2
8	5	10	1.19	1.32	1.42	11	1
9	4	8	1.11	1.23	1.33	9	1
10	3	7	1.04	1.13	1.25	8	1
11	2	7	.97	1.07	1.17	8	1
12	1	6	.91	1.00	1.10	7	1

FIGURE 122b. DATA FOR SAMPLE RATE STRUCTURE. VARIABLE WORTH RANGE. FIRST THREE QUARTERS OF GRADES ARITHMETIC INCREASE OF ONE; LAST QUARTER OF GRADES ARITHMETIC INCREASE OF TWO. SEMILOG ACCELERATION FOR TREND AND LIMIT LINES. CONSTANT 20 PER CENT MONEY SPREAD ($\sqrt{1.20} = 1.097$).

sions appropriate to highly skilled jobs. The three grades omitted from the right could each have eight ingrades of more value or an increasing number of ingrades where the degree of skill is extreme.

Figure 121a continues the constant worth range and the variable money spread, but applies the preferred numbers formula

$$f = \sqrt[N]{\frac{Z}{A}} \text{ as follows:}$$

C — Ceiling line \$1.05 to \$2.77 where $f = \sqrt[11]{\frac{2.77}{1.05}} = 1.09\,1/3$

T — Trend line \$1.00 to \$2.50 where $f = \sqrt[11]{\frac{2.50}{1.00}} = 1.08\,2/3$

F — Floor line \$ .95 to \$2.23 where $f = \sqrt[11]{\frac{2.23}{.95}} = 1.08$

Lower Ends	Upper Ends
$C = \sqrt{1.10}\,T$ or $1.10\,F$	$C = \sqrt{1.25}\,T$ or $1.25\,F$
$F = \dfrac{T}{\sqrt{1.10}}$	$F = \dfrac{T}{\sqrt{1.25}}$

The fifth and last sample in this study, Figure 122a, may seem strange to all who have been used to twenty-one points to the grade but it is undeniably a structure with merit. The feature that will need defending is the use of varying worth ranges. The reasons for doing this have already been discussed. In this instance we have started with fifteen points and added one more to each successive grade through the first nine grades, which puts the last of that arithmetic series at twenty-three points. We then double the increments to make twenty-five, twenty-seven, and twenty-nine point ranges. The semilog grid was then used to derive the trend and limit lines. The maximum line was shifted to pass the point values at the left side of each grade and the minimum line was shifted to the point values at the right side of each grade. This technique assures that the grade box corners will lie exactly within the limits. It does not alter the trend line position and is equivalent to setting up the grade boxes on the semilog grid. This structure has a better distribution of lapovers than usual and ample money spread throughout. Its special peculiarity is, however, the increasing room for job ratings per grade as the grades ascend. Such widening of worth ranges can be very helpful in the higher grades, particularly when straight lines are used, and we see no reason why a company starting fresh should not adopt it if the union can be sold on its practicality. The Metropolitan Life Insurance Company recommends a variable worth range to its group policy holders.[8] They use straight lines and extended corners.

Problem on Structure Building. Since the job of lowest worth is not likely to fall below about 34 per cent of the theoretical total, and the highest worth is not likely to go above about 83 per cent, we can use these percentages to represent point limits out of a 100-point potential. Now if we set aside nine points for one-point clearances between ten grades we will see that $83 - 34 - 9 = 40$, which means four points per box of constant worth range. As an alternative assumption we might arbitrarily start with a worth range of three points, use that for the lowest two boxes, take four points for the next two boxes, and then make the remaining ones five, six, seven, eight, and nine respectively with the effect of variable worth ranges. In working these problems we suggest:

a) Either of these techniques may be adopted. To retain some basis for comparison we suggest that all agree on ten labor grades and on $.83 to $2.50 per hour for the extreme trend line rates. Next the student might choose between:

b) Limit lines to be a constant ± 10 per cent from the trend line or limit lines to vary ± 6 per cent to ± 15 per cent from the trend line.

---

[8] Policyholders Service Bureau, *An Introduction to Job Evaluation, 1947.*

c) Straight lines for trend and limits lines or accelerating lines for same. A subchoice would be between preferred numbers values and semilog values translated to Cartesian coordinates.

If classes of graduate students are assigned these problems we suggest that each student be required to make two or more solutions each on a different set of assumptions. By this means they will see at first hand how the various combinations of techniques work out and how a change in one or more techniques can correct some undesirable condition, such as excessive vertical lapover at either end of the structure.

12

OPERATING AND ADJUSTING

An elaborate system of job evaluation which does not reflect current and changing conditions is worse than none at all . . . the only fair measure of the plan is whether it fits your company and can do the job you want done.

—J. A. RUHLMAN

Out-of-Line Rates. Every industry, if not every plant, has a wage rate history which often goes back over many years. Rates with background may be looked upon as very real rights. Yet, as George W. Taylor has said, "the forces which cause disparities in wage rates are usually more potent than those tending to force equality." There is no paradox here because disparities too have long histories and rightly or wrongly may be clung to as rights. We bring these phenomena together, as Taylor did, to account for the psychological resistance which often arises against job evaluation in general or against a particular description of job content. If there are many jobs whose loci lie without the limit lines, their descriptions, ratings, and perhaps the whole structure should be reviewed as to facts and practicality. If there are relatively few overpaid jobs they are usually left alone pending upgrading or "separation" of the job holders. These would not, however, benefit from a general wage rise if such should come to pass. The jobs whose loci are below the lower limit line should be revised upward as promptly as practicable. Both the ultimate decreases and the immediate increases may be included in making a trial payroll as a check on the structure. This trial should not run more than 5 per cent away from the existing one.

Job contents change continuously and until an official system is established to take care of changes it is possible that a foreman may have made some classification change by virtue of old habits. Perhaps some learner rates have been mixed in with regular rates and the average rate for a job class has been lowered thereby. If the records correspond perfectly with actual facts and there is still excessive irregularity, the management must decide what is to be changed, how, and when. This is a considerable problem for management until routines for all possible contingencies are arranged and in operation. This period of transition is also trying for the employees concerned. Although demotions will usually be barred by the agreement, transfers usually are not. Promotion, the best solution for overpaid individuals, is not a simple matter. If a sequential job can be opened there remains the training, breaking in, etc., which costs the employer money and the employee nervous strain if not loss in earning. The latter can at least be spared by use of a temporary guarantee. If there are many candidates for higher classification, some must be left where they have been despite overpay until openings occur. Some, of course, will not be promotable in any length of time and their unearned differentials should be looked upon as the penalty of earlier mismanagement. To isolate the data underlying this problem it is helpful to set up an Overpaid-Underpaid Record (Figure 123) on which the names of all individuals who are receiving rates outside the limits may be listed down the center in order of job worths and the dates of their last rate changes inserted under the appropriate cents column. Such a record may be made monthly until the list shrinks to zero.

Readjustment of Whole Structure. It may happen, we hope rarely, that a whole rate structure will come under criticism. This is most likely to occur toward the end of installation when numerous employees discover that their jobs are scheduled for reduction. In the case we are about to describe the current holders of such jobs were protected by an agreement against any cut themselves; nevertheless, they took a sudden dislike to the plan. The management had not ignored its employees during the development of the plan; in fact, it had consistently sought employee opinion and foreman concurrence in the job measurement. All seemed well until one of the consultant's men made a high-handed comment, so it was alleged. Suspicion was aroused and it looked as though the six months' work of development might be to no avail. Figure 124a shows the existing rates plotted against the new worth evaluations. Note that the union had already achieved rather high and uniform differentials. This fact alone might have caused some prejudice against the proposed rates with differentials to fit seventeen job classes as in Figure 124b. The union laid out a new structure with a few less classes, which might have been a good compromise, but it staked a higher trend line, which management objected to. There were several proposals and counter-proposals centering around the top rate and the amount of payroll increase involved. Then the

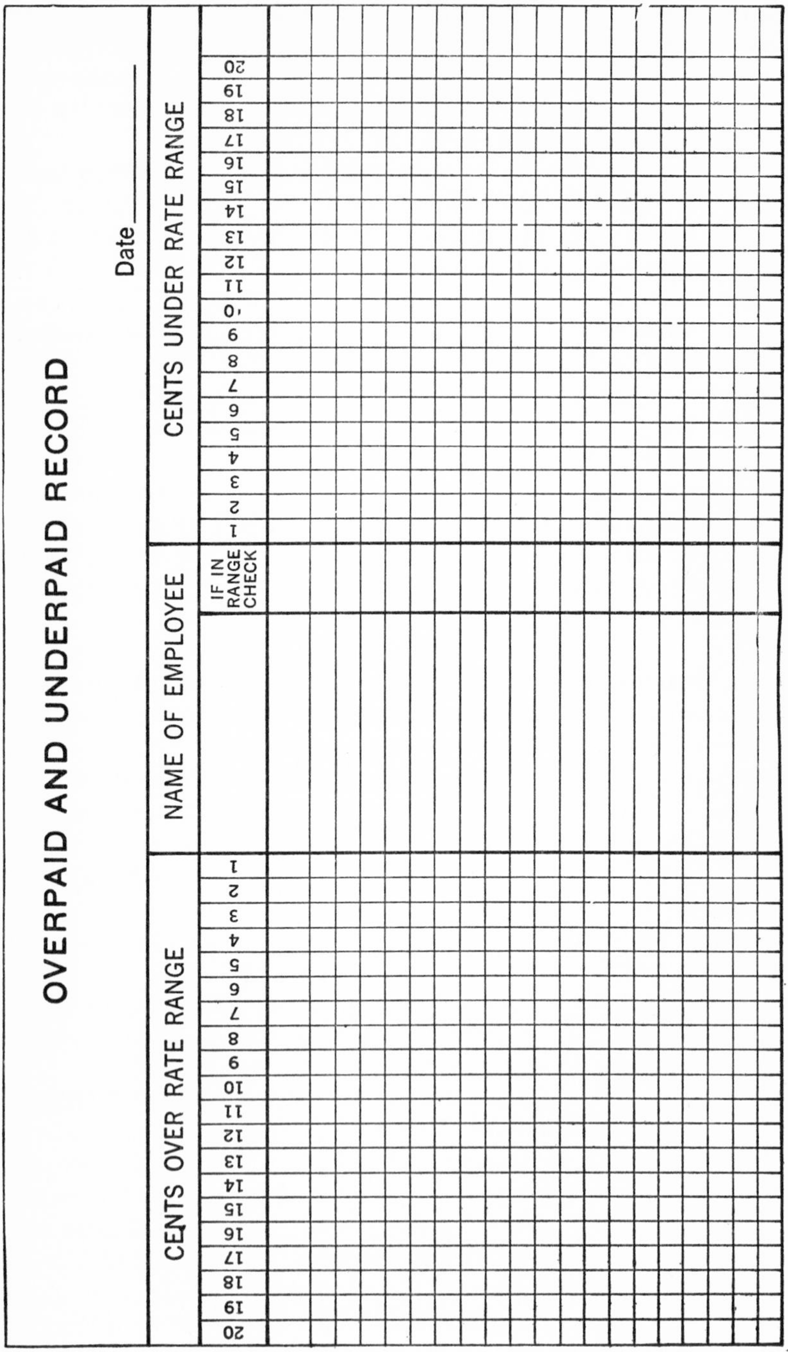

OVERPAID AND UNDERPAID RECORD

Date________

CENTS OVER RATE RANGE																				NAME OF EMPLOYEE		CENTS UNDER RATE RANGE																			
20	19	18	17	16	15	14	13	12	11	10	9	8	7	6	5	4	3	2	1		IF IN RANGE CHECK	1	2	3	4	5	6	7	8	9	10	11	12	13	14	15	16	17	18	19	20

FIGURE 123. OVERPAID AND UNDERPAID RECORD. (A modified N.M.T.A. form.)

local union repudiated the job evaluation in entirety and proposed a job "classification" of its own (Figure 124c). This was made in figures only so that visualization was missed. We believe the union never would have made its classification so unreasonable if it had seen the proportions graphically.

When the case was referred to a panel of the National War Labor Board it looked hopeless but analysis disclosed that the union had adhered to the new job worths more than it itself was aware and here the statistics gave insight to the graphs. The portions of the graphs which were most unreasonable included but a minority of the jobs. When this was realized it was possible to reconstruct the rate structure and meet the most essential wishes of both parties. The nonconforming jobs were re-sorted, some higher, some lower than the union had proposed, and a compromise structure was made (Figure 124d). In this structure we changed only 30 out of 173 jobs from their positions in the union classification, which amounted to an addition of $256.80 to the weekly payroll, to be distributed among 163 men. Many of these jobs were left as "strays" extending beyond the recommended worth limits. These extensions were contrary to good rate structure and were not intended to be left indefinitely but rather to be readjusted by the evaluation committee or, failing that, by bargaining. We were aware that such forced re-evaluation is contrary to the principles of job evaluation but as we stated at the end of the chapter on classification, we believe that job evaluation is not a science; when the results are protested honestly by any of the parties concerned it behooves those parties to get together, whatever the affront may be to normal rules. In this particular case it was rule of reason or obliteration of the whole evaluation. In the compromise 82½ per cent of the original evaluations were followed as to sequence and, best of all, the practice of systematic evaluation was given another trial. As C. R. Dooley has said, "in the last analysis the item of most importance is that all parties concerned agree to the grouping."

Day-to-Day Operation. When a rate structure and all that has preceded it is accepted the creative contributions to the program will be completed and the responsibility for applying the program can be taken over by other functionaries. Anticipating this change in requirements, the top steering committee would already have prepared one of the analysts, preferably the best one, to assume the continuing leadership as chief of the wage and salary administration. The steering committee should not, however, be disbanded, but retained to answer questions of policy. That it can do by meet-

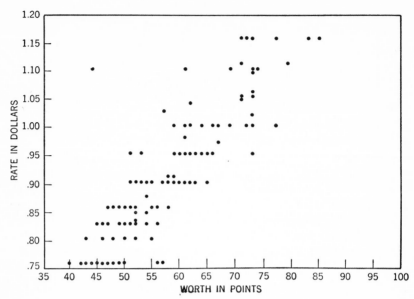

FIGURE 124*a*. SCATTER OF JOB LOCI BEFORE RATE CHANGE

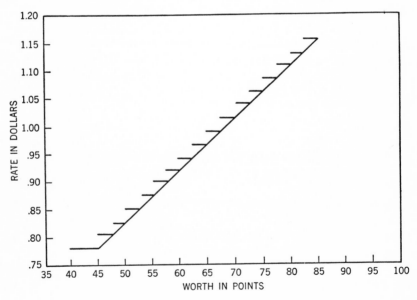

FIGURE 124*b*. RECOMMENDATION OF CONSULTANT

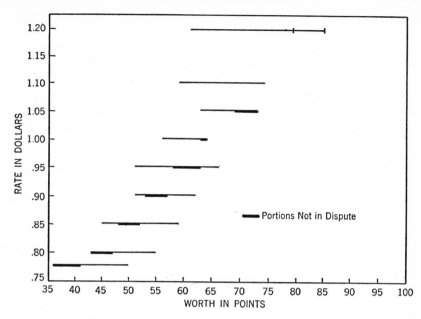

FIGURE 124c. UNION ATTEMPT AT "CLASSIFICATION"

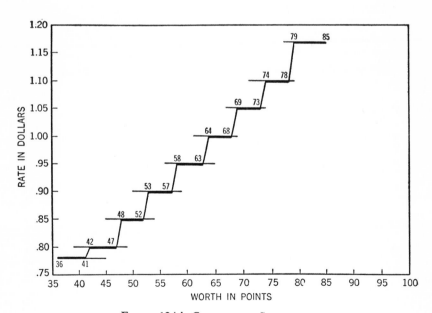

FIGURE 124d. COMPROMISE STRUCTURE

ing semiannually or on call. Most of the problems that remain can be solved within the limits of set policy and by the head of the division. Nevertheless, some companies have further use for committees, mainly to handle vexing questions of revision or reclassification. Such a committee may be called the Job Rate Reviewing Committee or Reclassification Committee. It may include: the plant superintendent, the personnel director, an industrial engineer, and perhaps someone from the payroll group. The head of the Wage and Salary Administration may be the chairman. If reclassification is covered by a union agreement as it often is there would be union representation on the committee. In either case they may meet regularly or on call. If there is only one such committee and its scope of activity is broad it may need to meet once a week, but bi-monthly or quarterly is usually sufficient. As promptly as practicable it should establish rules of procedure. For instance, to be eligible for reclassification the rule may require that the employee must be regularly doing at least 75 per cent of his work in the class in which he is to be reclassified. Second, if it has been necessary to transfer a man temporarily to a lower class job, such a man continues to receive his higher rate, but if he is not back on the higher class work by the time of the second merit rating period his transfer must be considered as a permanent reclassification. This means that he must change back at once or take the regular rate for that class. To be eligible for a rate increase a recommendation should come from the employee's immediate supervisor and should be approved by the head of Wage and Salary Administration. A. L. Kress gives four tests for approval:

1. What is the man's job?
2. Is the recommendation within the approved rate ranges for the job?
3. What does the man's record show?
4. When was his last increase?

Forms for Operating. Obviously several forms are needed, one of which, the job classification record, has already been described (see Chapter 9, Figure 87). All employees holding the same job are listed by name and their hourly rates are shown for the current period and for the period preceding, as per dates. The allowable rate range for the job is in view above the individual rates so that it can be seen readily whether or not anyone's rate has gotten out of line. The N.M.T.A. calls this checking a "perpetual inventory" of manpower and stresses its importance. All accessions, changes in status, dismissals, and the like must be added or subtracted on the cards for the jobs involved. Figure 125 provides a routine form for notifying all concerned. When a request for increase or transfer comes through with recommendation it can be considered in the light of all the facts pertaining to the jobs as well as the facts pertaining to the individual person. Only in rare instances should these be approved if by so doing the individual's rate is to be thrown out of the specified range. Promotion, of course, need not violate any range since that means a change in job class.

EMPLOYEE CHANGE NOTICE DATE

NAME DEPT. CLOCK NO.

☐ RATE CHANGE ☐ QUIT ☐ DISCHARGE ☐ MILITARY ☐ LAID OFF

NEW RATE EFFECTIVE DATE

REASONS EXPLAIN IN DETAIL

GRADE ✓

EXCELLENT

GOOD

FAIR

POOR

REHIRE O.K.?

NEW CLASSIFICATION

PRESENT RATE

PRESENT CLASSIFICATION

DUTIES AND OR RESPONSIBILITIES

LAST INCREASE

DATE

NEXT LAST INCREASE

DATE

FOREMAN OR SUPERVISOR

(SIGN FULL NAME NOT INITIALS)

HIRING DATE

APPROVED BY

HIRING RATE

CLASSIFICATION

DISTRIBUTION—White-Payroll, Yellow-Personnel, Pink-Dept. Head, Tan-Timekeeper, Blue-Union

FIGURE 125. EMPLOYEE CHANGE NOTICE.

For large companies where there are large numbers of employees per job it is better to leave the employee's names off the job classification record (Figure 126), and provide separate cards for the job holder's records. In that case there is room for the job ratings on the front and for the job description on the back of the card. These job cards are indexed by job classes and the employee classification records of different color (Figure 127) can be filed back of their respective job cards. See also Figure 141.

Hiring Rates. We have already shown graphically in Chapter 11 (Figures 106 and 107) how minimum rates are established for starting learners who know very little about their jobs. The second of these arrangements is by far the more satisfactory one because it schedules all advances according to predetermined time periods. That these "escalator" arrangements may be automatic without fail

JOB CLASSIFICATION RECORD

Date ____________ Job Code No. ____________

Department ____________

Job Name Class Labor Grade Total Points

EDUCATION					EXPERIENCE		EFFORT		RESPONSIBILTY				JOB CON'D	
Grades	High School	Blue Prints	Trades Training	Appren- ticeship	Months	Years	Physical	Mental	Equip.	Material	Safety Others	Work Others	Work Conditions	Unavoidable Hazards

RATE RANGE

Effective Date													
Minimum													
Maximum													

Figure 126. Job Record; Worth, Class, and Range. (A modified N.M.T.A. form.)

DATE	JOB CODE NO.	JOB NAME	DEPT	SHIFT	GRADE PTS.	GRADE	RATE RANGE	RATE	RATING	GROUP

EMPLOYEE CLASSIFICATION RECORD

Name of Employee_____   Clock No _____

Date of Employment_____

FIGURE 127. EMPLOYEE RECORD OF JOBS HELD. (A modified N.M.T.A. form.)

it is desirable to keep a tickler file showing every person who is due an advance on the move-up dates. Fully qualified accessions are also frequently hired below the minimum rates, but if the time needed for breaking in or for trial is very short the company policy or the agreement should call for the minimum at time of placement. Where skills are considerable it is common practice to hire at the rate for one grade below and automatically bring the individual to par through one, two, three, or four predetermined time steps. These vary as to total time from one to nine months. For probation alone, unions usually allow from one to two months, during which time the employer can dismiss an unsatisfactory probationer without being questioned by the union or he may be demoted to a lower-class job for which he is adequately qualified.

Production Rates for Incentive-Paid Jobs. Paying in terms of productivity or efficiency presupposes a quantity task and the rule is to set the rate per unit of quantity so that there will be an incentive of some agreed-upon percentage above the hourly base rate at the task efficiency. Since the average efficiency of an all-skilled incentive-paid group is well established at 114-115 per cent of "high task," it may be advantageous to ascertain the proper earning for 115 per cent efficiency. But even if that is the starting point it is simple to prorate the proper earning for 100 per cent efficiency. Obviously the concept of high task itself needs checking by this same fact, that is, do your best incentive-paid operatives average close to 114-115 per cent? If they do not, the chances are that your task is higher, or more likely lower, than the Taylor-Gantt task. If such a group is averaging 120 per cent you should find the proportion, 120 : 115 :: 100 : x, in which x = 96. In short, your task is 96 per cent of the traditional high task. Similarly if the group is averaging 110 per cent, the proportion will be 110 : 115 :: 100 : x, in which case your task is 104 per cent. If you are intentionally using the "low task" and a sharing earning line you can check that by prorating the high task, 100 per cent, to low task 60 per cent to

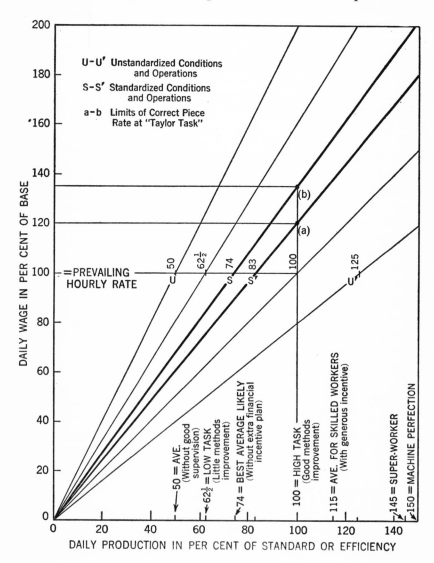

FIGURE 128. STRAIGHT PIECE RATE

65 per cent, say 62½ per cent, but there is no generally accepted average for operatives working under any sharing plan; there are too many variables. An additional check lies in the fact that the efficiency of a hypothetical operative who keeps up with a mechanical capacity is 150 per cent of high task. To use this, however, you must have some machine that runs evenly all day and which must be hand-tended constantly. The nearest approach to this "machine perfection" that we ever found was an exceptional female operator of a buttonholing machine. She held at 145 per cent efficiency compared to the machine's potential of 150 per cent but she was a veritable adjunct to the machine and such "super-workers" are rare.

How to Set a Correct Piece or Standard Hour Rate. Our pioneer industrial engineers spread earning curves all over the map but the best of them agreed perfectly on one thing. They all found that you must pay 120 per cent of the prevailing hourly rate to hold skilled operatives at 100 per cent high task. From this experiential point they projected back to the origin to locate the piece rate earning line. Thus they found, or would have found if they had used graphs, that the correct piece rate line passes through the (83–100) point, i.e., the "academic task" for (120–100) piece rate is 83 per cent efficiency relative to 100 per cent high task, (a) (Figure 128). We say academic task because there is no task designation with piece rate unless you happen to use the bonus type of formula for it.[1]

Lacking any task designation we hereby establish one, solely for management. That is not all, however, for a union may be smart and strong enough to ask for 125 per cent to 135 per cent of prevailing time payment at high task. Hence we must add another academic task and have dual limits. This we derive by taking the highest demand of 135 per cent and projecting a piece rate line from point (100–135) to the origin, (b) (Figure 131). In this case the academic limit becomes 74 per cent of 100 per cent high task. Certainly all good piece rates should pass between these limits. In summary, check your task and put on a graph whatever percentage you derive: 96 per cent, 100 per cent, or 104 per cent, etc. Then locate points (74–100) and (83–100). If your piece rate lies between these it is at least within the outside limits of present-day standardized practice. If it falls to the left it has too loose a task and will be too steep a pay slope. If it lies to the right it has too tight a task and too stingy a slope. Neither of these conditions can give mutual satisfaction. We consider this guide one of the most

[1] See the author's *Wage Incentive Methods*, 1944 or later printings.

important aids we can offer toward harmonious relations. It should shorten if not obviate many a negotiation.

Periodic Checks. We disapprove anything that might be interpreted as a means of limiting earning and we rejoice in the warning of Theodore Roosevelt that "nothing is more vicious in a democracy than to pay equal wages for unequal work," but we think it desirable to compile monthly data on all "take-home" for incentive-paid employees and for all time-paid employees. This is legally necessary where there is overtime and it should be done in all cases. Earnings that are above expectations must not be cut back merely because they are high, but any erratic figures may have symptomatic significance. If they are low there may be obstacles which management should uncover and remove, or perhaps a foreman has failed to report an upgrade in classification. If any earnings are surprisingly high there may have been mistakes in overclassification or overrating.

Tasks tend to loosen because of accumulating improvements in method. When the total of improvement is "substantial" the labor agreement should and usually does allow a job to be restudied. It is much better to investigate and correct the tasks regularly at least once a year than to neglect them for a while and then clean house. At the same time a truly honest management should watch out for employees who have not had their rightful advances; be sure they are doing the jobs on which they are classified. Of course the union will usually take care of this but why wait for a grievance? Similarly an honest union should not resist restudy of a substantially changed job. A good questionnaire for this is shown in Figure 129. Both parties should check wage scales periodically and cooperate in making adjustments to the current wage levels. In the case of minor market changes all that is necessary is to alter the rate range on the Job Classification Record and put it into application. In the case of numerous and considerable market changes a new scatter diagram or "correlation chart" may be necessary and in the extreme case a whole new rate structure is due. Probably that should be done biannually or at least every five years (see Figure 130).

Processing of Rate Changes. In the foregoing paragraphs we have explained why it is an essential duty of the wage and salary administration division to check every proposed rate change against the job classification and against previous rate changes. In "processing" this work each employee classification record must be checked to ascertain the frequency of changes and to stamp each card as to cause of change, such as, merit gain, promotion, etc. Only by complete recording will the division be able to assure top management that policies are being maintained. Routine can be established through which changes in jobs will be automatically reported to all concerned but in practice no processing is perfect and the following events may be used as occasions for recheck:

1. When employment requisition comes in.
2. When employee requests a restudy.
3. When management requests a restudy.
4. When employee is reviewed for merit rating.
5. When staff is caught up with new work.

Some companies go at this hit or miss, others schedule a certain number of jobs per week. There seems to be no universal practice but rechecking must be done and the interval should not be many months where changes are likely to occur. Not only should jobs be checked for change of content, inadequacy of description and records, but also for changes in merit rating of the job holders. In all cases have in mind company policy and check to see how faithfully that is being followed.

New Jobs. Changes in product, process, equipment, and method all create new jobs, some completely new but most of them simplified from older jobs. Psychologically the latter are the more difficult because they may still be recognizable as partly identical or similar to yesterday's jobs, in fact, they may go by titles that have not yet been revised. Motion study engineers and rate analysts may have new instruction sheets, new element times, new descriptions, and new point weightings, but the employees from shop steward to operator must also be enlightened. There are few shop questions today more difficult than this one concerning when an old job has become a different job. The coverage in the agreement relies on such words as "substantial change" or "material change" and always there is need of a convincing determination. We recall an arbitration case where by one issue the union denied a substantial change for certain jobs and by a second issue it insisted that all of another group of jobs ought to be restudied. Of course those issues were affected by a larger strategy but they were made possible by the illusive nature of the agreement wording plus the lack of any positive criteria on which to determine the right of restudy. Like everybody else we see little hope of a criterion other than an agreement that the change in job content shall be enough in points to alter the classification or in the case of an unevaluated but incentive-paid job the new standard time shall be a certain percentage below the

Rate ☐   Desc. ☐

Factory ☐   U ☐   C ☐

NC: Yes ☐   No ☐

'54: Yes ☐   No ☐

RESTUDY JOB QUESTIONNAIRE

Job Title..........................Code No.........Rate Range........

Paid LG....Point Range......: Eval. Points....LG....Point Range........

Date of Investigation...............Analyst............................

Using Departments.......................................Over 10   ☐

Total Number of Employees in Classification............................

Persons Contacted..

....

I. Has there been a material change in the assignments or duties of the
incumbents: Yes ☐   No ☐
Duties added or deleted—when?

II. Does the job description adequately cover the present assignments of
incumbents: Yes ☐   No ☐
Revised job description attached   ☐

Explain:

III. Miscellaneous comments: (Include position taken by operating management,
turnover problems, etc.)

(Use reverse side for additional comments)

FIGURE 129. FORM FOR RESTUDYING JOB CONTENT.

Job Title...

IV. Area Rates

Lockheed Rates are: Average ☐, Above Average ☐, Below Average ☐

Survey:

Company or Area Survey	Job Title	Rate Range *

* All rates include cost of living

Comments:

V. Evaluation—Factory Plan

Analyst or Job Factor	Deg.	Pts.	Deg.	Pts.	Deg.	Pts.	Deg.	Pts.	Deg.	Pts.	Deg.	Pts.	Deg.	Pts.
Skill														
Ment.														
Resp.														
Ment. Appl.														
Phy. Appl.														
Job Cond.														
Occ. Haz.														
L.G. & Total														
Rate Range														

(Lockheed Aircraft Corporation.)

PERFORMANCE AND SALARY REVIEW

RANGE NUMBER ____ OCCUPATION ____ GRADE ____ RATE RANGE: MIN. ____ CONTROL ____ MAX. ____ DATE ____

ORGANIZATION CODE	EMPLOYEE NUMBER	EMPLOYEE NAME	MAR. STA.	YR. OF BIRTH	DATE HIRED			CONSID. MONTH	ELIGIBLE FROM		LAST TWO INCREASES *						PRESENT RATE
					MO.	DAY	YR.		MO.	YR.	MO.	YR.	AMOUNT	MO.	YR.	AMOUNT	
FOR REVIEW:																	
FOR COMPARISON:																	
		AVERAGES: GROUP															
		COMPANY-WIDE															

RECOMMENDATION

TYPE OF INCREASE:
END OF PROBATION____ FIRST ANNIV.____ MERIT____
(Use Form 900 to initiate any other salary change.)

AMOUNT OF INCREASE: $________
(If no increase is recommended, indicate "None.")

RATING OF EMPLOYEE:
OUTSTANDING____ ABOVE AVERAGE____
AVERAGE____ UNSATISFACTORY____

FURTHER EXPLANATION:________

SIGNATURES

Recommendation ____ Date

Inter-approval or review ____ Date

Inter-approval or review ____ Date

Inter-approval or review ____ Date

Final approval ____ Date

Form 2884 Rev. 3-51

* 999 in amount column indicates decrease

FIGURE 130. FORM FOR ANNUAL REVIEW. (The Ohio Oil Company.)

old standard time. The latter is unascertainable without a restudy unless all are content with a synthetic task taken from standard data.

When a job is jointly accepted as new it is a simple matter to find its proper location among the old jobs. As we have mentioned previously, this can be established by repeating the process of indirect evaluation, that is, by measurement against the degree definitions or by direct evaluation through characteristic comparison. The latter technique is used by almost everybody, particularly if the job in question can be considered one of any known family of jobs. If it is a case of separating an old job into simpler jobs the data of job description should be especially helpful because thereby everyone will see how the worths can be less in divided parts than in the more general mixture. The reverse or combination of simple jobs may also happen if a company is reducing its scale of operations. With the tempo of tool and method improvement high as it is in most American industries it is well to look for substantial changes in the content of all jobs eventually. Hence an alert management may schedule the review of job descriptions so that all of them will be reconsidered in two, three, or at most five years.

Policy Regarding Classification of Employees. Policies regarding wage rates, hiring, transfer, promotion, etc., are limited on the one side by legislation and on the other by negotiated agreements. As the agreements vary widely it is hard to say what arrangements are typical. The example below probably is not typical as yet but it comes from a five-year contract which has been heralded as "epoch-making".[2]

The following excerpts are printed with the permission of the General Motors Corporation and by courtesy of the International Union, United Automobile, Aircraft, and Agricultural Implement Workers of America, CIO.

SENIORITY AND ADJUSTMENTS

(59a) When changes in methods, products, or policies would otherwise require the permanent laying off of employes, the seniority of the displaced employes shall become plant-wide and they shall be transferred out of the group in line with their seniority to work they are capable of doing, as comparable to the work they have been doing as may be available, at the rate for the job to which they have been transferred.

[2] Charles E. Wilson, "Progress Sharing Can Mean Industrial Peace," *Readers Digest,* September, 1952.

(61a) Each two months the Chairman of the Shop Committee shall be furnished a list of the names and seniority dates of employes who during the preceding period of two months have: (a) Acquired Seniority (b) Lost Seniority (c) Been granted leaves of absence for military service (d) Been granted other types of leaves of absence of more than sixty (60) days' duration.

(62) When an employe is transferred from one occupational group to another for any reason, there shall be no loss of seniority. However, in cases of transfers not exceeding sixty (60) days, an employe will retain his seniority in the occupational group from which he was transferred and not in the new occupational group, unless a longer period is specified for any plant or particular occupational group or groups by written local agreement.

(63) The transferring of employes is the sole responsibility of Management subject to the following: (a) In the advancement of employes to higher paid jobs when ability, merit, and capacity are equal, employes with the longest seniority will be given preference. (b) It is the policy of Management to cooperate in every practical way with employes who desire transfers to new positions or vacancies in their department. Accordingly, such employes who make application to their foremen or the Personnel Department stating their desires, qualifications and experience, will be given preference for openings in their department provided they are capable of doing the job. However, employes who have made application as provided for above and who are capable of doing the job available shall be given preference for the openings in their department over new hires. Any secondary job openings resulting from filling jobs pursuant to this provision may be filled through promotion; or through transfer without regard to seniority standing, or by new hire.

Any claim of personal prejudice or any claim of discrimination for Union activity in connection with transfers may be taken up as a grievance. Such claims must be supported by written evidence submitted within 48 hours from the time the grievance is filed.

In plants where departments are too small or in other cases where the number of job classifications within a department is insufficient to permit the practical application of this paragraph, arrangements whereby employes may make such application for transfer out of their department may be negotiated locally, subject to approval by the Corporation and the International Union.

CALL-IN PAY

(80) Any employe called to work or permitted to come to work without having been properly notified that there will be no work, shall receive a minimum of four hours' pay at the regular hourly rate, except in case of labor disputes, or other conditions beyond the control of the local Management.

WORKING HOURS

(For the purposes of computing overtime premium pay)

r the purposes of computing overtime premium pay, the regular
' is eight hours and the regular working week is forty hours.

(82) Employes will be compensated on the basis of the calendar day (midnight to midnight) on which their shift starts working, for the regular working hours of that shift. The employe's working week shall be a calendar week beginning on Monday at the regular starting time of the shift to which he is assigned.

(83) Hourly and piece-rate employes will be compensated as follows:

Straight Time

(84a) For the first eight hours worked in any continuous twenty-four hour period, beginning with the starting time of the employe's shift. (b) For the first forty hours worked in the employe's working week, less all time for which daily, sixth day, Sunday, or holiday overtime has been earned. (c) For time worked during the regular working hours of any shift which starts on the day before and continues into a specified holiday, sixth day, or Sunday.

Time and One Half

(85a) For time worked in excess of eight hours in any continuous twenty-four hours, beginning with the starting time of the employe's shift, except if such time is worked on a Sunday or holiday when double time will be paid as provided below. (b) For time worked in excess of forty hours in the employe's working week, less all time for which daily, sixth day, Sunday, or holiday overtime has been earned. (c) For time worked on the sixth day of the employe's work week, provided, however, that if the employe has lost time for personal reasons not to exceed eight hours per day during the first five days of the work week, he shall be paid straight time for work on such sixth day until such lost time has been made up. In addition to time not worked for personal reasons, time not worked during the first five days of the work week for the reasons listed below shall be considered as time lost for personal reasons in computing sixth day overtime: 1. Leaves of absence, formal and informal. 2. Disciplinary layoff. 3. New employes hired. 4. Employes with seniority rehired or recalled after a layoff of 30 days or more. 5. Layoff due to inventory requiring 4 or more days of the work week. 6. Strikes in same plant covered by this agreement.

Personal reasons, however, shall not include the following provided the employe had been properly excused for such purposes: 7. Induction requirements of the draft boards. 8. Hospitalization. 9. Other medical reasons.

Double Time

(86) For time worked during the regular working hours of any shifts that start on Sundays, and the following legal holidays: New Year's Day, Fourth of July, Labor Day, Thanksgiving, Christmas, and either Memorial Day or one other such holiday of greater local importance which must be designated in advance by mutual agreement locally in writing, and any time worked in excess of eight hours on a shift which starts the previous day and runs over into such Sunday or holiday.

(87) Employes working in necessary continuous seven-day operations whose occupations involve work on Saturdays and Sundays shall be paid time and

one half for work on these days only for time worked in excess of eight hours per day or in excess of forty hours in the employe's working week, for which overtime has not already been earned, except as otherwise provided in paragraphs (*a*), (*b*) and (*c*) below: (*a*) Such employes shall be paid time and one-half for hours worked on the employe's sixth work day in the week, provided that if the employe has lost time for personal reasons not to exceed eight hours per day in the preceding days in the week, he shall be paid straight time on the sixth work day until such lost time has been made up. (*b*) Such employes shall be paid double time for hours worked on the 7th consecutive day worked in the calendar week under the following conditions: (1) The 7th consecutive day of work results from the employe being required to work on his scheduled off day in that calendar week. (2) If the employe has lost time for personal reasons not to exceed 8 hours per day during the first six days of the calendar week he shall be paid straight time or time and one-half as the case may be on the 7th day until such lost time has been made up. (*c*) Such employes will be paid double time for hours worked during the regular working hours of any shifts that start on any of the six legal holidays listed in Paragraph 86. In the case of employes who work 6 or 7 days during the work week, the first 8 hours worked at double time on shifts starting on such holidays shall be counted in computing overtime for work in excess of 40 hours in the employe's working week.

Premium payments shall not be duplicated for the same hours worked under any of the terms of this Section.

Change in Shift Hours

(88) Any change in the established shift hours or lunch period shall be first discussed with the Shop Committee as far in advance as possible of any such change.

(89) A night shift premium of five per cent of night shift earnings, including overtime premium, will be paid to all hourly rated employes working on shifts half or more of the working hours of which are scheduled between the hours of 6:00 p.m. and 6:00 a.m.; except that in the case of three shift operations, employes working on third shifts regularly scheduled to start between the hours of 10:00 p.m. and 4:45 a.m. will receive a night shift premium of seven and one-half per cent of night shift earnings, including overtime, for all hours worked. Employes working on special shifts not covered by the above, wherein half or more of the regular straight time working hours are scheduled between the hours of 12 midnight and 8:45 a.m. shall be paid seven and one-half per cent premium of night shift earnings, including overtime, for all hours worked.

For the purpose of calculating shift premium, overtime on a regularly scheduled shift shall be considered as part of that shift except as otherwise provided in the following paragraph.

In two shift operations where the second shift is regularly scheduled to work more than nine hours, and the shift is regularly scheduled to work until or beyond 3:00 a.m., employes working on such shifts shall receive seven and one-half per cent premium of night shift earnings, including overtime, for all hours worked after 12 midnight.

WAGE PAYMENT PLANS

(90) Wage payment plans are a matter of local negotiation between the Plant Managements and the Shop Committees, subject to appeal in accordance with the Grievance Procedure.

(91) Any change from an incentive plan to an hourly rate method of pay is a matter for local determination and any such changes must be made on a sound and equitable basis which does not increase average production costs, and which provides for maintaining efficiency of the plant.

WAGES

(97) The establishment of wage scales for each operation is necessarily a matter for local negotiation and agreement between the Plant Managements and the Shop Committees, on the basis of the local circumstances affecting each operation, giving consideration to the relevant factors of productivity, continuity of employment, the general level of wages in the community, and the wages paid by competitors.

(98) Wage rates for women shall be set in accordance with the principle of equal pay for comparable quantity and quality of work on comparable operations. Any dispute arising as to the question of quality, quantity, or comparability, as herein defined shall be settled within the procedural framework of the grievance provision in the Agreement. In application of this Paragraph the Parties shall be guided by Appendix A. (Wage Rates for Female Employes.)

(99) New employes shall be hired at a rate no lower than ten (10) cents below the rate of the job classification and shall receive an automatic increase of five (5) cents at the expiration of thirty (30) days. Every employe who is retained by the Corporation in the job classification shall receive an increase to the rate for the job classification within ninety (90) days or as soon as he or she can meet the standard requirements for an average employe on the job, whichever occurs first, provided however, that deviation from the above rule may be made pursuant to negotiation between the local Shop Committees and local Managements, for jobs requiring more than ninety (90) days to attain average proficiency. The foregoing paragraph shall not apply to tool and die rooms or to any job classification previously covered by upgrading agreements.

(100) It is understood that local wage agreements consist of the wage scale by job classification as set up by Paragraph 98 and as submitted to the Shop Committee in accordance with Paragraph 99 of the June 3, 1941 Agreement, and any negotiated local wage agreements or additions thereto.

(101a) The *annual improvement factor* provided herein recognizes that a continuing improvement in the standard of living of employes depends upon technological progress, better tools, methods, processes, and equipment, and a cooperative attitude on the part of all parties in such principle that to produce more with the same amount of human effort is a sound economic and social objective. Accordingly, all employes covered by this agreement shall receive an increase of 4 cents per hour, effective May 29, 1950, and an additional increase of 4 cents per hour annually on May 29, 1951, May 29,

1952, May 29, 1953 (then raised to 5 cents) and May 29, 1954, which will be added to the base rate of each wage classification. (*b*) In addition, the cost-of-living allowance formula (which was provided for in the previous National Agreement between the parties) will be continued, and such allowances shall be determined in accordance with the provisions of this Paragraph 101.

It is agreed that only the cost-of-living allowance will be subject to reduction so that, if a sufficient decline in the cost of living occurs, employes will immediately enjoy a better standard of living. Such an improvement will be an addition to the annual improvement factor provided for in 101 (*a*).

(*c*) The improvement factor increases in base rates provided for in Paragraph 101 (*a*) shall be added to the wage rates (minimum, intermediary, and maximum) for each day-work classification. The cost-of-living allowance provided for in Paragraph 101 (*b*) shall be added to each employe's straight time hourly earnings and will be adjusted up or down each three months in line with the cost-of-living allowance provided for in Paragraphs 101 (*f*) and 101 (*g*). (*d*) In the case of employes on an incentive basis of pay the increases in base rates provided for in Paragraph 101 (*a*) shall be added to the earned rate of all incentive workers until local Plant Managements and the local Unions reach an agreement for factoring this increase into the wage structure of incentive classifications. The cost-of-living allowance provided for in Paragraph 101 (*b*) shall be added to each employe's hourly earned rate and will be adjusted up or down each three months in line with the cost-of-living allowance provided for in Paragraph 101 (*f*) and 101 (*g*). (*e*) The Cost-of-Living Allowance will be determined in accordance with changes in the "Consumers' Price Index for Moderate Income Families in Large Cities"—"All Items," published by the Bureau of Labor Statistics, U. S. Department of Labor (1935–1939 = 100) and hereafter referred to as the BLS Consumers' Price Index.* (*f*) The Cost-of-Living Allowance as determined in Paragraph 101 (*b*) beginning with the first pay period following June 1, 1950, shall continue in effect until the first pay period beginning after September 1, 1950. At that time, and thereafter during the period of this Agreement, adjustments shall be made quarterly at the following times:

* "Old Series" Consumers' Price Indexes are being compiled for the months January–June 1953, at the direction of the President and the Secretary of Labor, to facilitate orderly transition to use of the Revised Index in wage escalator clauses under collective agreements. The Bureau of Labor Statistics has no authorization or appropriation to continue the "Old Series" beyond the June Index (issued at the end of July). The Revised Index only will be issued thereafter, on the 1935–39 = 100 base as well as on the official 1947–49 = 100 base period.

For a description of the Revised Index, see "The Consumers' Price Index—A Short Description of the Index as Revised, 1953." For discussion of the arithmetic problems of transition from the "Old Series" to the Revised for wage contract purposes, see "The Revised Consumers' Price Index—A Summary of Changes in the Index and Suggestions for Transition from the 'Interim Adjusted' and 'Old Series' Indexes to the Revised Index."

Effective Date of Adjustment	*Based Upon*
First Pay Period Beginning on or after:	BLS Consumers' Price Index as of:
June 1, 1950 and at quarterly intervals thereafter to March 1, 1955.	April 15, 1950 and at quarterly intervals thereafter to January 15, 1955.

In no event will a decline in the BLS Consumers' Price Index below 164.7 provide the basis for a reduction in the wage scale by job classification. (g) The amount of the Cost-of-Living Allowance which shall be effective for any three-month period as provided in Paragraphs 101 (b) and 101 (f) shall be in accordance with the following table:

BLS Consumers' Price Index	*Cost-of-Living Allowance, In Addition to Wage Scale by Job Classification*
164.6 or less	None
164.7 – 165.8	1¢ per hour
165.9 – 166.9	2¢ per hour
167.0 – 168.1	3¢ per hour
168.2 – 169.2	4¢ per hour
169.3 – 170.3	5¢ per hour
170.4 – 171.5	6¢ per hour
171.6 – 172.6	7¢ per hour
172.7 – 173.8	8¢ per hour
173.9 – 174.9	9¢ per hour
175.0 – 176.0	10¢ per hour
176.1 – 177.2	11¢ per hour
177.3 – 178.3	12¢ per hour
178.4 – 179.5	13¢ per hour
179.6 – 180.6	14¢ per hour
180.7 – 181.7	15¢ per hour
181.8 – 182.9	16¢ per hour
183.0 – 184.0	17¢ per hour
184.1 – 185.2	18¢ per hour
185.3 – 186.3	19¢ per hour
186.4 – 187.4	20¢ per hour
187.5 – 188.6	21¢ per hour
188.7 – 189.7	22¢ per hour

and so forth, with 1¢ adjustment for each 1.14 point change in the Index.

h) The amount of any Cost-of-Living Allowance in effect at the time shall be included in computing overtime premium, night shift premium, vacation payments, holiday payments, and call-in pay. (i) In the event the Bureau of Labor Statistics does not issue the Consumers' Price Index on or before the beginning of the pay period referred to in Paragraph 101 (f), any adjustments required will be made at the beginning of the first pay period after receipt of the Index. (j) No adjustments, retroactive or otherwise, shall be made due to any revision which may later be made in the published figures for the BLS Consumers' Price Index for any base month. (k) The parties to this Agreement agree that the continuance of the Cost-of-Living Allowance is dependent upon the availability of the official monthly BLS Consumers' Price Index in its present form and calculated on the same basis as the Index for April, 1950, unless otherwise agreed upon by the parties. (l) The Memorandum of Understanding between the parties dated

August 24, 1949, shall become Appendix C and will continue in full force and effect during the life of the May 29, 1950 Agreement, unless terminated earlier in accordance with the provisions of said Memorandum.

New Jobs

(102) When new jobs are placed in production and cannot be properly placed in existing classifications by mutual agreement, Management will set up a new classification and a rate covering the job in question, and will designate it as temporary. 102(a) The temporary rate for such job shall be consistent with the terms of Paragraph 97 of this Agreement, and a copy of the temporary rate and classification name will be furnished to the Shop Committee. 102(b) The new classification and rate shall be considered temporary for a period of 30 calendar days following the date of notification to the Shop Committee. During this period (but not thereafter) the Shop Committee may request Management to negotiate the rate for the classification. The negotiated rate, if higher than the temporary rate, shall be applied retroactively to the date of the establishment of the temporary classification and rate except as otherwise mutually agreed. If no request has been made by the Union to negotiate the rate within the thirty (30) day period, or if, within sixty (60) days from the date of notification to the Shop Committee, no grievance is filed concerning the temporary classification and rate as provided below, or upon completion of negotiations, as the case may be, the temporary classification and rate shall become a part of the local wage agreement.

The following provisions of Paragraphs 102(c) through 102(e) shall apply to temporary classifications and rates established on or after the date of this Agreement.

102(c) If the Shop Committee requests Management to negotiate and the Shop Committee and Management are unable to agree on a classification and rate for the new job, the disputed rate and/or classification may be treated as a grievance. Such grievance may be filed at the Management-Shop Committee Step of the grievance procedure. If the grievance is still unresolved after it has been considered at the Third Step, it may be referred to the Personnel Staff of the Corporation and the General Motors Department of the International Union, for consideration. If the grievance is not resolved at this point, it may, by mutual agreement, be referred to the Impartial Umpire who shall be empowered to determine the proper classification and/or rate for the new job as provided herein. The classification and/or rate established by the Umpire shall become a part of the local wage agreement.

102(d) The Umpire's authority to establish a classification and/or rate shall be limited to new jobs in grievance cases submitted to the Umpire as provided above and his decision shall be limited to the area of dispute.

102(e) In determining the proper rate and/or classification for a new job, the Umpire shall be guided by the specific criteria stipulated and agreed to in writing by the parties hereto, in each individual case.

If after one year of experience, the provisions of Paragraph 102 through Paragraph 102(*e*) place an undue burden upon the parties or the Umpire, either party may, by written notice to the other party, terminate Paragraphs 102 through 102(*e*), in which event the provisions of Paragraph 102 through 102(*b*) of the former Agreement between the parties dated March 19, 1946, shall be automatically substituted therefor.

——

Grievances. Either a job evaluation program or a wage incentive plan can work well in one place and fail in another. Failure may be said generally to be due to different conditions, but better fitting of plans to conditions will not always guarantee success either. The matter of administration alone, personalities if you please, can do much to make or break any plan. Even when this is top-notch there are bound to be grievances. Various schemes have been devised through which employee and management views can be exchanged, many of them eminently successful. The one that predominates today, at least for a union shop, is the system of committees and paired representatives who are regularly authorized to receive and judicate grievances. A plant if large is divided into districts by agreement between the manager and a union-elected shop committee. In the large plants of General Motors Corporation each district includes about two hundred and fifty employees per shift. One union committeeman represents each of these districts and is called the district committeeman. There is also an alternate to act in his absence. Some or all of these union officers constitute the shop committee, which meets once a week or bi-weekly with the plant management. The committeemen are allowed a limited amount of time per week to spend on grievance work.

For details on the committeemen we refer the reader to the General Motors-U.A.W. Agreement of May 29, 1950, but from the same we print the four steps of the procedure in full, also the powers of the umpire.

——

GRIEVANCE PROCEDURE

Step One. Presentation of Grievance to Foreman

(28) Any employe having a grievance, or one designated member of a group having a grievance, should first take the grievance up with the foreman who will attempt to adjust it.

(29) Any employe may request the foreman to call the committeeman for that district to handle a specified grievance with the foreman. The foreman will send for the committeeman without undue delay and without further discussion of the grievance.

(30) If the grievance is not adjusted by the foreman, it shall be reduced to writing on forms provided by the Corporation, and signed by the employe involved and one copy shall be given to the foreman. The committeeman may then take the grievance up with higher supervision with or without another committeeman, according to the agreed local practice.

Step Two. Appeal to Shop Committee

(31) If the case is not adjusted at this step, it may be referred to the Shop Committee (or sub-committee where established).

(32) In plants in which sub-committees are established, cases not adjusted by the sub-committee and the representative of Management may be appealed to the Shop Committee as a whole to be taken up with the highest local Management.

(33) After a written grievance signed by the employe making the complaint has been appealed to the Shop Committee by a committeeman, the Chairman of the Shop Committee may designate one of its members to make a further investigation of the grievance in order to discuss the grievance properly when it is taken up by the Shop Committee at a meeting with the Management.

(34) A final decision on appealed grievances will be given by a representative of the highest local Management within a maximum of fifteen working days from the date of first written filing thereof unless a different time limit is established by local agreement in writing. Any grievance not appealed from a decision at one step of this procedure in the plant to the next step within five working days of such decision, shall be considered settled on the basis of the last decision and not subject to further appeal. However, in plants where there are less than twenty-five hundred employes, the Shop Committee may upon notifying the Plant Management in writing, substitute a ten (10) day period for the fifteen (15) day period and a three (3) day period for the five (5) day period. Provided further, however, that within the applicable time limits of this Paragraph a grievance may be withdrawn by mutual agreement without prejudice to either party.

(35) Written answers will be given by the Management to all written grievances presented by the Shop Committee.

(36) The question of supplying minutes of the Shop Committee meetings with the Management to the Shop Committee and the form of such minutes is a matter to be negotiated with the Management of each plant by the Committee involved. The minutes of regular Shop Committee meetings will be furnished to the Chairman of the Shop Committee within five (5) working days from the date of the meeting.

Such minutes should include: (1) Date of meeting. (2) Names of those present. (3) Statement of each grievance taken up and discussed, also, in summary fashion, of the Union's contention in the event of failure to adjust. (4) Management's written answer on each grievance, with reason for same if answer is adverse. (5) "Highlights" of the meeting, these including specific questions asked by the Committee on policy matters and any answers to such questions given by Management. (6) Date of approval, and signatures as agreed upon locally.

The above provisions shall not interfere with any mutually satisfactory local practice now in effect.

Step Three. Appeal to Corporation and International Union

(37) If the grievance is not adjusted at this step and the Shop Committee believes it has grounds for appeal from the Plant Management decision, the Chairman of the Shop Committee will give the Plant Management a written "Notice of Unadjusted Grievance," on forms supplied by the Corporation, and the Chairman or designated member of the Shop Committee will then prepare a complete "Statement of Unadjusted Grievance" setting forth all facts and circumstances surrounding the grievance, signed by the Chairman of the Shop Committee. The Plant Manager or his designated representative will also prepare a complete "Statement of Unadjusted Grievance" and the Management's reasons in support of the position taken, signed by the Plant Manager or his authorized representative. Three copies of the Union's statement will be exchanged with the Management for three copies of the Management's statement as soon as possible and in any event within five (5) working days after the Committee has given the Management the "Notice of Unadjusted Grievance," unless this time is extended by mutual agreement in writing. Each Shop Committee shall consecutively number each "Statement of Unadjusted Grievance" from one upward for identification purposes.

(38) The Chairman of the Shop Committee shall then forward copies of the "Statements of Unadjusted Grievance" to the Regional Director of the International Union. The Regional Director will review the case and determine if an appeal shall be made. The Regional Director or a specified representative and the Director of the General Motors Department of the International Union or a specified member of his staff will be granted permission to visit the plant for the purpose of investigating the specific grievance involved in "Statements of Unadjusted Grievance," providing such a grievance or investigation will aid in: (1) Arriving at a decision as to whether or not a grievance exists; (2) Arriving at a decision as to whether or not such grievance shall be appealed; (3) The purpose of its proper presentation in the event of appeal.

Such visits will occur only after the following procedure has been complied with: (a) The names of the individuals who will be permitted to enter the plant must be submitted in writing to local Management previous to the date such entry is requested. Such names will be submitted to the Corporation by the General Motors Department of the International Union. (b) The Regional Director shall give notice in writing to Plant Management of the request for entry and will identify the representative whom he wishes to make the visit and the specific grievance to be investigated. In the case of the Director of General Motors Department or a specified member of his staff, notice may be given either verbally or in writing. (c) Plant Management will acknowledge receipt of the request and set a time during regular working hours which is mutually agreeable for such visit. (d) A member of the Shop Committee or a district committeeman may accompany the Union representative during such visit should he request their presence. Management representatives may accompany the Union representatives during such visit. (*e*) Only one such visit on a specified grievance shall be made by the Regional Director or his specified representative unless otherwise mutually agreed to. (*f*) Such visits shall be restricted to the time mutually agreed upon in Point (*c*) above and shall be subject to all plant rules and regulations which apply to employes and all regulations made by the United States Army, Navy, and Federal Bureau of Investigation.

It is mutually agreed that the purpose of this provision is solely to facilitate the operation of the grievance procedure; and that the Union representative shall confine his visit to its stated purpose. If it is necessary the Union representative may interview the employe or employes signing the grievance.

Any dispute developing out of the application of these provisions may be finally determined by the Umpire.

If the Regional Director shall decide to appeal the case, he shall give notice on the form "Notice of Appeal" supplied by the Corporation, sending one copy each to the local Plant Management and the Chairman of the Shop Committee. Such "Notice of Appeal" will carry the same case number as the "Statement of Unadjusted Grievance." Any case not appealed within thirty days of the date of the written decision by the local Plant Management to the Shop Committee shall be finally and automatically closed on the basis of that decision and shall not be subject to further appeal. No case shall be reopened unless the Regional Director shall submit new evidence to the Plant Management and it is mutually agreed by them that such case should be reopened. The case shall then date from the date it is reopened. (**39**) The case will then be considered by an Appeal Committee consisting of four members as follows: For the Union, the Regional Director or one specified representative of the Regional Director who is permanently assigned to handle all cases arising under this Agreement, in all plants in his region, and the Chairman or another designated member of the Shop Committee of the plant involved; and two representatives of local or Divisional Management, one of whom has not previously rendered a decision in the case. No person shall act as a representative of a Regional Director in meetings of the Appeal Committee unless his name has been given to the Corporation in writing by the International Union. A representative of the International Office of the Union and/or a representative of the Personnel Staff of the Corporation may also attend such meetings at any time. Upon the written request of the Chairman of the Shop Committee and the Regional Director, or his specified representative, to the Plant Management, twenty-four (24) hours in advance of the meeting, a member of the Shop Committee (or the district committeeman, in lieu of such Shop Committeeman, who has previously handled such case) will be permitted to participate in the appeal meeting on such case. Whenever the Union requests the presence of a third representative at the appeal hearing, Management may also select a third representative who has previously handled the case, to participate in the appeal meeting on such case.

(40) Attendance of committeemen at the meetings of the Appeal Committee shall be considered as absence from the Plant under Paragraph 19 of the Agreement. Such committeemen shall not be paid for time spent in such meetings of the Appeal Committee.

(41) Meetings of the Appeal Committee shall be held not more frequently than once each two weeks for each bargaining unit, unless mutually agreed otherwise. In event no meetings of the Appeal Committee have been held for more than two weeks, meetings will be arranged within seven days after "Notice of Appeal" has been received.

(42) If an adjustment of the case is not reached at this meeting, the Management will furnish a copy of its decision in writing, and a copy of a summary of the minutes of the meeting, to the Chairman of the Shop Committee and the Regional Director within five working days after the meeting, unless this period is extended by mutual agreement in writing.

Step Four. Appeal to Impartial Umpire

(43) In the event of failure to adjust the case at this point, it may be appealed to the Impartial Umpire, providing it is the type of case on which the Umpire is authorized to rule. Notice of appeal of such cases to the Umpire by the Union shall be given by the Regional Director to the Plant Management of the plant in which the case arose, with copies to the Personnel Staff of the Corporation in Detroit and to the International Union Office at Detroit; in cases appealed to the Umpire by the Corporation, notice of such appeal will be given by the Corporation to the International Union Office in Detroit. Cases not appealed to the Umpire within twenty-one days from the date of a final decision given after review in an Appeal Committee meeting shall be considered settled on the basis of the decisions so given; provided, however, that within the twenty-one (21) day time limit of this paragraph a case may be withdrawn by mutual agreement without prejudice to either party. After a case has been appealed to the Umpire by either the Union or the Corporation, the briefs of both parties shall be filed with the Umpire within twenty-one days from the date of receipt of "Notice of Appeal."

(43a) After a case has been appealed to the Umpire but prior to the Umpire's hearing of the case, the Director of the General Motors Department of the International Union or a specified member of his staff will be granted permission to visit the plant for the purpose of investigating the specific grievance in accordance with all of the provisions of Paragraph 38 regarding plant visits.

(44) The impartial Umpire shall have only the functions set forth herein and shall serve for one year from date of appointment provided he continues to be acceptable to both parties. The fees and expenses of the Umpire will be paid one-half by the Corporation and one-half by the Union and all other expenses shall be borne by the party incurring them. The office of the Umpire shall be located in Detroit.

(45) All cases shall be presented to the Umpire in the form of a written brief prepared by each party, setting forth the facts and its position and the

arguments in support thereof. The Umpire may make such investigation as he may deem proper and may at his option hold a public hearing and examine the witnesses of each party and each party shall have the right to cross-examine all such witnesses and to make a record of all such proceedings.

Powers of the Umpire

(46) It shall be the function of the Umpire, after due investigation and within thirty days after submission of the case to him, to make a decision in all claims of discrimination for Union activity or membership and in all cases of alleged violation of the terms of the following sections of this Agreement, and written local or national supplementary agreements on these same subjects: Recognition; Representation; Grievance Procedure; Seniority; Disciplinary Layoffs and Discharges; Call-in Pay; Working Hours; Leaves of Absence; Union Bulletin Boards; Strikes, Stoppages, and Lock-outs; Wages, except paragraph (97); General Provisions; Skilled Trades; Vacation Pay Allowances; Holiday Pay; Paragraph (79) relative to procedures on Production Standards; Paragraphs (95) and (96) relative to employment of laid off General Motors employes; and of any alleged violations of written local or national wage agreements. The Umpire shall have no power to add to or subtract from or modify any of the terms of this Agreement or any agreements made supplementary hereto; nor to establish or change any wage except as provided by Paragraphs 102 (c), 102 (d), and 102 (e) herein; nor to rule on any dispute arising under Paragraph (78) regarding Production Standards. The Umpire shall have no power to rule on any issue or dispute arising under the Pension Plan and Insurance Program Section or the Waiver Section. Any case appealed to the Umpire on which he has no power to rule shall be referred back to the parties without decision.

(47) The Corporation delegates to the Umpire full discretion in cases of discipline for violation of shop rules, or discipline for violation of the Strikes, Stoppages, and Lock-outs Section of the Agreement.

(48) No claims, including claims for back wages, by an employe covered by this Agreement, or by the Union, against the Corporation shall be valid for a period prior to the date the grievance was first filed in writing, unless the circumstances of the case made it impossible for the employe, or for the Union as the case may be, to know that he, or the Union, had grounds for such a claim prior to that date, in which case the claim shall be limited retroactively to a period of thirty days prior to the date the claim was first filed in writing.

(49) In claims arising out of the failure of the Corporation to give the employe work to which he was entitled, the Corporation, before his next seniority layoff and within six months from the answer given by Management at the Third Step, shall give him extra work for a number of hours equal to the number of hours that he had lost prior to the written filing of his claim, and this work shall be paid for at the hourly rate he would have received had he worked, or if paid for at a less rate, the Corporation will make up the difference in cash. By extra work is meant work to which no other employe is entitled. Failing to give the employe work within six months, the Corporation will pay the back wages.

(50) All claims for back wages shall be limited to the amount of wages the employe would otherwise have earned from his employment with the Corporation during the periods as above defined, less the following: 1. Any Unemployment Compensation which the employe is not obligated to repay or which he is obligated to repay but has not repaid nor authorized the Corporation to repay on his behalf. 2. Compensation for personal services other than the amount of compensation he was receiving from any other employment which he had at the time he last worked for the Corporation and which he would have continued to receive had he continued to work for the Corporation during the period covered by the claim.

(51) No decision of the Umpire or of the Management in one case shall create a basis for a retroactive adjustment in any other case prior to the date of written filing of each such specific claim.

(52) After a case on which the Umpire is empowered to rule hereunder has been referred to him, it may not be withdrawn by either party except by mutual consent. Grievances filed prior to the date of notification of ratification of this Agreement by the Union may be appealed to the Umpire under the provisions of the Agreement dated May 29, 1948, and its supplements.

(53) There shall be no appeal from the Umpire's decision, which will be final and binding on the Union and its members, the employe or employes involved, and the Corporation. The Union will discourage any attempt of its members, and will not encourage or cooperate with any of its members, in any appeal to any of its members, in any appeal to any Court or Labor Board from a decision of the Umpire.

(54) Any grievances which the Corporation may have against the Union in any plant shall be presented by the Plant Management involved to the Shop Committee of that plant. In the event that the matter is not satisfactorily adjusted within two weeks after such presentation, it may be appealed to the third step of the Grievance Procedure upon written notice to the local Union and the Regional Director of the Union. Thereafter the matter will be considered at the third step of the Procedure as provided in Paragraph (39). If the matter is not satisfactorily settled at this meeting or within five days thereafter by agreement, the case may be appealed to the Umpire by the Corporation upon written notice to the International Union at Detroit and to the Umpire.

(55) Any issue involving the interpretation and/or the application of any term of this Agreement may be initiated by either party directly with the other party. Upon failure of the parties to agree with respect to the correct interpretation or application of the Agreement to the issue, it may then be appealed directly to the Umpire as provided in Paragraph (43).

General Motors and U. A. W. have been fortunate in the selection of Dr. H. A. Millis and Dr. George W. Taylor as the first two umpires. Mr. H. W. Anderson,[3] who also has had much to do with the work, has this to say about it in general:

[3] A.M.A. *Personnel Series*, No. 52.

1. It is important that local management place the responsibility for handling grievances upon a member of the staff who has the proper qualifications for the job and the necessary understanding.
2. There must be proper cooperation on the part of both the union and the management if grievances are to be settled.
3. It is much easier to settle grievances at their source than it is to settle them after they advance through the grievance procedure.
4. Grievances have a tendency to gather extraneous matter as they roll up through the procedure, and for this reason it is important to reduce them to writing if a settlement cannot be reached at the initial stage.
5. It is more constructive to settle a grievance on the basis of equity than it is to say "no" on the basis of a technicality or because of a rigid interpretation of a paragraph in an agreement when no policy question is involved. By this I do not mean appeasement.
6. There is no panacea for grievances. It requires hard work, patience, fair dealing, an understanding of human nature, and assumption of responsibility on both sides if better labor relations are to result.
7. While it is the responsibility of the management to settle legitimate grievances, no settlement that impairs the efficiency or discipline of the working force should be made.

Grievance procedures in nonunion shops have been outlined by the National Industrial Conference Board in its *Management Record,* Vol. XI, No. 8 and *Studies in Personnel Policy,* No. 109.

13

MERIT RATING

Job Evaluation and merit rating, combined with some system of
paying extra wages for extra work, seem to offer an opportunity
to settle wage disputes on the basis of fact.

—J. E. WALTERS

Job Rating Plus Man Rating. You could have reliable job evaluation without merit rating and without extrafinancial incentives but it would be like having a meal without drink and without dessert. The diners might not do their whole duty on the spinach. It is true that merit rating has but recently come to industry, mostly since World War I, and is not yet accepted by all unions, nor by all managements. Some have made half-hearted attempts at it only to give it up. A survey made by L. G. Spicer [1] several years ago, covering 176 companies, showed that 100 had no such system, 15 applied it only to hourly workers, 17 applied it only to salaried workers, and 32 applied it to both. Twelve submitted incomplete replies.

Like other activities of the personnel function, formal merit rating could not come until staffs were provided to round out the work of line supervision. It *has* been generally recognized for a long time that many hourly paid employees have been losing their hope of promotion and that what rate increases may be expected are often badly handled. So in recognizing the disease it may not be long before many will accept the cure. On the other hand tendencies of unions to prefer rigid seniority, and across the board increases in base rates, are causing employers to postpone new ventures in this direction. Furthermore, on Oct. 11, 1948, the Supreme Court upheld a decision of the U. S. Circuit Court in Cincinnati to the effect that an employer must bargain with its unions before giving merit raises to individual workers.

When given a fair chance, merit rating has been beneficial to all types of employees and, aside from promotion, it is the only

[1] *Personnel*, XXVII, No. 6.

systematic means of providing extra financial incentive for time-paid employees. Since it is man rating, it puts individual or man differentials on the same systematic basis that job rating provides for base rates. It is unlike job evaluation in that it must be personal, but it is like job evaluation in that it can be impartial and according to predetermined procedures. Merit rating is also unlike job evaluation in that the latter precedes hiring while the former follows hiring.

Definition and Nature. Merit rating is a systematic, periodic, and, so far as may be humanly possible, an impartial rating of an employee's excellence in matters pertaining to his present job and to his potentialities for a better job. Naturally this must be judged, for any one individual, relative to the excellence of other individuals. Like job evaluation this can be done directly or indirectly. The direct approach through ranking is more used than in job evaluation because the indirect approach, that is, appraising against predetermined and detached criteria, is unsatisfactory for some of the most important qualities. Hence we cannot claim that man rating is ever as objective as job rating. In fact, it is conceded that embarrassing situations may occasionaly arise.[2] Nevertheless, fair-minded raters, when trained, can attain a high degree of impartiality, and fair-minded employees can take their ratings without irritation. That achievement does not, however, just happen. What we have previously said about the need for confidence in connection with evaluation goes double for merit rating. Furthermore, tact and kindly consideration must be added. Destructive criticism is taboo. Obviously, there is great opportunity here for management to make or mar personnel relations. So far as it can establish facts as the basis for decisions and adhere to them with unquestionable fairness it can do much to promote justice and consequent harmony. All employees have some good qualities, make some praiseworthy achievements, and naturally are gratified when these things are recognized. It is along this latter line that merit rating must put the emphasis. If it succeeds in that it can also point out the soft spots and solicit self-discipline toward the mutually desired development. Not only in-grade advances but up-grade promotions can be made contingent on the findings of merit rating. This helps a policy of "hiring from within."

Claims for Merit Rating. There have been many other claims for merit rating. Certainly the uncultivated variety of employee

[2] W. R. Mahler, *Twenty Years of Merit Rating* (New York: The Psychological Corporation, 1947). Roland Benjamin, Jr., "A Survey of 130 Merit Rating Plans," *Personnel*, XXIX, No. 3, and L. F. Van Houten, "Merit Rating Case Histories," *Personnel Adm. Service,* The Dartnell Corporation, 1952.

rating, which always goes on until replaced by a cultivated variety, leaves ample room for improvements. Taking a hopeful but conservative attitude on this, we prefer to quote the claims of Jesse T. Hopkins of Edgar T. Ward's Sons Company and Affiliated Companies.[3] In his candid article Mr. Hopkins says, "Altogether too many people have thought that merit rating was actually a measuring tool, when it is only an orderly method of recording the opinions of one or more members of the supervisory staff of those who work under them." He follows this and other cautions with what we think is a pretty fair merit rating of merit rating:

1. Merit rating establishes a method by which the supervisor can talk with his men. From such interviews comes a much better understanding of many things on the part of both. We would say further that it can recognize and reward the employee's contribution to the organization as a whole, an appreciation which job evaluation alone can not provide.
2. It provides an excellent means of taking the sting out of necessary criticism. The tactful supervisor will point out the good qualities as well as the bad. It is a chance to appeal to the best in the man.
3. It stimulates men to self-analysis and puts them on the road to self-improvement and development.
4. It is a process which assists management to discover men of special talent or with capacities for greater responsibilities.
5. A merit rating form can almost serve as a pattern to the employee for standards of job performance and relations to others.
6. Merit rating is an excellent recruiting device in that the desirable worker is attracted to the company where he knows he will not be sidetracked, where his good work will not go unnoticed, and where he will work under intelligent and understanding supervision.
7. In general, merit rating can become a very effective means of individual employee analysis which stimulates and develops not only the employee rated but the supervisor who does the rating.
8. Then, too, it has a public-relations value. Confidence is inspired among customers and the public in general when it is known that company interest in its employees is expressed by carefully developed methods such as merit rating.

Background of Merit Rating. Someone has said that double merit rating occurs every time one person contacts another person.

[3] *Some Fallacies and Virtues of Merit Rating,* A.M.A. Production Series No. 124.

Certainly there has always been something of the sort between parents and children, teachers and pupils, salesmen and customers, etc. The formal kind of merit rating seems to have stemmed from the school; it was applied to U. S. teachers themselves in 1915. In 1916 the Bureau of Salesmanship Research was organized at Carnegie Institute of Technology, partly to improve the rating of salesmen, and it adopted a rating scale in 1917. In the meantime the U. S. Army had developed the Scott man-to-man comparison scale for rating the graduates of officer training courses and promptly extended it as a means of selecting suitable candidates for the training courses. It further extended its merit rating to all commissioned officers in 1919. In all applications the rater would select records of five men, each to represent one degree of a quality, another set of five men for the next quality, etc. These representatives were used as a "Man-to-Man Scale." [4] In 1919–20, forty-five companies and associates started man rating experiments in industry. This led to rating men on one quality at a time. Many techniques and methods followed:

a) Carlson's recognition that the qualities, work, attitude, and knowledge each gave a regular distribution curve for any normal group of individuals.

b) The National Metal Trades Association [5] added degrees with definitions to regularize the rating of two qualities.

c) Wonderlic substituted illustrations of behavior for the too general qualities.

d) The Farm Credit Administration used ten degrees across one sheet.

e) Stevens and Wonderlic used a separate sheet for each of ten qualities, on which a group of men are ranked.

f) Scott applied graph scales during World War I.

g) Lawshe, Kephart, McCormick, and others adapted an old experimentation technique to merit rating—the "Paired-Comparison Method."

h) The Acme Steel Company devised their "Chart" system in which each supervisor's ratings are leveled to 70 per cent on each quality, thereby correcting the personal error.

[4] *The Personnel System of the U. S. Army,* Vol. II.

[5] Other groups which have assisted much in this development are: The American Management Association. The National Electric Manufacturers Association, The National Industrial Conference Board, and the Metropolitan Life Insurance Company. See A.M.A. *Rating Employee and Supervisory Performance, A Manual of Merit Rating Techniques.*

i) Richardson, Sisson, and others developed the "Forced-Choice" method for the armed services.

j) Flanagan developed the "Critical-Incidents" technique for the Air Force.

Practical Considerations. Omitted by Mr. Hopkins, but doubtless taken for granted by him, is the need for putting all individual differentials on a reliable basis. We have already discussed the problem of eliminating out-of-line base rates and we have explained that much of the misalignment is due to mistaken individual differentials. Actually some of these accumulations are justified by real man-worth variations so that after base rates are put in order there remains the problem of ascertaining which and how much extra rating should be recognized as bona fide. Practical questions arise such as: How much more or less is one man worth than another doing the same job? Which men have promotional potentialities? Is the man who asks for an increase most worthy of it or is another who has not said a word more worthy? A well-thought-out policy, plus reliable information as a basis for decision, is needed here as much as it is in the matter of base rates. It may be impossible to rectify all the previous mistakes but it is possible to get ready for better answers in the future. Questions regarding probationers, learnees, layoffs, and discharges can all be answered more justly if merit rating data are perpetually gathered and recorded on all the man-record cards. Dealings between union representatives and management are freer from argument and ill feeling if all merit facts are available and unassailable. True, there is the clash between merit and length of service which must be settled by bargaining. Fortunately many union leaders are respectful toward a merit record, in which case they will write the seniority clause somewhat as follows:

In all cases of increase or decrease in the working force of the company, or in the promotion or demotion or transfer within the working force, the following factors shall be considered: (1) seniority or length of continuous service; (2) knowledge, training, ability, skill, and efficiency; (3) physical fitness; (4) family status, number of dependents, etc.; (5) place of residence. When the last four factors are relatively equal, then factor (1), seniority, shall govern.

We urge unions to follow this policy in the interest of justice and efficiency for all concerned.

Methods Less Regular Than in Job Evaluation. We see no basis of classification for merit rating methods which will provide clean-cut separation. Some plans make use of more than one principle, as we will show presently. Nearly all the plans end with some kind of score, usually in points. Hence it is hardly feasible to set up classes on points or no points, straight points or weighted points, etc., as we did for job evaluation. Yet there are plans that could be so classified. For instance, Cheney Brothers' original plan had five qualities, Service, Attendance, Quality, Production, and Citizenship, with an additional one, Versatility, which was not applied to everybody. Twenty points were allotted to each of the five, straight. The Kollmorgan Optical Company plan has six qualities and these are weighted in points (see Figure 131).

CHENEY PLAN		KOLLMORGAN PLAN
Service (cumulative)..... 20 pts.		10 pts. Service (cumulative)
Attendance .... 20 "		8 " Attendance
Production .... 20 "		20 " Quantity
(This factor is allowed		24 " Quality
to go 5 pts. above par)		24 " Adaptability and Skill
Quality .... 20 "		14 " Conduct (Cooperation)
Citizenship .... 20 "		
100 pts.		100 pts.

FIGURE 131. COMPARISON OF POINTS RATING IN TWO COMPANIES USING MERIT RATING PLANS

These two plans may be used also to illustrate another variation in application. The Cheney plan applied whatever percentage of the potential total an employee might get in rating above 50 per cent to the money range between the minimum rate and the maximum. The Kollmorgan plan requires a 65 per cent man rating to qualify for the prevailing rate, that is, the trend line, leaving only 35 per cent further rating for the upper portion of the money range. Such differences would necessitate somewhat different attitudes on the part of the raters.

The most satisfactory solution to classification we can contrive is to carry over the two techniques from job evaluation (see Chapter 3) in order to distinguish them from "methods" and for the latter set up four headings: Grouping,[6] Numerical Gradations, and Check Lists of Specific Questions and Record of Occurrences. These seem to be different enough in principle to make method cleavages, but when we come to subdivide them similarities begin to show. For

[6] Ultimate grouping can be made from any set of scores. As a classification we mean the more immediate purpose of gathering into grades or groups.

instance, the Probst Service Rating plan distributes individuals into eleven groups which are lettered $-$ E, E, $-$ D, D, $-$ C, C, $+$ C, B, $+$ B, A, $+$ A. The basis of grouping is a set of about 100 descriptive items—character traits, habits, work qualities, and personality. The evaluating is done by a "scoring device," etc.[7] In applying the methods and techniques to create a tailor-made plan the tendency toward similarities is pronounced, and seems to be characteristic of merit rating. Furthermore where degrees are predetermined (see Technique B below) their application may be made by direct comparison (see Technique A). Even so we think our attempt at classification does clarify some differences in principle, thereby isolating elements which can be studied and put together more understandingly.

CLASSIFICATION OF TECHNIQUES AND METHODS

TECHNIQUES:

    A. Direct Comparison of Qualities—"Paired Comparison."

    B. Indirect Comparison of Qualities, i.e., against predetermined degree definitions.

METHODS:

    1. Grouping, All on Selected Qualities.

        a) "Man to Man" Examples, with Technique B.

        b) Ranking for Each Quality, with Technique A.

        c) Grading by Letters or by Numbers with Technique A or B.

        d) Grading by Weights, may be $\pm$, with Technique A.

            (A code may be used to withhold weights from the raters.)

    2. Numerical Gradations or Steps, All on Selected Qualities (visible or by stencil).

        a) Arbitrary Scales, with Technique B.

        b) One to Ten or Percentage Scales, with Technique B.

        c) Graphic Scales, with Technique B.

    3. Check List of Specific Descriptions or Questions (visible or by code).

        a) Check Closest Description, with Technique B (also A).

        b) Yes or No Answers to Questions, with Technique A.

        c) Comments as Answers to Questions, with Technique A.

        d) Most Descriptive Statements (Forced Choice), with Technique A.

    4. Record of Occurrences.

        a) Critical Incidents, with Technique A.

[7] J. B. Probst, *Measuring and Rating Employee Value* (New York: The Ronald Press Co., 1947).

One or More Samples from Each Method

CLASS 1. GROUPING, ALL ON SELECTED QUALITIES.

1. (*a*) "Man-to-Man" Examples for the Degrees, with Technique B:

	Degrees	Points
Leadership.	Highest	15
Initiative, force, self-reliance, decisiveness, tact,	High	12
ability to inspire men and to command their	Middle	9
obedience, loyalty, and cooperation.	Low	6
	Lowest	3

Potential maximum for all qualities 100, minimum 20.

There were five qualities: Physical Qualities (3–15), Intelligence (3–15), Leadership (3–15), Personal Qualities (3–15), and General Value to the Service (8–40). A rater chose from his acquaintances a man to typify each degree of each quality. He then compared the man to be rated with the five men per quality and in each case designated the closest similarity, thereby determining the point value of the rates. These values were totaled for all the qualities and the ratees grouped. Despite the lack of uniformity of these human scales, the average groups ran closely to 60 points and the distribution of the groups gave usually a normal curve. The method was copied in civilian activities and is still used by a few manufacturing companies, but has been discarded by most of them and by the Army itself as being too cumbersome.

1. (*b*) Ranking for Each Quality, with Technique A (roughly graphic as per class 2*c*):

First Example:

Ability				
Consider his success in doing things in new and better ways and in adapting improved methods to his own work.				
	Routine worker	Fairly progressive	Resourceful	Highly constructive

This plan, used by The Kimberly-Clark Corporation for executives-supervisors, has seven "abilities" listed down the left of the blank and horizontal scales in which the degrees are defined as illustrated.

Second Example:

Initiative	Wastes time walking about, talking to everyone	He needs prodding occasionally	Works steadily	Habitually drives himself
Names of Persons				

This plan, used by The Atlantic Refining Company for office employees, has ten "traits" and a separate sheet is used for each trait; the degree headings given above are for the trait initiative.

1. (c) Grading by Letters or by Numbers, with Technique A:

Character of Service	Excellent	Good	Fair	Poor
Quantity of Work				

This plan, anonymous, uses six characteristics listed down the left with four degrees across the horizontal as indicated. The rater simply checks under the appropriate degree but there are no definitions either of the characteristics or the degrees. Similar forms use A, B, C, D in place of the Excellent, Good, Fair, and Poor. The Curtiss-Wright Corporation, Buffalo, used six factors and four degrees, all of which were defined. In addition it divided each factor degree into five A, B, C, D, E subdegrees which were not defined. Revere Copper and Brass, Inc., does much the same but in place of the A, B, C's it uses numbers, 1 to 15, 1 to 20, and 1 to 30, running from lowest to highest subdegree.

1. (d) Grading by Weights, May Be Plus or Minus, with Technique A (a code may be used to withhold weights from the raters):

First Example:

Qualities	Dates Rater				Averages of Periodic Ratings		
* 5. Dependability: Does he follow instructions? Will he do what you expect him to do and do it conscientiously and thoroughly?							

Degree:	5	4	3	2	1
* 5 Key:	(Outstanding)	(Above Average)	(Average)	(Below Average)	(Weak)
Weight:	10	9	8	7	6

This plan, anonymous, uses ten qualities which are roughly defined. There are five degrees which are weighted on a separate key table, from which the appropriate weight is transferred to the current date column opposite the quality being rated. An additional set of columns is provided for averaging the values for the four ratings. The degrees are not defined.

Second Example:

Qualities		Unsatisfactory (negative)		Aver-age	Satisfactory (positive)		Totals	
							Detail	For Whole
Quality of Work	Accuracy of Production	many errors −4	careless −2	aver-age 6	careful +2	most accurate +4		
	Care of Working Space	slovenly −2	careless −1	aver-age 3	keeps clean +1	very clean +2		
	Handling of Material	rough −2	careless −1	aver-age 3	careful +1	very careful +2		

This plan, of the Spark Plug Division, General Motors Corporation, uses six major qualities, subdivided into three or four minor qualities (except attendance). Whatever the grading may be, it is added algebraically to the average weight and entered in the next-to-last column. The values for all the minor qualities are totaled and this total is entered in the last column. For accuracy of production it might be $6 − 4$ or $6 − 2$ or $6 + 2$ or $6 + 4$. The maximum potentials vary from 2 to 10 and all together give a maximum potential of 100. At first glance this plan seems commendable but elaborateness of weighting cannot alone bring fair results. It seems to us wiser to define the qualities in terms of concrete examples rather than in terms of subdivisions. The latter merely multiply the considerations and make the 15 to 20 weightings per major quality a matter of arbitrary guessing, for those who predetermine the weights. It may be easier for those who select the appropriate values. Foremen do not take naturally to academic grading. They have to be trained in grading. Doubtless the company using this form does have some more explicit descriptions of the qualities, perhaps of the degrees, but if so they ought to be on or attached to the forms. As it is there is bound to be great variance in the grading done by different foremen and also in that done by the same foreman at different times.

Grouping Supported by Theory. The distribution either of things or of persons on any measurable quality will in general take the shape of a bell curve. About 50 per cent of the individuals so measured will constitute the so-called average group with approximately 25 per cent above the actual average and approximately 25 per cent below. The theory back of grouping is, therefore, sound.

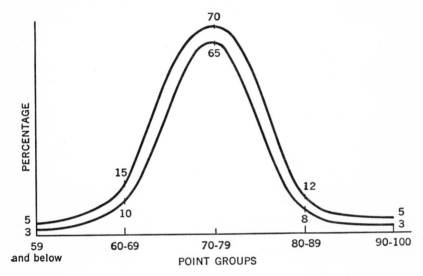

FIGURE 132. NORMAL DISTRIBUTION BAND.

Briefly, it starts on the hypothesis that if a random sample of workers is normal the parent distribution curve is also normal (Figure 132) or, conversely, if the sample is skewed the whole will also be skewed in the same way (Figure 133). Next it assumes that if the qualities are properly chosen they will occur normally, that is, if the frequence of occurrence and the degree of intensity are plotted, a normal distribution curve will result,[8] but there are usually irregularities caused by such influences as selection for the job, leadership, custom, and last but not least the way the statistical group is put together. Effects of these forces should not be credited to, nor charged against, the individual being rated. In short, the method has possibilities if it is used correctly. The National Metal

[8] "A Case History in Merit Rating," by R. S. Driver, *A.M.A. Personnel*, XVI, No. 4; also *Personnel Series* No. 93.

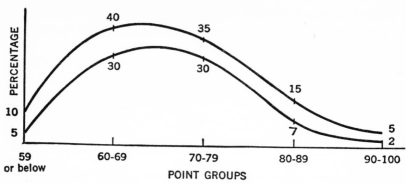

FIGURE 133. SKEWED DISTRIBUTION BAND.

Trades Association derives five groupings from merit rating as shown in Figure 134.

Group	Point Range	"Normal" Distribution	Money Range
1	91–100	3– 5% of personnel	Max.
2	81 and under 91	8–12% " "	.75%
3	71 " " 81	65–70% " "	.50%
4	61 " " 71	10–15% " "	.25%
5	60 or below	3– 5% " "	Min.

FIGURE 134. GROUP METHOD USED BY THE NATIONAL METAL TRADES ASSOCIATION.

CLASS 2. NUMERICAL GRADATIONS OR STEPS, ALL ON SELECTED QUALITIES.

2. (*a*) Arbitrary Scales, with Technique B:

Factors	R–1 R–2	R–3 R–4	R–5 R–6	R–7 R–8
4. Job Knowledge This factor appraises how well the employee knows his job.	☐ ☐ Is he an expert on his job? Does he make the most of his knowledge and experience? Is he a self starter?	☐ ☐ Is he well informed on his job and related work, rarely needing assistance and instruction but asking for them when it will save time?	☐ ☐ Does he know his job fairly well? Does he regularly require supervision and instruction?	☐ ☐ Is his knowledge of his job limited? Does he show little desire or ability to improve himself?

This plan used by the National Metal Trades Association has six "factors" and carries excellent instructions, stresses impartiality, and the consideration of "instances that are typical of his work and way of acting." The left square is used when the degree specification is a perfect fit and the right square is used "if he does not quite measure up to the specification but is definitely better than the specification for the next lower degree." Scoring is sometimes made by a stencil as per key of weights. Also the ratings may be punched and the cards sorted mechanically. Acceptable low score is 60 per cent.

Factor	R_1	R_2	R_3	R_4	R_5	R_6	R_7	R_8
Job Knowledge	20	18	16	14	12	10	8	6

The maximum potential for all six factors is 100.

2. (*b*) One to Ten Scales, with Technique B:

First Example:

Factors	Rater	Reviewer

1. Quality of Performance:
    (a) Thoroughness: adequacy of results
    (b) General dependability: accuracy of results
    (c) Technical skill with which the important procedures or instruments are employed in performing his duties
    (d) Original contributions to method or knowledge
    (e) Effectiveness in getting good work done by his unit		

In boxes mark:
1 or 2 if excellent
3 or 4 if very good
5 or 6 if good
7 or 8 if fair
9 or 10 if unsatisfactory

Interpretation of sum:
3–7 Excellent
8–13 Very Good
14–19 Good
20–24 Fair
25–30 Unsatisfactory

This "Service Rating" plan, anonymous, but obviously modified from The U. S. Civil Service Commission, uses only three major factors but the subdivisions come to twenty. The scoring is unique in that it is in reverse order to usual practice, that is, the lower the score the better the rating.

Second Example:

The "Acme Chart Plan" has been in use by the Acme Steel Company since 1937. Thus it is not new and it would not be novel except for one feature. There are ten qualities: (1) accuracy, (2) quantity, (3) use of time, (4) ability to work with others, (5) ability to learn, (6) safety, (7) initiative and acceptance of responsibilities, (8) conduct on the job, (9) care of equipment, tools, materials, supplies, and power, (10) punctuality and attendance. On each of these each employee is rated independently in percentage by two or more raters. The feature that makes this noteworthy is the assembling of all ratings made by each rater on each given quality and then doctoring them to give an average of 70 per cent. This wipes out any exaggerated ratings but keeps the series in proportion. The average corrected rating for each employee can then be made, which will be free from subjective errors, either high or low. These corrected ratings are used to supplement seniority when promotion is being considered. Minor variations are further disregarded by treating all employees, in approximately the highest 10 per cent rating, as equal in rated merit. This keeps the verdicts within the statistically determined reliability of the rating. Then the one of that group who has the longest seniority is given the promotion. By this means only the ratings of employees in a given unit are compared, which obviates the situation of having every employee on one job rated higher or lower than any employee on some other job, which sometimes occurs.

2. (*c*) Graphic Scales, with Technique B:

This type of plan was used by 87 per cent of the seventy-five companies surveyed in 1952.

First Example:

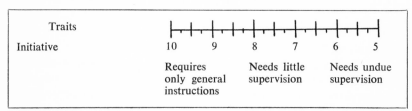

This plan, anonymous, has four major traits as follows: (1) value of assigned work, (2) capacity for future growth, (3) aptitude and leadership, (4) personality traits. The last one is subdivided into five minor traits from which we have taken the first. This plan shows the scoring numerically and graphically.

Second Example:

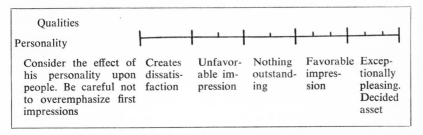

This "review of service" plan, used by The Armstrong Cork Company, has twelve qualities and they are not subdivided. No scoring is given but there is space for explanation and three columns, not shown here, to be checked annually under the headings: Has improved, Little or no change, Has gone back. Note that the scales for some of these examples run in opposite directions.

Third Example:

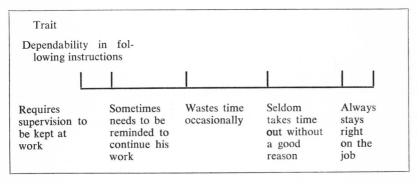

Eighteen of these "Test Research Rating Scales" were developed by E. K. Taylor and G. E. Manson while on the staff of the Civilian Personnel Research Subsection of the Adjutant General's Office.[9] Only four or five scales most suitable to a given set of job situations are used, plus one more for over-all effectiveness. The jobholder's names are all listed on each separate trait form. Stress is placed on the degree definitions, which are more extensive than here shown, rather than on a trait name.

Evaluation is made in the presence of, and under the close supervision of, a qualified personnel technician and every precaution is taken to avoid disturbance. The two persons to get extreme ratings are identified first, then the persons next to them; the process is re-

[9] *Personnel*, XXVII, No. 6.

peated for all the scales in use. Of course the raters are given explanations and training before the actual rating begins. Reliability tests show that the "pile-up" of cases at the upper ranges is conspicuously absent from the distributions but the means still come somewhat above the exact center. This deviation from symmetry is, however, much less than in usual practice. Naturally, this sort of practice is more costly, both in form construction and in administration, than the ordinary practices but the authors believe "that employee evaluations (whether undertaken as a means of establishing a criterion for the validation of personnel techniques and procedures or for providing data on the basis of which administrative decisions are to be made) serve an important function. If such evaluations are to be made, the time and effort required to develop a system, such as has been described, may more than pay for itself in the greater value of the data that result."

CLASS 3. CHECK LIST OF SPECIFIC DESCRIPTIONS OR QUESTIONS (VISIBLE OR BY CODE). This type of plan was used by 9 per cent of the seventy-five companies surveyed in 1952.

3. (a) Check Closest Description, with Technique B:

Quality	Suited to Job	Unsuited to Job
8. Adjustment to job	☐ Satisfactory; worth considering for advancement. ☐ Efficient; satisfied; has reached limit of development. ☐ Capable; interested; but needs more training.	☐ Could do higher type of work of another variety, but not satisfactory on present job. ☐ Capable; but interests not satisfied. ☐ Underqualified; shows little promise of development.

This "Progress Report," anonymous, has the advantage of bringing out information other than the degree of a qualification, that is, it can serve as an all-round follow-up. It does not, however, lend itself to scoring. Hence it is usually applied only to the less measurable qualities; the measurable qualities may be given numerical or graphical scales on the same sheet. There are nine qualities, six of which have 3- or 4-degree graphic scales.[10]

3. (b) Yes or No Answers to Questions, with Technique A (A yes may carry a weighting, a no may mean zero value).

[10] For a seven-quality twelve-degree plan see H. A. Stackman, "A Case Report from Scovill," *Personnel*, XXIII, No. 6, pp. 410–24.

Quality			
Production ⊢―――――――――――――――――――――――――――⊣			
High	Increasing	Steady	Low, Shrinking

1. Does executive guard against waste of supplies?   Yes —.   No —.
2. Does executive think of new and more efficient
   operations?   Yes —.   No —.
3. Does executive handle lunch hours efficiently?   Yes —.   No —.
4. Does executive tolerate laxness on part of employees?   Yes —.   No —.
5. Does executive try to improve himself while on the
   job?   Yes —.   No —.
6. Does executive consistently get results?   Yes —.   No —.

This plan, anonymous, combines a graphic scale with the specific questions. Answers to the latter are not weighted; they serve merely as information and guidance to checking the scale. This plan has five major qualifications: Appearance, Attendance, Attitude, Efficiency, and Promotional Quality. Attitude is subdivided into: Cooperation, Manner, and Industry. Efficiency is subdivided into: Knowledge of Job, Leadership, and Production. Note that Question 4 is in reverse so that the *no* answer is the favorable one and that Question 6 covers the net result of all the others. Sometimes neither yes nor no is the correct answer!

Figure 135 provides an excellent example of combining Method 3*b* with Method 2*a*. Notice that the yes answers are allowed the minimum count of one each and that the measurable qualities will always predominate in any score.

3. (*c*) Comments as Answers to Questions, with Technique A:

Quality	On this quality give factual information about the person's
Description of Selling Technique	Knowledge of merchandise. Interest in the customer's needs. Ability to present the merchandise attractively. Ability to increase the average salescheck. Ability to sell to all kinds of customers. Ability to close a sale.

This "Salesclerk's Review Ratings," anonymous, has five qualities besides the one above: Speed, Appearance, Attitude, Accuracy, and Social Factors or Nonselling Responsibilities Influencing the Job. For these five, not given here, there are no set comments but each carries a sentence suggesting the kind of comments wanted. Answers of yes or no are precluded. Obviously any scoring on this

I CUMULATIVE SERVICE

1 yr......1	22 yrs........11
2 yrs.....1	24 " 12
3 " 2	26 " 14
5 " 3	28 " 16
8 " 4	30 " 18
10 " 5	32 " 20
12 " 6	34 " 22
14 " 7	36 " 24
16 " 8	38 " 26
18 " 9	40 " 28
20 " 10	42 " 30

II DEPENDENTS

4 persons...................4
3 " 3
2 " 2
1 " 1

III MARITAL STATUS

Married Man................1
Single Woman..............2

IV CITIZENSHIP

Citizen 5
Alien (service 25 yrs. or more)
with or without 1st papers..4
First Papers.................3
Alien (service 20–25 yrs.)......2
Alien (service 15–20 yrs.).....1

V ATTENDANCE

Perfect 4
1–2 absences................3
3–4 " 2
5–6 " 1
Over 6 " 0

VI QUANTITY

Day Workers
Above average..............6
Average 4
Below average..............2
Unsatisfactory 0
Bedaux Workers
80 pts. per hr & over..........6
70–79 pts. per hr............4
60–69 pts. per hr............2
Below 60-pt. hr..............0

VII QUALITY

A. To what degree is the product up to the dept's standard of quality?
   1. Above standard requirements? Yes..1
   2. Meets standard requirements? Yes..1
   3. Occasionally below? Yes..1
   4. Is job of high quality req.? Yes..1
B. Workmanship
   1. Is this person orderly in his work? Yes..1
   2. Does he handle materials economically? Yes..1
C. Degree to which supervision is necessary to maintain quality.
   1. Needs little or no checking Yes..1
   2. No more than average checking Yes..1

VIII VERSATILITY, ADAPTABILITY, SKILL

1. Has this person learned new work within expected time? Yes..1
2. Can he fill 2 major jobs? Yes..1
3. Can he fill 3 major jobs? Yes..1
4. Can he adjust to radical change in his present job? Yes..1
5. Can he learn different work? Yes..1
6. Would he adjust readily to transfer to another major job? Yes..1
7. Can he actually fill his job with better than ordinary skill? Yes..1
8. Can he perform a highly skilled job with apparent ease and dexterity? Yes..1

IX CONDUCT, COOPERATION

1. Is this person one who does not play pranks which might endanger other workmen? Yes..1
2. Does he refrain from objectionable language and actions? Yes..1
3. Is he always willing to carry out instructions on the job? Yes..1
4. Is he willing to try new methods? Yes..1
5. Is he helpful to supervisor? Yes..1
6. Does this person call to the attention of the supervisor defective work received? Yes..1
7. Is this person one who does not offer excuses or alibis to avoid accepting his proper responsibilities? Yes..1

TOTAL RATING...............

FIGURE 135. COMPLETE EXAMPLE OF PLAN COMBINING 3*b* WITH 2*a*. (Bausch & Lomb Company.)

kind of information would be very rough indeed but the picture shown may be just as accurate, perhaps more significant, as an aid to employee improvement.[11]

3. (d) Most Descriptive Statements (Forced Choice), with Technique A:

The "Forced Choice" method came from researches conducted by the armed forces during World War II. It was aimed to eliminate favoritism that crowded ratings toward the good end of the scale.[12] The basic method provides blocks of descriptive statements, two equally favorable and two equally unfavorable per block. The rater checks two of each four statements—the one most descriptive and the one least descriptive of the individual being rated. Indices of the favorability and unfavorability are established from independent pooled judgment. The subtlety of the plan lies in the fact that only one of the favorable and one of the unfavorable statements differentiate between good and poor ratees and only those two statements are considered in the scoring. The whole form contains thirty to fifty blocks and is scored by counting these discriminating statements as checked. Favorable checks are plus and unfavorable ones are minus. The raters do not see the scoring key so that they are unaware of which statement in each pair counts. Under test the method has been found not to give a much higher rating when the raters try to show favoritism! It is thought to be particularly effective in identifying men who are giving the best performances; it is not so suitable if the ratings must be defended in bargaining or in arbitration.

CLASS 4. RECORD OF OCCURRENCES.

4. (a) Critical Incidents, with Technique A:

The "Critical-Incidents" method [13] came from researches conducted by the Air Force during World War II and several industries have since adapted it to their needs. It presumes that employees do or do not do certain things on the job that make the difference between success, mediocrity, or failure. Therefore supervisors are coached to record certain kinds of occurrences, namely, *critical in-*

---

[11] H. S. Belinky, "Developing Effective Service Ratings," *Personnel Administration*, November, 1940.
[12] M. W. Richardson, "Forced-Choice Performance Reports," *Personnel*, XXVI, pp. 205–12, and E. D. Sisson, "Forced Choice," *Personnel Psychology*, I, pp. 365–81.
[13] J. C. Flanagan, and R. B. Miller, *Handbook for the Performance Record for Production Employees* (Chicago: Science Research Associates, 1951).

cidents connected with the work of each ratee. A Manual guides the supervisor in this observing and recording. He does not make any attempt to evaluate the items. The Manual identifies thirty-five types of incidents classified into five areas: (1) physical qualification, (2) mental qualifications, (3) work habits and attitudes, (4) temperament, and (5) personal characteristics. Four breakdowns are laid out for each area as illustrated [14] in Figure 136. The record is accumulated over several weeks or months and separated on forms to show the favorable and unfavorable incidents. This method should be acceptable to unions because it provides tangible evidence without any tricks. It is also suggested as being illuminating in the matter of where training would lead to improvement of performance.

Conclusion of One Experienced in Merit Rating.

Regardless of all the techniques designed to guide and control the rating process, evaluations of employees in the final analysis are only opinions, and their value will depend largely upon the capacity of the persons doing the rating. Hence . . . we have favored keeping it (the plan) as simple as possible. We believe the main emphasis for improvement should be directed toward a better training of supervisors and foremen who are the raters in most instances.[15]

Many Qualities Have Been Used. J. B. Probst [16] has used as many as seventy-five actions or behavior characteristics for man rating. The instructions, cautions, etc., given by Mr. Probst are excellent and have been influential but we believe a smaller number of qualities can suffice.

The survey Figure 137 made by L. G. Spicer in 1949, when compared with a similar one made in 1940, indicates for hourly paid workers less stress on initiative and adaptability, more on job knowledge. Of these, Numbers 1, 2, 8, and 9 are measurable, whereas the others lack tangibility and must be graded. Of the qualities for salaried workers, Numbers 3, 4, and 14 are measurable. In either case the qualities can be broadly classified as: (A) pertaining directly to the job, and (B) pertaining to general worth. Note that the measurable qualities belong to class (A).

---

[14] J. C. Flanagan, "Principles and Procedures in Evaluating Performance," *Personnel*, XXVIII, No. 5.

[15] National Industrial Conference Board, *Studies in Personnel Policy*, No. 8, from which the "anonymous" examples have also been selected.

[16] Chicago Bureau of Public Personnel Administration, etc., *Technical Bulletin*, No. 4.

PERFORMANCE RECORD
WORK HABITS AND ATTITUDES

13. Response to Departmental Needs

4	3	2	1		1	2	3	4
5								5
6								6

a. Tried to get others to slow down, refuse tasks; b. Criticized equipment, facilities, methods unnecessarily; c. Was unwilling to perform work beyond his assignment or responsibility; d. Refused to pass along his idea for an improvement.

A. Tried to get co-workers to accept new rate, job, etc.; B. Increased his efficiency despite co-workers' resentment; C. Accepted extra work in spite of inconvenience; D. Accepted more difficult jobs; E. Suggested improved production procedures.

14. Getting Along with Others

4	3	2	1		1	2	3	4
5								5
6								6

a. Became upset or angry over work; b. Quarreled with fellow employees; c. Criticized, annoyed co-workers; d. Bossed co-worker; e. Interfered with equipment of another; f. Refused help to co-worker.

A. Remained calm under stress; B. Kept temper under provocation; C. Helped co-worker at inconvenience to self; D. Avoided friction by tact, consideration; E. Assisted fellow employee needing help.

15. Initiative

4	3	2	1		1	2	3	4
5								5
6								6

a. Failed to plan work when necessary; b. Failed to obtain tools until need arose; c. Failed to point out defective parts or operation; d. Failed to take action in an emergency.

A. Planned efficient ways of doing work; B. Stocked materials and tools ahead of time; C. Prepared work area, machine in advance; D. Volunteered for more responsible tasks; E. Voluntarily did work in addition to that expected; F. Pointed out defects on the line.

16. Responsibility

4	3	2	1		1	2	3	4
5								5
6								6

a. Passed up chance for more training; b. Passed up chance to learn more about the job; c. Gave misleading, incorrect instructions; d. Poorly directed work in foreman's absence.

A. Got additional information on his job, department; B. Took additional outside training; C. Got information on improving work; D. Planned a schedule for others; E. Trained, instructed other employees; F. Got cooperation between employees.

FIGURE 136. EXAMPLE OF CRITICAL INCIDENTS. (American Management Association.)

Number of Traits Used on Rating Scales	Hourly Employees	Salaried Employees
Most frequent number of traits used	6	10
Second most frequent number used	5	6

NAMES OF TRAITS MOST FREQUENTLY USED

Number	Hourly Employees	Number of Cos.	Number	Salaried Employees	Number of Cos.
1	Quality of Work	40	1	Job Knowledge	26
2	Quantity of Work	38	2	Initiative	26
3	Dependability	24	3	Quantity of Work	23
4	Job Knowledge	21	4	Quality of Work	22
5	Cooperation	21	5	Dependability	19
6	Initiative	19	6	Judgment	18
7	Attitude	17	7	Cooperation	18
8	Safety Habits	16	8	Attitude	14
9	Attendance	14	9	Leadership	13
10	Working Conditions	12	10	Working Relations	12
11	Learning Ability	12	11	Learning Ability	12
12	Adaptability	10	12	Appearance	11
13	Physical Condition	10	13	Personality	10
14	Personal Habits	9	14	Attendance	9

FIGURE 137. SURVEY OF QUALITIES IN USE. (From a survey made by Life Office Management Association, it appears that the five traits most used by life insurance companies for rating their clerical workers are: (1) accuracy, (2) dependability, (3) knowledge of work, (4) ability to work with others, and (5) efficiency.)

Again they may be more specifically classified as:

   a)   Present performance.
   b)   Supervision needed—responsibility.
   c)   Potential performance—promotability.
   d)   General behavior.
   e)   Personality assets.

Here classes (*a*) and (*b*) are the most definitely measurable. We draw this dividing line sharply because many managements include personality, cooperativeness, attitude, or other qualities belonging to classes (*c*), (*d*), and (*e*) which are scarcely measurable at all. Of course they have important bearings on the worth of the employee and perhaps they ought to be kept in for rating; if you weight them at all, however, you should weight them down, or train the raters to keep them down so they cannot predominate in the score or verdict. The aim is to base the scoring on incontestable facts as far as practicable. The intangible qualities, which can only be graded, can be helpfully kept in sight without trouble so long as they are minimized or excluded from the score. It is possible that information for guidance may prove more valuable than a scoring that cannot be taken at face value. The design of the plan would be influenced by this choice of emphasis.

Choice of Qualities. Obviously the limits to choice lie between what information is needed and what can be reliably obtained. Coupled with this is the question of whether over-all rating will be satisfactory or whether some analysis will be worth while. Over-all rating by means of ranking allows comparison of individuals who are not on the same job but it does not give all the specific information needed by the personnel department. To gain both objectives it is necessary to confine the rating to a few qualities that are important to most of the jobs and ignore other qualities. Another consideration is that the qualities should sample widely divergent aspects of each man's performance and at the same time be common enough in occurrence to be based on observable facts, not guesses. If seven to ten such qualities can be recognized, and described with definiteness, you have found the basis for a custom-made plan. By all means compare the choices made by other companies but follow principles in making your own choice and try to make simple but clean-cut definitions for both qualities and the degrees on which they are to be measured or graded. For the sake of simplicity we would confine the choice to (a), (b), and (c) using the most tangible on-the-job representations of these and without further subdivision.

If the objective in merit rating is special, such as establishing a guide to hiring, variation must be made for each distinct type of occupation, such as engineering, research, etc. If the objective is solely character appraisal, acquired traits can be ignored and such traits as initiative, responsibility, and leadership concentrated upon.

Complete Example. To represent the many different sorts of scales we have been showing fragments. We will now show one complete example, one portion for hourly jobs, Figure 139, and another for salaried, professional, or administrative positions, Figure 138. They constitute the plan of the Essex Rubber Company and are taken from *Merit Rating, Selected Case Histories,* a study prepared recently by L. F. Houten for the Dartnell Corporation of Chicago. In this report Mr. O. L. Evans, Essex's Director of Industrial Relations, explains that the ratings are made at four-month intervals by department heads who are trained to rate by means of group meetings. By way of appraisal he says, "the use of these forms definitely aids supervisors in improving the caliber of their

INSTRUCTIONS

READ CAREFULLY

1. Base your judgment on the entire period covered and not upon isolated incidents alone.

2. If ratings are made by more than one individual a complete understanding should be reached between them as to the exact meaning of the terms described below.

3. Place a check in the block which most nearly expresses your judgment on each factor.

4. For those employees who are rated at either extreme of the scale on any factor, for example, outstanding, deficient, limited, etc., please enter a brief explanation for the rating in the appropriate space below the factor.

5. Remember that your opinions are used also as a measure of your judgment.

6. Make your rating an accurate description of the employee rated.

Factors to be considered and rated:

1. PERSONAL PERFORMANCE:
Quality and amount of work done personally.

a. Quality of work performed:

| Inferior. Lacking in several respects. | Passable. Without marked merit. | Satisfactory. Meets standard requirements in all respects. Work results usually accurate and complete. | Above standard requirements. Very thorough and accurate. | Outstanding. Far exceeds normal requirements of accuracy and thoroughness. |

In your opinion has this employee's performance during the last six months with respect to this factor tended to (check one)

Improve   Remain the same   Deteriorate

Comments:...

b. Quantity of work performed:

| Exceptional. Volume is unexcelled | Produces a large volume of work. Consistently exceeds production of others doing similar work satisfactorily. | Satisfactory. Reasonable and adequate volume at all times. | Limited but passable. | Deficient. |

Improve   Remain the same   Deteriorate

Comments:...

☐ Improve ☐ Remain the same ☐ Deteriorate

☐ Requires close supervision. Often behind schedule.

☐ Work occasionally lags. Requires more than normal supervision.

☐ Performs work with reasonable promptness under normal supervision.

☐ Consistently reliable under normal conditions. Dues special as well as regular assignments promptly. Little or no supervision required.

☐ Work always on schedule, even under most difficult circumstances. Rises to emergencies and assumes leadership without being requested to do so.

Comments:

☐ Improve ☐ Remain the same ☐ Deteriorate

☐ Analyses and conclusions subject to frequent error and are often based on bias. Decisions require careful review by supervisor.

☐ Judgments usually sound on routine, simple matters but cannot be relied upon when any degree of complexity is involved.

☐ Capable of carefully analyzing day-to-day problems involving some complexity and rendering sound decisions. Decisions rarely influenced by prejudice or personal bias.

☐ Decisions can be accepted without question except when problems of extreme complexity are involved. Little or no personal bias enters into judgment.

☐ Possesses unusual comprehension and analytical ability. Complete reliance may be placed on all judgments irrespective of degree of complexity. Decisions and judgments are completely free of personal bias or prejudice.

Comments:

☐ Improve ☐ Remain the same ☐ Deteriorate

3. RESOURCEFULNESS:
Initiative, vision, originality. Ability to seek and find new ideas and new ways to do a job.

☐ Work is consistently characterized by marked originality, alertness, initiative and imagination. Can be relied on to develop new ideas and techniques in solving the most difficult problems.

☐ Frequently develops new ideas and methods of merit. Handling of emergencies is generally characterized by sound decisive action.

☐ Meets new situations in satisfactory manner. Occasionally develops original ideas, methods, and techniques.

☐ Follows closely previously learned methods, and procedures. Slow to adapt to changes. Tends to become confused in new situations.

☐ Limited. Requires frequent reinstruction. Has failed to demonstrate initiative or imagination in solving work problems.

Comments:

FIGURE 138. COMPLETE EXAMPLE OF MERIT RATING FOR SALARIED EMPLOYEES (Dartnell Personnel Administration Service.)

In your opinion has this employee's performance during the last six months with respect to this factor tended to (check one)

☐ Improve   ☐ Remain the same   ☐ Deteriorate

4. COOPERATION:
Teamwork, attitude toward work, company and associates and his willingness to work with and for others.

| ☐ Obstructive. Has frequently exhibited undesirable attitude toward cooperation with associates and superiors. | ☐ Sometimes difficult to handle. Occasionally tactless. | ☐ Satisfactory. Usually cooperative in most matters. | ☐ Willingly contributes extra effort and energy to cooperate with other people. Has enthusiastic work attitude. | ☐ Habitual cooperation, helpfulness, loyalty, and enthusiasm toward job, associates and company. Sets example for other employees. Makes an outstanding contribution to morale. |

Comments: ....

THIS ITEM TO BE ANSWERED BY MERIT RATING SECTION ONLY.

5. SERVICE RECORD:
Length of service.
Seniority

| ☐ 1 year | ☐ 2 years | ☐ 3 years | ☐ 4 years | ☐ 5 years or more |

Absences

| ☐ 10 or more | ☐ 7 to 10 | ☐ 4 to 6 | ☐ 1 - 3 | ☐ none |

DO NOT RATE EMPLOYEE ON FACTORS 6 AND 7 UNLESS HE OCCUPIES A SUPERVISORY POSITION.

6. SUPERVISION & LEADERSHIP:
a. Selection and assignment of personnel:

| ☐ Deficient. Subordinates considered as a group are weak. Capable personnel are not utilized to full extent of abilities. | ☐ Selection tends to be spotty. Full utilization of abilities of staff is not secured. | ☐ Satisfactory. Average or above. Selection and utilization generally adequate. | ☐ Considered as a group, staff selections are of a superior character. Makes effective assignments. | ☐ An excellent judge and analyst of the abilities and capacities of people. Selections and assignments are outstanding. |

☐ Improve   ☐ Remain the same   ☐ Deteriorate

Comments: ....

b. Training, guidance and development of subordinates:

☐ An excellent instructor whose organization is always well informed. Is recognized as outstanding in his ability to train and develop personnel.

☐ Recognizes need and value of a development program. Trains and develops subordinates in an effective, competent manner.

☐ Does a satisfactory job, particularly if needs and methods are outlined.

☐ Does not fulfill all requirements of satisfactory performance. Either fails to recognize need or not inclined to undertake constructive positive effort.

Comments: ....

☐ Improve   ☐ Remain the same   ☐ Deteriorate

c. Relationship to subordinates—ability to develop a harmonious and effective organization:

☐ Lacks full support and cooperation of associates. Easily prejudiced for or against. Maintains weak or poor discipline.

☐ Enjoys only passive support and cooperation of subordinates. Not sufficiently objective or impersonal in relationships.

☐ Obtains good support and cooperation. May encounter occasional difficulties in relationships with subordinates, but none of a serious nature.

☐ Is a strong leader who has the willing support and cooperation of his subordinates. Rarely experiences even minor difficulties.

☐ Is an outstanding example of leadership. Always has the enthusiastic support and cooperation of his subordinates even under difficult circumstances.

Comments: ....

☐ Improve   ☐ Remain the same   ☐ Deteriorate

d. Delegation of responsibilities and authority:

☐ Exercises excellent judgment in delegation of responsibility and authority. Subordinates know exactly what is expected under all circumstances.

☐ Subordinates have better than average understanding of their functions and relationships. Devotes adequate time to planning and direction.

☐ Satisfactory. Generally exercises good judgment. May occasionally experience a lack of understanding on the part of subordinates.

☐ Does not delegate wisely. Subordinates have too much or too little authority. Subordinates sometimes lack a clear understanding of what is expected of them.

☐ Overburdens himself with unnecessary detail which prevents giving time and attention to supervision and direction. Conflicts frequently arise between subordinates as to responsibility.

Comments: ....

☐ Improve   ☐ Remain the same   ☐ Deteriorate

FIGURE 138. *(Continued.)*

In your opinion has this employee's performance during the last six months with respect to this factor tended to (check one)

☐ Improve   ☐ Remain the same   ☐ Deteriorate

7. UNIT PERFORMANCE:
Quality and amount of accomplishment of unit under his supervision. Consider economy of operation.

Quality of work performed:

☐ Deficient.
☐ Usually passable but does not meet standard of satisfactory.
☐ Satisfactory. Meets normal requirements.
☐ Superior. Above normal requirements.
☐ Outstanding.

Comments: ....

b. Quantity of work performed:

☐ Limited. Below average.
☐ Average to below standard requirements.
☐ Satisfactory. Reasonable and adequate volume at all times.
☐ Produces a large volume of work. Consistently exceeds production of others doing similar work satisfactorily.
☐ Exceptional. Volume is unexcelled.

Comments: ....

c. Dependability in getting work done:

☐ Work always on schedule even under most difficult circumstances. Rises to emergencies and assumes leadership without being requested.
☐ Consistently reliable under normal conditions. Does special as well as regular assignments promptly. Little or no supervision required.
☐ Performs work with reasonable promptness under normal supervision.
☐ Work occasionally lags. Requires more than normal supervision.
☐ Requires close supervision. Often behind schedule.

Comments: ....

8. TO BE MORE EFFECTIVE ON PRESENT JOB, THIS EMPLOYEE SHOULD:

1. Be given additional instruction on ....
2. Be given additional experience on such jobs as ....
3. Study such subjects as ....

4. Change his attitude as follows: ....

5. There is nothing more that I can do for him because. ....

6. Remarks: ....

9. **Without reference to the foregoing factors, please describe briefly your opinion of this man's overall value to the Company.** ....

10. **PROMOTION POTENTIAL:**
In your considered judgment—during the next six months or year—should this employee be:
(Please check your reason)

☐ Kept on the same job?

  ☐ a. Satisfactory on this job but no promotion "potential" shown yet.

  ☐ b. Not ready for promotion, though is promotional material.

  ☐ c. No replacement available, though is promotional material.

  ☐ d. No other job in line of promotion or transfer.

  ☐ e. Undecided.

☐ Promoted? To what job?
  Describe: ....

☐ Released?
  ☐ a. Unsatisfactory.
  ☐ b. Temporary work.

☐ Transferred?
  ☐ a. For further training and experience.
  ☐ b. Not suited to this job; try on some other job.
  Describe: ....

This review   was   was not   discussed with employee on ....

His reactions were ....

Signature.................... Date....................
                  Rating supervisor

Signature.................... Date....................
                  Reviewing supervisor

FIGURE 138. (*Concluded.*)

employees. Supervisors in turn are partly rated (indirectly) through the composite scores of their departmental employees." In practice Figure 141 has an additional front page listing: employee's name, job title, division, department—section, and rating period.

Training Raters Important. As R. S. Driver says, "be prepared to devote considerable energy to merit rating maintenance as well as to its installation." The important factor in this maintenance is training. Every care must be taken to see that all raters understand the meanings of the qualities, precautions to keep in mind, etc. This is best accomplished through meetings called and conducted by the merit rating staff of the Personnel Department. Best practice devotes forty hours to this training but it must be repeated.

Ingrades for Man-Differentials. When the contest over automatic time progressions vs. management-determined progressions was raging before the National War Labor Board, 1943–45, the unions were vehement in claiming that "the merit increase system resulted in favoritism, delay, and inefficiency; that retention by management of complete discretion in making promotions in effect removed rates of a large portion of workers from the sphere of collective bargaining." The second Maxson decision gave the union the right to negotiate concerning the standards which were to govern the granting of merit increases but the parties failed to agree on the "objective standards," so that the Board had to reconsider its own decision. In 1945 the Washington Board therefore reverted to the first Maxson formula as written by Regional Board No. 2. We have already explained in Chapter 11 how this gave the union the victory on progressions below the mid-line. Increases above the mid-line were thereafter to be determined by the employer on the basis of merit with the employee right of appeal. Thus the Board finally recognized "the propriety of management making the initial determination as to granting or withholding merit increases and . . . the propriety of the union filing and prosecuting grievances as to whether these determinations are in accordance with the agreed standards through the grievance procedure of the contract, including arbitration if necessary." For Supreme Court decision see p. 327.

Figure 140 repeats the sample rate structure used in Chapter 11 to illustrate the use of ingrades below the mid-line and here illustrates the use of ingrades above the mid-line. We have arbitrarily made four such ingrades for all job classes. This fits the use of 60 per cent for qualifying only, plus 10 per cent steps to the 100 per cent limit. When merit rating scores are so tied to ingrades there can be a semi-automatic progression for man-differentials.

NAME & CLOCK NO. _____ DEPARTMENT _____

OCCUPATION _____ CLASS _____ GROUP _____ DATE _____

WHAT HAS HE DONE?

QUALITY OF WORK—THIS FACTOR APPRAISES THE EMPLOYEE'S PERFORMANCE IN MEETING ESTAB-LISHED QUALITY STANDARDS.

☐ ☐	☐ ☐	☐	☐ ☐
Does he consistently do an excellent job? Are rejects and errors very rare?	Does he usually do a good job? Does he seldom make errors?	Is his work usually passable? Must you sometimes tell him to do a better job?	Is he careless? Does his work only get by? Does he often make mistakes?

QUANTITY OF WORK—THIS FACTOR APPRAISES THE EMPLOYEE'S OUTPUT OF SATISFACTORY WORK.

☐	☐	☐	☐ ☐
Is his output unusually high? Is he exceptionally fast?	Does he usually do more than is expected? Is he fast?	Does he turn out the required amount of work, but seldom more?	Is he slow? Is his output frequently below the required amount?

WHAT CAN HE DO?

ADAPTABILITY—THIS FACTOR APPRAISES THE EMPLOYEE'S ABILITY TO MEET CHANGED CONDITIONS AND THE EASE WITH WHICH HE LEARNS NEW DUTIES.

☐ ☐	☐ ☐	☐	☐ ☐
Does he learn new duties and meet changed conditions very quickly and easily?	Can he turn from one type of work to another or grasp new ideas if given a little time and instruction? Does he adjust himself to new work with little difficulty?	Is he a routine worker? Does he require detailed instruction on new duties and methods?	Is he slow to learn, requiring repeated instructions? Does he have great difficulty in adjusting himself to new work?

JOB KNOWLEDGE—THIS FACTOR APPRAISES HOW WELL THE EMPLOYEE KNOWS HIS JOB.

☐ ☐	☐ ☐	☐ ☐	☐ ☐
Is he an expert on his job? Does he make the most of his knowledge and experience? Is he a self-starter?	Is he well-informed on his job and related work, rarely needing assistance and instruction, but asking when necessary?	Does he know his job fairly well? Does he regularly require supervision and instructions?	Is his knowledge of his job limited? Does he show little desire or ability to improve himself?

CAN YOU RELY ON HIM?

DEPENDABILITY—THIS FACTOR APPRAISES YOUR CONFIDENCE IN THE EMPLOYEE TO CARRY OUT ALL INSTRUCTIONS CONSCIENTIOUSLY.

☐ ☐	☐ ☐	☐ ☐	☐ ☐
When you give him a job to do, have you the utmost confidence that you will get what you want when you want it?	Does he follow instructions and do what you expect him to do with little follow-up?	Does he generally follow instructions but occasionally need following up?	Does he require frequent follow-up even on routine duties?

ATTITUDE—THIS FACTOR APPRAISES THE EMPLOYEE'S OPEN-MINDEDNESS, AND HIS WILLINGNESS TO COOPERATE IN CARRYING OUT SAFETY AND OTHER COMPANY POLICIES.

☐ ☐	☐ ☐	☐ ☐	☐ ☐
Is he an exceptionally good team worker? Does he invariably go out of his way to cooperate? Is he always ready to try out new ideas?	Does he meet others half way and go out of his way to cooperate? Is he usually ready to try out new ideas?	Does he usually cooperate, but with some reluctance to accept suggestions and try out new ideas?	Does he cooperate only when he has to? Is he unwilling to try out new ideas? Does he have little interest in his job?

RATED BY _____ APPROVED BY _____ TOTAL POINTS _____

(OVER)

FIGURE 139. COMPLETE EXAMPLE OF MERIT RATING FOR HOURLY PAID EMPLOYEES. (Dartnell Personnel Administration Service.)

GENERAL COMMENTS

1. ALL IN ALL, ARE YOU SATISFIED WITH THIS EMPLOYEE AND HIS PROGRESS? EXPLAIN.

2. IN YOUR OPINION, IS THIS EMPLOYEE PERFORMING THE TASK BEST SUITED TO HIS ABILITY? DO YOU RECOMMEND PROMOTION, TRANSFER, DEMOTION OR DISCHARGE?

3. WHAT ESPECIALLY DESIRABLE GOOD TRAITS DOES HE HAVE?

4. ALONG WHAT LINES DO YOU FEEL THAT HE NEEDS TO IMPROVE HIMSELF?

5. IS HE DOING ANYTHING TO IMPROVE HIMSELF?

6. WHAT IS HIS RECORD AND ATTITUDE AS TO SAFETY?

7. WRITE HERE ANY ADDITIONAL COMMENTS, GOOD OR BAD, WHICH YOU FEEL HAVE NOT BEEN COVERED.

REASON FOR RE-RATING PRIOR TO REGULAR PERIODIC RATING:

DATE OF RE-RATING _____ **RE-RATED BY** _____

FIGURE 139. (*Concluded.*)

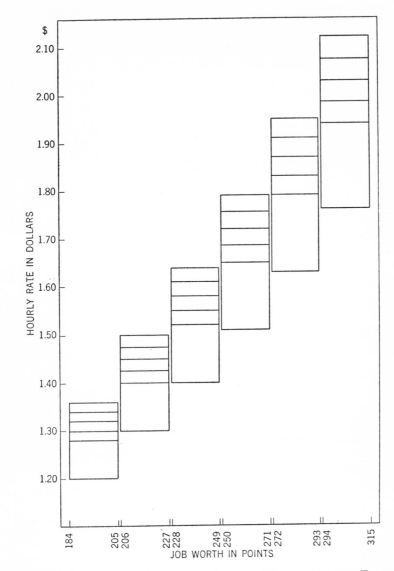

FIGURE 140. SAMPLE RATE STRUCTURE. CONSTANT WORTH RANGE OF TWENTY-ONE POINTS. SEMILOG ACCELERATION FOR TREND AND LIMITS. LOWER END 10 PER CENT MONEY SPREAD. UPPER END 25 PER CENT MONEY SPREAD. UPPER HALVES DIVIDED INTO FOUR INGRADES FOR SEMIAUTOMATIC MERIT PROGRESSIONS.

YEAR________ NAME________ PR NO.________

DATE	SERVICE MAX. 20 POINTS			ATTENDANCE MAX. 20 POINTS		QUALITY MAX. 20 POINTS		PROD. MAX. 25 POINTS		CITIZEN MAX. 20 POINTS	VERSAT'Y MAX. 20 POINTS	TOTAL CREDIT RATING	OPERATION		HOURLY RATE			
	YRS.	MO.	PTS.	%	PTS.	%	PTS.	%	PTS.	PTS.	PTS.		NO.	NAME	MAX.	CALC.	DATE	PRE-SENT
JAN.																		
FEB.																		
MAR.																		
APR.																		
MAY																		
JUN.																		
JUL.																		
AUG																		
SEP.																		
OCT.																		
NOV.																		
DEC																		
JAN.																		
FEB.																		
MAR.																		
APR.																		
MAY																		
JUN.																		
JUL.																		
AUG.																		
SEP.																		
OCT.																		
NOV.																		
DEC.																		

EAP 4377 CREDIT RATING CARD

FIGURE 141. EMPLOYEE CREDIT RATING CARD. (Cheney Bros.)

Forms for Operation. Only two forms are necessary besides the original data sheets for rating. They are: (1) an employee rating record (Figure 141) which can be made a complete follow-up or progress record and (2) an employee rating summary (Figure 142). The former is kept for each employee separately and the latter brings together a group of employees such as a department; if the department is large, it can be broken down by functional or location centers. Besides employee names and jobs, both have such headings as classification, group identification, total rating, detailed

OCC. NO._____ MIN. RATE_____ MAX. RATE_____										
Clock No.	Name	Quality	Quantity	Adapt-ability	Job Know-ledge	Depend-ability	Attitude	Total Points	Pres. Rate	Rev. Rate

FIGURE 142. MERIT RATING COMPARISON SUMMARY. (Farrel-Birmingham Company.)

rating by qualities, names of raters, dates, etc. The employee card should also show the money rate range. The employee card used by the National Metal Trades Association provides, on the back, columns for adaptability—Good At, Fair At, Some Knowledge, Remarks, etc., as a guide to transfer or promotion. Some use a summary sheet to check the ratings for consistency and incidentally as an aid to training the raters. Average ratings for departments are also used as checks.

Use of Employee Ratings. Full benefit of a merit rating plan cannot be attained if it is carried on unbeknown to the employees. Each employee should be given an appointment with his adviser in the Personnel Department every six months or more frequently if desired, and the whole thing should be gone over, tactfully, of course. Conversely, the employees should not be allowed to see or hear about one another's ratings. If this is done wisely it can have a tremendous effect for the better. This means that each employee must know the criteria on which he is rated as well as the ratings.

Eli Lilly and Company of Indianapolis has even made a lay-out which anticipates the several possible outcomes of a corrective interview (see Figure 143). Below the graphic layout are explanations for the numbered steps. In their own words,

These phrases are suggested as being helpful when beginning to use this pattern. They are not insisted upon, and once the pattern is mastered, you will probably find better phrases for carrying you over the critical points in the pattern, where if you know what to say, you are prepared to carry through your corrective interview smoothly.

Period Between Ratings. Rerating is usually done every six months, although some companies do it only on the anniversary of an employee's entrance. The Lincoln Electric Company rates every six weeks. A committee studies the employees who have the highest ratings and uses transfer as a preparation for promotion. New employees should be rated at least every three months if not every month for a while for the sake of guidance, even though there is little chance of their achieving a higher differential at once. If an employee's rating indicates that his individual differential should be reduced, he can be shown the facts by way of warning and then be allowed another three or four months before the scheduled reduction must go into effect. Under these circumstances he will usually achieve a subsequent and satisfactory rating that will make the change unnecessary. Thus it is possible to stimulate all toward self-discipline, which is the surest path to upgrading. Every rate, base plus individual differential, will be acquired according to policy, deliberately set in advance, or mutually bargained.

Limited Merit Rating for Incentive Workers. The Bliley Electric Company has an eleven-characteristic, weighted point plan of job evaluation from which it fixes "pay brackets" for all jobs. The line of bottom bracket rates is gauged for qualified workers and the ranges from that to the line of top bracket rates are used for recognition of merit, that is, as an employee achieves merit points above 60, he moves up in rate until his maximum limit is attained on 100 points. New employees who are not already qualified are guaranteed subbracket rates which advance automatically on a time schedule from the date of hiring but may be enhanced by merit ratings.

After the twelve-week training period each employee gets the bottom rate of his bracket plus any increments earned through merit rating, which is redetermined at regular four-week intervals for incentive workers, trainees, and new transfers, but only at twelve-week intervals for qualified hourly workers. No merit rating is made until two weeks have elapsed after hiring. The novel feature of this

BEFORE	DURING				AFTER
Consider	I. State Problem	II. Get Employee's Reaction	III. Consider Appropriate Action with Employee	IV. State Plan of Action	
Facts	(1) Purpose				Initiate Action
Probable Causes	(2) Good Points	Agree	(8) N.G. (9) Sup's None Sug.		Observe Results
Possible Actions	(3) Weak Points	(4) (Stop)	(7) Emp's O.K. Sug.	(10) Corrective Action	Follow-up
		(6) No Point			
		Disagree	Requires Study	(11) Rain Check	
Approach		(5) Point			
Self					

Statement (1) is: ". . . I'd like to talk to you about your job to see if we can help you improve . . ." This statement would fit in very well at the beginning of the interview. It would explain the purpose of the discussion.

Number (2) is: ". . . There are some things you're doing very well . . ." This could be used to begin telling the employee about his outstanding points in brief and specific terms.

Number (3) is: ". . . But I'm concerned about these facts . . ." This could be used to tell the employee about his weaknesses. These weak points are merely mentioned as *facts* on the same footing as any other points brought out in this first step. The supervisor is careful not to raise any question of motives. So far as he is concerned, all motives are good motives. The employee wants to do the right thing if he can find out what it is and if it is within his ability. Therefore, in this step, the supervisor essentially compares things which the employee does well with things in which he needs to improve.

Number (4) is: ". . . Do you think I've interpreted the situation properly? By using this question, the supervisor can commence getting the employee's reaction to the weaknesses that have just been stated.

Number (5) is: ". . . I'm glad you told me those things; they may change the picture somewhat . . ." This phrase might be used if the supervisor had received some material facts from the employee.

Number (6) is: ". . . Yes, but there are still these facts which need attention . . ." The supervisor would use this phrase if the employee has replied with facts which were immaterial.

Number (7) is: ". . . Do you have any suggestions as to what we can do?" This question would be used to obtain the employee's suggestion for the plan of action.

Number (8) is: ". . . I'm sorry, but because of . . . , I don't think that would work." This phrase would be used by the supervisor in case the employee came up with a suggestion that would not be satisfactory.

Number (9) is: ". . . Suppose we try . . ." If the supervisor has to make a suggestion, this phase might be used.

Number (10) is: ". . . I'm sure you'll work this out." The supervisor might use this phrase in closing the interview.

Number (11) is: ". . . I'll check on this and discuss it with you further." In giving the employee a rain check, this phrase might be used.

FIGURE 143. A LAYOUT AND SUGGESTED LEADS FOR THE CORRECTIVE INTERVIEW. (Eli Lilly & Company, Indianapolis.)

EMPLOYEE RATING SHEET
BLILEY ELECTRIC COMPANY
BLILEY MFG. CORPORATION

Effective Date _____

	Unsatisfactory or Untrained	Below Requirements	Meets Requirements	Exceeds Requirements	Very Superior
WORK (Mental and Physical) Are necessary physical and visual effort and required mental concentration being used?	7	11	15	18	20
SKILL (Education and Experience) Does employee have necessary job knowledge and proper mastery of all skills required?	13	21	27	32	36
RESPONSIBILITY (Mat'l, Equip., Safety, Supervision) How much care is taken to turn out good work, use equipment properly, work safely? (or to supervise same?)	7	11	15	18	20
INITIATIVE AND INGENUITY How well does employee make necessary decisions and use initiative and ingenuity when required?	7	11	15	18	20

SENIORITY

Less than 3 Months	3-9 Months	9-18 Months	18 Months and Over
0	6	8	10

TOTAL POINTS _____

Eff. Date _____

New Rate _____

Rate Remains at _____

REASON: _____

Employee Rating _____

Transfer _____

Guar. Min. _____

Other _____

Remarks _____

Rated by _____ Ck'd. by _____

Signed _____

FIGURE 144a. EMPLOYEE RATING SHEET. (Bliley Electric Company.)

EMPLOYEE RATING SHEET

BILEY ELECTRIC COMPANY — BLILEY MFG. CORP.

Effective Date

PER CENT OF STANDARD PRODUCTION

	Less than 33%	33 to 37	38 to 42	43 to 47	48 to 52	53 to 57	58 to 62	63 to 67	68 to 72	73 to 77	78 to 82	83 to 87	88 to 92	93 to 97	98 to 102	103 to 107	108 to 112	113 to 117	118 to 122	123 to 127	128 to 132	133 or over
19 pt.	22	25	29	32	35	38	42	45	48	51	54	58	61	64	67	70	74	77	80	83	86	

RESPONSIBILITY FOR MATERIAL

Extreme Spoilage	Exceeds Allowed Spoilage	Allowed Spoilage	No Spoilage
0	3	4	5

RESPONSIBILITY FOR EQUIPMENT

No Regard for Equipment	Careless Use of Equipment	Required Care of Equipment	Great Care in Use of Equipment
0	3	4	5

SENIORITY

Less than 3 Months	3-9 Months	9-18 Months	18 Months and Over
0	6	8	10

TOTAL POINTS

Eff. Date_____

New Rate_____

Rate Remains at_____

REASON·

Employee Rating_____

Transfer_____

Guar. Min._____

Other_____

Remarks_____

Rated by_____ Ck'd by_____

Signed_____

FIGURE 144b. EMPLOYEE RATING SHEET. (*Reverse.*)

Standard Form No. 51
Appr. Jan. 5, 1942
C. S. C. Dept. Cir. No. 302

REPORT OF EFFICIENCY RATING

REGULAR ( ); INTERIM ( )
PROBATIONARY—1ST ( ) 2D ( )

Classification Symbols

(Service) (Grade) (Class)

As of _____ based on performance during period from _____ to _____

_____ (Name of employee)

_____ (Title of position)

_____ (Bureau)

_____ (Division) _____ (Section) _____ (Subsection or unit) _____ (Field office)

ON LINES BELOW MARK EMPLOYEE

√ if adequate
— if weak
+ if outstanding

1. Underline the elements which are especially important in the position.
2. Rate only on elements pertinent to the position.
   a. Do not rate on elements in *italics* except for employees in administrative, supervisory, or planning positions.
   b. Rate administrative, supervisory, and planning employees on all elements pertinent to the position whether in *italics* or not.
3. Before rating, become thoroughly familiar with instructions in the rating manual.

CHECK ONE

Administrative, supervisory, or planning _____ ☐

All others _____ ☐

(1) Maintenance of equipment, tools, instruments.
(2) Mechanical skill.
(3) Skill in the application of techniques and procedures.
(4) Presentability of work (appropriateness of arrangement and appearance of work).
(5) Attention to broad phases of assignments.
(6) Attention to pertinent detail.
(7) Accuracy of operations.
(8) Accuracy of final results.
(9) Accuracy of judgments or decisions.
(10) Effectiveness in presenting ideas or facts.
(11) Industry.
(12) Rate of progress on or completion of assignments.

(21) *Effectiveness in planning broad programs.*
(22) *Effectiveness in adapting the work program to broader or related programs.*
(23) *Effectiveness in devising procedures.*
(24) *Effectiveness in laying out work and establishing standards of performance for subordinates.*
(25) *Effectiveness in directing, reviewing, and checking the work of subordinates.*
(26) *Effectiveness in instructing, training, and developing subordinates in the work.*
(27) *Effectiveness in promoting high working morale.*
(28) *Effectiveness in determining space, personnel, and equipment needs.*
(29) *Effectiveness in setting and obtaining adherence to time limits and deadlines.*

(13) Amount of acceptable work produced. (Is mark based on production records? _____ (Yes or no))

(14) Ability to organize his work.

(15) Effectiveness in meeting and dealing with others.

(16) Cooperativeness.

(17) Initiative.

(18) Resourcefulness.

(19) Dependability.

(20) Physical fitness for the work.

(30) Ability to make decisions.

(31) Effectiveness in delegating clearly defined authority to act.

STATE ANY OTHER ELEMENTS CONSIDERED

(A) _____

(B) _____

(C) _____

STANDARD

Deviations must be explained on reverse side of this form

	Adjective rating	Numerical rating
All underlined elements marked plus, and no element marked minus	Excellent	1
A majority of underlined elements marked plus, and no element marked minus	Very good	2 or 3
All underlined elements marked at least with a check, and minus marks fully compensated by plus marks, or—a majority of underlined elements marked at least with a check, and minus marks on underlined elements overcompensated by plus marks on underlined elements	Good	4, 5, or 6
A majority of underlined elements marked at least with a check, and minus marks not fully compensated by plus marks	Fair	7 or 8
A majority of underlined elements marked minus	Unsatisfactory	9

	Adjective rating	Numerical rating
Rating official	_____	_____
Reviewing official	_____	_____

On the whole, do you consider the conduct of this employee to be satisfactory? _____ (Yes or no) _____ (See back of form)

Rated by _____ (Signature of rating official) _____ (Title) _____ (Date)

Reviewed by _____ (Signature of reviewing official) _____ (Title) _____ (Date)

Rating approved by efficiency rating committee _____ (Date) Report to employee _____ (Adjective rating) . _____ (Numerical rating)

16—26177-1

FIGURE 144c. REPORT OF EFFICIENCY RATING. Reverse contains a conduct report and an explanation of deviations from standards, each with provision for signatures of reporting persons. The Personnel Research Section, Adjutant General's Office, War Department, has recently completed an Army-wide study of efficiency rating.

plan is the differentiation in merit qualities and weights to supplement the two kinds of payment, by the hour or "nonproduction" (Figure 144*a*), and by efficiency-bonus or "production" (Figure 144*b*). Furthermore, each incentive job has its specific merit rating sheet in order to use different weightings as may be suggested by job evaluation. This allows adjustment between quality and quantity, etc. These harmonious but varied arrangements may be compared as follows:

EXAMPLE OF AVERAGE RATING

Time Paid "Nonproduction"				Incentive-Paid "Production"
Work	15	} 57	60	{ Efficiency in per cent of standard production
Skill	27			
Initiative	15			
				Responsibility
Responsibility	15	12 {	8	for Material
			4	for Equipment
Seniority	8		8	Seniority
	—		—	
	80		80	

Note that in the nonproduction arrangement the first four parts are combinations of characteristics used in job evaluation. These are in a brace. The merit rating qualities are supposed to be "tied in" with the others. This idea comes from the depression fad called "Measured Day Rate," which we have never accepted as sound practice, but the separate arrangement for production payment looks very good. The merit part is kept to minority influence and avoids the double credit which comes for production when a single arrangement is used alike for incentive and hourly paid work. Even here there is a compromise. Four weeks is overlong for calculating production efficiency and overshort for calculating other merits (Figure 144*c*).

Case of Full Cooperation. A case of union-management cooperation in both job evaluation and merit rating which has brought distinct improvement in all respects is that of the Air Associates, Inc., and the I. U. U., A. A. and A. I. W. of A., CIO. The rating is done quarterly by the foreman and the shop steward concerned, with assistance of personnel staff.[17]

Merit Rating for Higher Job Holders. For holders of higher jobs rating once a year may be sufficient. Scales for rating may be similar to those used for holders of hourly paid jobs but should be readapted to bring out in part additional or different attributes.

[17] See also N. L. A. Martucci, "A Joint Management-Labor Merit Rating Program," *Personnel*, XXIV, No. 1.

MERIT RATING REPORT FOR EXEMPT EMPLOYEES

DATE _____   SCORE _____

NAME OF EMPLOYEE _____ RATED BY _____
                                                                SUPERVISOR

CLASSIFICATION _____ DEPT. _____ REVIEWED BY _____
                                                         DIV. OR DEPT. HEAD

QUALITY OF WORK - ABILITY TO MEET QUALITY STANDARDS IN DUTIES NOT DELEGATED TO SUBORDINATES.

[ ]20 [ ]18	[ ]16 [ ]14 [ ]12	[ ]10 [ ]8 [ ]6	[ ]4 [ ]2
Exceptionally accurate - practically no mistakes.	Meets normal standards - very few errors.	Often below standard - work needs checking.	Frequent errors - slipshod work.

QUANTITY OF WORK - SPEED AND EFFICIENCY IN PERFORMING DUTIES NOT DELEGATED TO SUBORDINATES.

[ ]20 [ ]18	[ ]16 [ ]14]]12	[ ]10 [ ]8 [ ]6	[ ]4 [ ]2
Unusually high - more than required.	Speed and efficiency satisfy normal job requirements.	Needs prodding - does not always do his best.	Efficiency poor - turns out less than he should.

JOB KNOWLEDGE - EXTENT OF JOB INFORMATION AND UNDERSTANDING POSSESSED BY EMPLOYEE.

[ ]20 [ ]18	[ ]16 [ ]14 [ ]12	[ ]10 [ ]8 [ ]6	[ ]4 [ ]2
Thorough grasp of job and more besides.	Good working knowledge of job.	Knowledge limited - needs to be shown.	Lacks sufficient knowledge of job.

ADAPTABILITY - CAN HE MEET CHANGED CONDITIONS? HOW FAST DOES HE LEARN NEW DUTIES?

[ ]10 [ ]9	[ ]8 [ ]7 [ ]6	[ ]5 [ ]4 [ ]3	[ ]2
Highly flexible - does well on several types of work.	Makes satisfactory adjustments on new or different work.	Has some difficulty on new or different work.	Can do only his own job.

INITIATIVE - EXTENT TO WHICH EMPLOYEE IS A "SELF-STARTER" IN ATTAINING OBJECTIVES OF JOB.

[ ]10 [ ]9	[ ]8 [ ]7 [ ]6	[ ]5 [ ]4 [ ]3	[ ]2
Unusual initiative - beyond that which present job can fully utilize.	Usually goes ahead on own initiative - satisfies job requirements.	His application of initiative is spotty.	Lacks sufficient initiative to attain required job objectives.

DEPENDABILITY - EMPLOYEE'S RELIABILITY IN DOING AN ASSIGNED JOB.

[ ]10 [ ]9	[ ]8 [ ]7 [ ]6	[ ]5 [ ]4 [ ]3	[ ]2 [ ]1
Always reliable on important and complex matters. Justifies utmost confidence.	Applies himself well - occasional supervision.	Not always reliable - needs considerable supervision.	Cannot be relied on - needs constant supervision.

TEAMWORK - EXTENT TO WHICH EMPLOYEE COOPERATES WITH AND EFFECTIVELY INFLUENCES PEOPLE HE CONTACTS.

[ ]5 [ ]4.5	[ ]4 [ ]3.5 [ ]3	[ ]2.5 [ ]2 [ ]1.5	[ ]1 [ ].5
Obtains highest respect and cooperation from others.	Maintains effective working relations with others- Generally cooperative.	Shows reluctance to cooperate - does not always get along well with others.	Relations too ineffective to retain in job without improvement.

ATTENDANCE - REGULARITY WITH WHICH EMPLOYEE REPORTS TO WORK.

[ ]5 [ ]4.5	[ ]4 [ ]3.5 [ ]3	[ ]2.5 [ ]2 [ ]1.5	[ ]1 [ ].5
Rarely absent.	Occasional excused absence	Frequently absent without good reason.	Habitually absent.

_____ NET SCORE (FOR NON-SUPERVISORY EMPLOYEES, THIS IS THE TOTAL ENTERED AT TOP OF PAGE.)

ITEMS BELOW THESE LINES ARE MARKED ONLY IN RATING SUPERVISORY EMPLOYEES.

PERFORMANCE OF GROUP SUPERVISED - AMOUNT AND EFFECTIVENESS OF ACCOMPLISHMENTS OF THE GROUP.

[ ]20 [ ]18	[ ]16 [ ]14 [ ]12	[ ]10 [ ]8 [ ]6	[ ]4 [ ]2
Unusual amount of effective accomplishments.	Group effort meets and may at times exceed normal requirements.	Efficiency below requirements.	Performance completely inadequate.

ABILITY TO ORGANIZE - CAPACITY FOR PLANNING WORK WELL AND GETTING SUBORDINATES TO EXECUTE PLAN.

[ ]15 [ ]13.5	[ ]12 [ ]10.5 [ ]9	[ ]7.5 [ ]6 [ ]4.5	[ ]3 [ ]1.5
Exceptional ability to plan and make plan work.	Activities well planned and carried out.	Planning and/or execution of plan inadequate in some respects.	Planning too poor to retain in job without improvement.

ABILITY TO DEVELOP SUBORDINATES - EXTENT TO WHICH SUPERVISOR UTILIZES ABILITIES OF SUBORDINATES.

[ ]15 [ ]13.5	[ ]12 [ ]10.5 [ ]9	[ ]7.5 [ ]6 [ ]4.5	[ ]3 [ ]1.5
Unusual ability to utilize subordinates.	Effective in utilizing subordinates.	Deficient in utilization of subordinates.	Not enough ability to satisfy job requirements.

_____ NET SCORE FOR SUPERVISORY EMPLOYEES. (ENTER AT TOP OF PAGE)

FIGURE 145. MERIT RATING REPORT FOR EXEMPT EMPLOYEES. (W. L. Maxson Corporation.)

The W. L. Maxson Corporation merely adds three attributes for application to supervisors. One of these is measurable, namely, Performance of Group Supervised—Amount and Effectiveness of Accomplishments of the Group. The other two attributes must be graded by the department head or whoever is immediately over the supervisor. See Figures 145, 146, and 147.

As indicated previously any merit rating should be designed to bring out information regarding the promotability of each employee and used as an aid to development for holding higher jobs. This has been increasingly recognized and is now assisting in making correct replacements promptly. A further use for merit rating occurs where annual bonuses are to be paid in proportion to employee contibution, as at the Lincoln Electric Company. Mr. Joseph H. Ball in a recent report [18] on labor-management relations of that company says:

> . . . the importance of the merit rating with respect to the employee's annual income, and his relative standing in his department based upon the merit rating, have developed a competitive spirit among the employees which reacts as a further incentive to effective job performance. The merit rating has had the effect of raising the level of performance of entire departments.

APPRAISAL MEETING AGENDA

I. Statement of purpose
   A. Committee to appraise individual's present worth.
   B. Committee to appraise individual's future worth to company.

II. Appraisal—Factors considered by the Appraisal Committee, with specific incidents in mind wherever possible, are as follows:

   A. PERFORMANCE
      1. Measurable results accomplished:
         a) Quality of work done.
         b) Quality, cost, and time element of work done.
         c) Customer relations.
         d) Employee relations.
         e) Extension beyond assignment.
         f) Problem solving ability.

      2. Methods:
         a) How he goes about getting job done.
         b) How he works with and through other persons.
         c) Kind of records he keeps.
         d) Follow-through on activities.
         e) Ability to delegate responsibility.
         f) Ability to organize work.
         g) Ability to develop his subordinates.
         h) Work attributes, such as job knowledge or personality factors which are especially helpful.

FIGURE 146. MANAGEMENT INVENTORY AND DEVELOPMENT, APPRAISAL MEETING AGENDA. (W. L. Maxson Corporation.)

[18] *Report of the Joint Committee on Labor-Management Relations,* Congress of the U. S.

B. PERSONAL QUALIFICATIONS
1. What do you think of first when you think of this individual? Use only factors particularly noticeable.
2. After general discussion, determine:
   a) Strongest single qualification.
   b) Most noticeable weakness.

C. POTENTIAL
1. Consider what is the next step ahead for the person being appraised; whether he has a potential beyond the next step. This must be specific, in terms of positions now in existence.
2. Consider all the jobs in the company for which the individual might be qualified.
3. Decide whether further development or experience is needed before his potential can be realized.

D. ACTION
1. Decide whether this person will be left on his present job or what other action needs to be taken.
2. State the development steps to be recommended or taken to help the individual improve.

E. CURRENT STATUS should be stated in one of the following degrees of status, paying close attention to the definition here presented:
1. IMMEDIATELY PROMOTABLE. Individual can fill immediately a specific job at a *higher* management level without need for any further training.
2. PROMOTABLE. Individual can fill a specific job at a *higher* management level with further training. Such training may be accomplished within a stated time interval, such as six months or two years.
3. SATISFACTORY PLUS. Individual is supplying what can reasonably be expected on his present job and could accept additional responsibilities and authorities within his present management level.
4. SATISFACTORY. Individual is supplying what can reasonably be expected on his present job, but we do not see him going beyond his present management level in the immediately foreseeable future.
5. QUESTIONABLE. Individual's performance on his present assignment is not completely satisfactory.
6. UNSATISFACTORY. Individual's performance is not acceptable on his present job. He may be able to improve his performance with further help and encouragement. In other words, we are not giving up on him.
7. UNSATISFACTORY—ACTION DATE SET. Individual's performance is not acceptable and his personal qualifications are such that he will not be able to improve his performance. The date is set when we expect to have made the necessary changes.

III. The SUMMARY APPRAISAL and the APPRAISAL REPORT
A. After the Summary Appraisal has been written and unanimously agreed on, each Committee member should sign the blue sheet.
B. The chairman of the Committee, soon after the Appraisal meeting, fills out the Appraisal Report, which is intended to be given to the appraisee after the Review.
C. Both papers are given to the Section Supervisor for keeping until the Review.

FIGURE 146. (*Concluded.*)

SUMMARY APPRAISAL

MANAGEMENT INVENTORY AND DEVELOPMENT

NAME _____ POSITION _____ DATE _____

DEPARTMENT _____ SECTION _____

AGE _____ COMPANY SERVICE _____ YEARS ON PRESENT JOB_____

THIS SUMMARY APPRAISAL IS A NARRATIVE DESCRIPTION DEVELOPED FROM A DETAILED ANALYSIS OF THE EMPLOYEE'S WORK.

PERFORMANCE

RESULTS (What has this individual accomplished in measurable results since his last appraisal? Consider quantity, quality, cost, and time element of work. Be specific. Give facts and figures wherever possible.)

....

....

....

....

....

....

....

....

....

....

....

....

METHOD (How does this person go about getting his job done? How does he work with and through people? Be specific.)

....

....

....

....

....

....

....

....

....

....

....

THE W. L. MAXSON CORPORATION

FIGURE 147. SUMMARY APPRAISAL

PERSONAL QUALIFICATIONS

GENERAL ....

....

.••••.•••••...••... ...

....

STRONGEST SINGLE QUALIFICATION ... .

....

MOST NOTICEABLE WEAKNESS ....

....

POTENTIAL

What is the next step ahead for this individual and does he have further potential beyond next step. If so, outline.

....

... .

ACTION

[ ] LEAVE ON PRESENT JOB
(Recommend action for improvement, such ....
as Training, Change of Attitude, Change
in Pay, Encouragement, etc. ....

    [ ] Put on Probation   From ....   To ....

[ ] REPLACE

    [ ] Promote   [ ] Terminate   [ ] Transfer to job of
    [ ] Demote to ....   same classification

    Date recommended action to be taken ....

CHECK THE CURRENT STATUS ON THIS INDIVIDUAL

IMMEDIATELY	SATISFACTORY	DECISION DEFERRED	
[ ] Promotable	[ ] Plus	[ ] Because New	[ ] Unsatisfactory
[ ] Promotable	[ ] Satisfactory	[ ] Questionable	[ ] Unsatisfactory– Action Date Set

---

APPRAISAL MADE BY

NAME ....   TITLE ....

NAME ... .   TITLE ....

NAME ....   TITLE ....

NAME . ...   TITLE ....

---

*THE PERFORMANCE AND PERSONAL QUALIFICATION SECTIONS OF THIS REPORT HAVE BEEN DISCUSSED
WITH THE EMPLOYEE BY:*

NAME ... . *DATE* ....

FIGURE 147. (*Concluded.*)

14

APPLYING EVALUATION TO OFFICE
AND SUPERVISORY POSITIONS

> There is no difference between office and plant with respect to
> the principles involved in labor relations and no difference be-
> tween salaries and wages as compensation to individuals em-
> ployed.
>
> —J. O. Hopwood

Background of Position Classification. As we mentioned once
before the Civil Service Acts undoubtedly brought the first suggestions of work classification. The early acts were somewhat negative
in nature, prompted by revolts against the spoils system, or by scan-
dalous abuses of government employment, but in time they became
constructive.[1] Government offices, not always looked upon as
models, did benefit and provided examples of orderliness. In the
meantime the proportion of people working in all offices, to the
whole population, gained increasingly. For instance the number of
employees engaged in clerical tasks in the United States, *per million
of population, has been increasing per decade* from a minimum of
2.9 per cent to a maximum of 5.0 per cent. According to the census
of 1950 there were about sixteen million white-collar workers of
whom two million belonged to unions.

During each of the World Wars there were upheavals in office
personnel and in their rates of pay despite all attempts at control.
The greater dependence on women, for one thing, led to duplication
of duties and to double ranges of salary for similar work. Titles lost
their original significance. Worst of all, there was a lot of favoritism and "gross inequality." Turning to the positive forces we find
large offices becoming mechanized so that they could and did begin
to copy the management techniques already maturing in the shops.
Consultants in office management sprang into being. A new profes-
sion and position, that of office manager, arrived. Groups of punch

[1] See Classification Act of 1923.

374

key operators were segregated, that is, functions became centralized. Group tasks were set for incentive payment. Employment techniques were applied. Out of these negative and positive influences came job analysis-description-specification and classification for office work. It even had a name all of its own, "salary standardization." The latter was more empiric than present-day evaluation and was often predetermined without direct consideration of the particular requirements, but it brought order to the lower levels of clerical work and has continued to evolve.[2] E. N. Hay made the first application of "Factor Comparison" to salaried jobs in 1938. Since then office analysts have generally followed the patterns of job evaluation so that much of what we have already described can be applied to the office. In 1945 a survey of 252 companies indicated that 90 had job evaluation for office jobs as follows: 70 per cent of the plans were the ranking-grading or "classification" type, 24 per cent were weighted point plans, and 6 per cent were characteristic comparison.

Policy. We have discussed this at length in Chapter 3 and think it sufficient to give a single example of salary policies. For this we select the eight simple statements made by Edward N. Hay of The Pennsylvania Company.[3]

The following rules are among policies governing salary adjustment that have proved practical at The Pennsylvania Company:

1. Do not make salary increases beyond the maximum salary established for a given position.
2. Normally, award only one "step" increase at a time.
3. As a rule, increases should be awarded only once a year. In boom times it should be possible to give the more valuable employees more than one increase in a year in order to discourage turnover.
4. Award salary increases only where they are deserved.
5. Give preference, if any choice is possible or necessary, to those whose work is of the highest quality, as compared with those who are receiving salaries in the upper half of the range.
6. Give preference to those persons whose present salary is in the lower half of the salary range as compared with those who are receiving salaries in the upper half of the range.
7. Special treatment is ordinarily given to new employees. A liberal policy is to consider them for increases, if work is

[2] For Dr. Marion Bill's Classification Plan see L.O.M.A., *Clerical Salary Study Committee Report 2*, pp. 69–107.

[3] A.M.A. *Financial Management Series*, No. 79. For a fuller guide see H. A. Hopf, *Executive Compensation and Accomplishment, ibid.,* No. 78.

satisfactory, after three months, six months, and twelve months of employment. If it is necessary to reduce the total amount awarded annually in increases, these periods can be lengthened so that increases do not come so frequently in the first year.

8. Often it is desirable to make exceptions in favor of employees whose work is unusually good or who are exceptionally- promotable. These exceptions may include increases more frequent than once a year or larger amounts than the standard "step" increases. When it is necessary to restrict the amount of money given in salary increases, these special exceptions should be kept at a minimum.

Organization. We think it is not inconsistent to assert on the one hand that the rating of nonmanual jobs and the rating of manual jobs is a single problem and on the other hand that each of these should be applied by different committees, perhaps by different analysts. We have only to remember that all this work is primarily organizational, the operational part being definitely secondary. Hence when it is carried to the top it must be steered from the very top. The Westinghouse Electric Company started with a Salary Administration Committee consisting of the president, the comptroller, the director of budgets, and the assistant to the vice-president in charge of industrial relations. The last-named acted as chairman and executive officer. Any committee of lower standing could not have done an all-inclusive job. Incidentally, the grouping that this committee achieved is looked upon as the functional organization of the company. Possibly a smaller committee might be adequate for the subsequent operation but it would be questionable to lower it in level. As an operating or classifying committee it is responsible for all relations between the company and its salaried employees although some of this load may be delegated to the personnel department.[4] This committee should meet regularly to coordinate departmental proposals and to take final action on all rate questions. Here also are formulated the recommendations for change in policy regarding rates. In short, it should be the intermediary between the general management and the departmental management on all salary matters. At The Atlantic Refining Company a Wage Control Committee acts as a mediating and arbitrating body. The same committee attends to all administrative work in

---

[4] There is sometimes a job classification manager in the industrial relations department. See A. L. Kress, *Job Evaluation Problems,* A.M.A. Office Management Series No. 102.

connection with the salary plan. Alexander Smith and Sons has used a company-union committee to evaluate office jobs.

Direct Classification. Methods and techniques used for non-manual jobs are today little different from those already described except that direct classification of whole jobs is still used in the office. It probably is also used in some shops but it is so unsuited to most shop jobs that we have ignored it in Chapter 3. As used by the Federal Civil Service,[5] the classification is shaped according to five basic groups as follows:

P.—The Professional and Scientific Service.
S.P.—The Subprofessional Service.
C.A.F.—The Clerical, Administrative, and Fiscal Service.
Cu—The Custodian Service.
C.M.—The Clerical Mechanical Service.

These major groups are subdivided into grades of difficulty and responsibility, starting with the easiest and most routine positions and ending with the most exacting and difficult positions. Thus the chemist's positions would be graded as P2 Assistant Chemist, P3 Associate Chemist, and P4 Head Chemist. As a guide to the grading there are five "allocation factors":

a) Subject matter.
b) Difficulty and complexity of duties.
c) Nonsupervisory responsibilities.
d) Supervisory and administrative responsibilities.
e) Qualifications required for the position.

Each of these factors is described as to meaning and ways of determining its application to any particular situation. Certainly this framework is broad enough to allow wide variations in skill or in responsibility, but as Riegel points out,[6] it is difficult to recognize the varied and complex allocation characteristics of higher postions, say those priced above $4,000. Below that level the decisions are mostly of routine nature and their characteristics can be more definitely recognized. Hence he thinks this basis is suitable at and below the $4,000 level but less and less suitable as the levels ascend beyond. Wilmerding [7] suggests an inversion of the classifica-

---

[5] A. W. Proctor, *Principles of Public Personnel Administration*, and Ismar Baruch, *Position Classification Analysis*.

[6] J. W. Riegel, *Salary Determination* (Ann Arbor: Bureau of Industrial Relations, University of Michigan, 1940).

[7] L. Wilmerding, Jr., *Government by Merit* (New York: McGraw-Hill Book Co., Inc., 1935).

tion method, that is, instead of building a series of graded positions from job descriptions, he would start by considering the problem as a total, such as a series of positions from top to bottom and then proceed by division and subdivision until a workable set of levels is depicted. This is about what was done by the original office consultants and managers who set up "predetermined" levels or classes. For instance, the late Dr. W. V. Bingham classified typists, stenographers, and secretaries as follows:

S1   Typists doing simple typing or copy work on machine where outside training is necessary in the operation of the machine.

S2   Typists doing especially difficult typing such as setting up schedules and tables, or operating comptometers, or doing a minor portion of stenographic or Ediphone work.

S3   Ediphone operators or stenographers receiving dictation or departmental correspondence.

S3a Bookkeeping machine operators.

S3b Elliott-Fisher operators.

S3c Comptometer operators.

S4   Secretaries to officers or stenographers taking and transcribing technical dictation.

S5   Secretaries for senior officers with extraordinary duties, particularly those of a highly confidential nature.[8]

Broad Classification Made by Ranking. One of the few unlimited applications was that of the Westinghouse Electric Company, which was completed in ten months. Reporting the whole case E. B. Roberts comments: [9]

To be genuinely effective and to engender universal confidence that each receives his just due, a salaried position analysis must embrace all positions from the highest to the lowest, and every worker must come within the scope of its provision, the work of each being the subject of the same analysis and classification that is applied to every other.

As the first step the employees wrote on a standard form their own job descriptions under four headings: duties, supervision of others, contacts, and equipment used. These were corrected by the department heads, passed through two levels of supervision, and were scrutinized jointly by the departmental manager and the industrial relations representative. When all descriptions had been compared, edited, etc., the employee names were removed and each

[8] See also L. C. Lovejoy, *Salary Standardization at the Fisk Rubber Corporation,* A.M.A. Office Management Series No. 88.

[9] "Position Analysis and Classification," *Management Review,* XXIV, No. 7.

functional series of jobs was ranked as to relative worths. This was done on the concept of total worths, but those doing the ranking did try to consider the main variables such as: difficulty of work, volume of work, responsibility, supervision required, supervision of others, experience, knowledge, and training. It was done jointly by the industrial relations supervisor, a representative of the functional division concerned, a major staff executive, or a divisional consultant. The latter was brought in for "his sense of the significance of the industrial relations problem and its objectives." The several lists of positions were then grouped and a definition was prepared outlining the significance of each group. The same fundamental groups were recognized throughout the functional divisions such as sales, engineering, works, accounting, etc., and used as the basis of establishing class levels regardless of functional division. In other words a parallelism of importance was discernible even where the actual duties were considerably different. At this point all titles were revised and made consistent. Definitions for the groups within the "Works" division or manufacturing are as follows:

WORKS POSITIONS

NAMES, GROUPS, AND GROUP DESCRIPTIONS

GROUP VI—ADMINISTRATIVE

Administer the broad manufacturing responsibility, universally, functionally, or within a prescribed division of the manufacturing organization. By negotiation and arbitration bring into harmonious arrangement individual and divergent interests. Promulgate general rules and procedures for the manufacturing organization as a whole, or within the limits of jurisdiction. Shape broad plans and apply them. The position involves executive responsibility of the first order for large or small groups of subordinates depending upon the sphere of activity.

Positions in Group VI:

    General Works Manager
    Director, General Works Staff
    Works Manager
    Assistant Works Manager

GROUP V—EXECUTIVE

The function is that of the executive who translates plan into action, by the control of the direction in which those of the lower groups will apply their efforts, and the interpretation to them of the meaning or intent of the policy or procedure. They advise with superiors on policy and procedure reflecting to them broad knowledge of and experience with operating conditions.

Positions in Group V:

Superintendent
Captain of Police
Assistant Superintendent
General Foreman

GROUP IV—CREATIVE

The function is that of the creation of material values. The positions call for familiarity with techniques and a breadth of conception of their application and withal the ability to discriminate and choose or reject. They observe phenomena by study of a manifold of situations, and collect data for the construction of patterns for use in formulating general procedures, thereby establishing standards of practice. Their influence extends downward in the organization, carrying with it the tone of superiors, and upward to those superiors influencing the tone and character of the executive instructions that are promulgated in those higher groups to set policy in action.

Under their technical leadership, the operation of the creation of things is carried out by the hourly paid workers, the integrated result of which effort is to be recognized on this level. However, the individual hourly paid jobs are of the skilled and unskilled groups. The function of the staff supervisors and engineers of this group is the accomplishment of that integration.

Positions in Group IV:

Supervisor, General Works Staff
Supervisor, Works Manager's Staff
Division Staff Supervisor
Assistant Division Staff Supervisor
Manufacturing Engineer
Maintenance Engineer
Tool (Design) Engineer
Plant Layout Engineer
Test Engineer

GROUP III—INTERPRETIVE

These are jobs of interpretation. The function is to meet, classify, and cope with situations clearly recognized as within the scope of the established system. These things are done by applying the standards created in the higher groups. Those who function in this group must clearly see the situation in hand, and fit it into the established pattern. The work may involve secondary executive responsibility for the control of the efforts of large or small groups of workers.

Positions in Group III:

Foreman
Assistant Foreman

Shipper
Police Sergeant
Buyer
Office Manager
Secretary
Time Motion Analyst
Chief Clerk (Chief of Clerical Section)
Layout Draftsman
Inspection

GROUP II—SKILLED

These are the jobs of skilled workers. The tasks require discrimination and choice, technique of hand or brain, and often artistry.

Positions in Group II:

Production Clerk
Detail Draftsman
Assistant Buyer
First (Power Plant) Engineer
Process Demonstrator
Statistician
Second (Power Plant) Engineer
Secretary-Stenographer
Interviewer
Ledgerman
Stenographer
Typist

GROUP I—UNSKILLED

The job is the accomplishment of assigned tasks in an established, routine fashion. To function in these jobs accuracy and dependablity are necessary, but neither experience nor training is required.

Positions in Group I:

Storekeeper
Shipping Clerk
Schedule Clerk
Order Stock Checker
Record Clerk
Transcribing Clerk
Switchboard Tender
Store Room Attendant
File Clerk
Duplicating Machine Operator
Office Boy (Girl)

Choice of Methods. The considerations for choice of a method are little different from what we have described in Chapter 3, except that the jobholders are better able to make their own job descriptions and the descriptions are likely to be more on duties or responsibilities than on effort or working conditions. The skills are decidedly different. We will refer to these differences again presently.

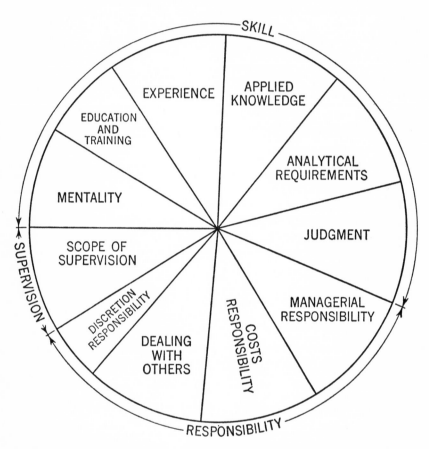

FIGURE 148. MAJOR AND MINOR CHARACTERISTICS, LOCKHEED PLAN FOR SUPERVISORY POSITIONS. (Lockheed Aircraft Corporation.)

Choice of Characteristics. In this matter there is considerable difference. Skill and responsibility usually need different subdivisions if not greater proportions of worth. At Lockheed's skill that had only two subdivisions for hourly paid jobs (see Figure 16a) is given six subdivisions, for supervisors, Figure 148. Only one of the

latter subdivisions retains the same name, "mentality." The percentage for the major characteristic, skill, is not greatly changed—
56.08 per cent in the office against 59½ per cent in the shop. Job
conditions and efforts, sometimes called "deterrent," are dropped
entirely and responsibility is expanded to 35.15 per cent from 12
per cent in the shop. The rest, 8.77 per cent, is given to "scope of

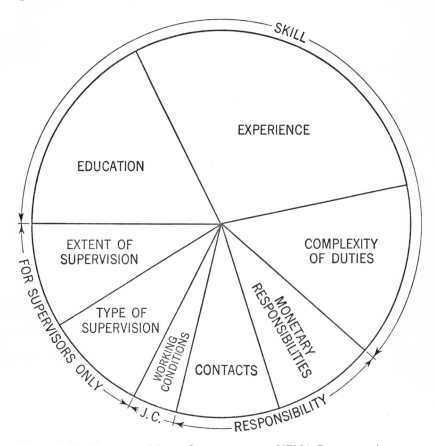

FIGURE 149. MAJOR AND MINOR CHARACTERISTICS, NEMA PLAN, FOR ACCOUNT-
ING, CLERICAL, SUPERVISORY, AND TECHNICAL POSITIONS

supervision." The NEMA plan, Figure 149, intended for broader
application than to supervisory jobs alone, expands the major characteristic of skill to 61.35 per cent from 50 per cent in the shop (see
Figure 14) while responsibiilty contracts to 17.50 per cent from
20 per cent in the shop. "Working conditions" is retained for 3½
per cent and the remaining 17.50 per cent is given to supervision,

which is divided equally for "type and extent." In comparing those two plans one would have expected the percentages given supervision to be the other way around. The Lockheed plan for supervisors reduces experience and education to include more specific components. Otherwise the differences from the NEMA plan are somewhat a matter of names: costs for monetary, dealing with others for contacts, and in part judgment for complexity of duties.

When designing a plan we strongly recommend that the committee begin with the major characteristics for the sake of broad comparisons, but such comparison is not absolute because such characteristics as "contacts" and "type of supervision" combine certain kinds of skill with responsibility. At the same time "complexity" may put some responsibility within the skill group. The definitions of these characteristics usually make it clear as to what is being measured, but it seems highly desirable to choose names for characteristics that would preclude any possible mixing of responsibility with any of the "skills." This is not easy to do because in life they are often blended. For evaluation purposes they must be treated separately.

As an example of readaptation from shop to office with minimum change we submit the characteristics and point allotments for the revised Western Electric plans.

Points for Hourly Jobs	Characteristics	Points for Salaried Jobs
39.0% { 60 / 25 / 75	Mental Development / Job Knowledge / Analysis & Judgment	60 / 30 / 100 } 45.1%
19.5% { 30 / 50	Mental & Visual Demands / Physical Demands	50 / 25 } 17.9%
23.2% { 40 / 30 / 25 / —	Loss Responsibility / Work Responsibility / Responsibility for Safety of Others / Business Relations	45 / 25 / — / 60 } 31.0%
18.3% { 40 / 35	Working Conditions / Job Hazards	25 6.0% / 0
410		420

Below we tabulate point allotments to the major characteristics for six representative point plans to show the present wide variance which should probably be lessened as the experimental period runs out.

Characteristics	Plan Names					
	Walters	Western Electric	Weed	Lockheed	NEMA	LOMA
Skill	44.6	45.1	54.0	56.08	61.35	63.0
Effort	6.6	17.9	4.0	0	0	6.8
Responsibility	15.3	31.0	26.0	35.15	17.50	22.0
Job Conditions......	3.3	6.0	0	0	3.65	8.2
Supervision	....	....	....	8.77	17.50	Separate
Nonvariables if used..	30.0	....	16.0	....	....	....

Too Many Characteristics. As in plans for hourly paid jobs there is considerable waste of effort because of the inclusion of characteristics that in reality measure the same things. In 1951 the eighteen-characteristic plan of the Aluminum Company of Canada was tested to see if a smaller number of characteristics would not give much the same results.[10] The Wherry-Doolittle multiple correlation technique was used and it was found that six characteristics would evaluate all jobs within one labor grade of that derived by using the full set of eighteen characteristics. The six characteristics accounted for 98 per cent of the variance in total points while the remaining twelve characteristics accounted for less than 2 per cent of the variance. The original set of characteristics follows with the selected ones in italics.

SKILL

1. Scholastic Training
2. Previous Experience
3. Learning Period
4. *Technical or Mechanical Knowledge*
5. Dexterity
6. *Complexity*

RESPONSIBILITY

7. Employees
8. Materials
9. Equipment

10. *Methods*
11. *Records*
12. Money
13. Plant Service
14. *Company Policy*

EFFORT

15. Mental
16. Physical

WORKING CONDITIONS

17. Surroundings
18. *Hazards to Self*

A similar but more extensive study [11] came up with four very different "primary factors," namely: (1) work experience; (2)

[10] J. A. Oliver and A. Winn, "An Abbreviated Job Evaluation Plan for Salaried Personnel." *Personnel,* XXVIII, No. 3.

[11] D. J. Chesler, "Abbreviated Job Evaluation Scales Developed on the Basis of 'Internal' and 'External' Criteria." *Journal of Applied Psychology,* XXXIII, No. 2.

character of supervision received; (3) character of supervision given; (4) responsibility for confidential matters. The author concedes that "in all three companies some jobs were displaced by two or three labor grades."

The Pilot Study. If there is anything untried about a proposed plan, such as the efficacy of a small number of characteristics, it is worth while to make a pilot study before closing the plan for installation. A pilot study means trying out the tentative plan in one small division or, better yet, on key jobs throughout all divisions. By keeping the number of jobs small and then selecting them for representative variations it is easy to test the suitability of the characteristics, degree definitions, and point allotments. The jobs can be ranked successively on each characteristic and checked as to distribution and the like. Some of the assumptions will work out to the satisfaction of all concerned while others may not. This shows up the errors in design so that they can be corrected with a minimum of disturbance. Such a tryout should be continued, perhaps adding more jobs, until general agreement and confidence are attained. In the meantime the committee, staff, and even department heads will have acquired considerable practice and education as to how to procede when the plan is closed and applied officially. Here and here only is it legitimate to let past practice in job pricing be an influence, but only so far as the past pricing has been mutually acceptable.

Job Evaluation Still Experimental in This Field. The plans included in this chapter and the next are not all comparable because there are several concepts as to what the scope should be. Alexander Smith and Sons [12] has a plan for union members only, excluding supervisory personnel. Lockheed Aircraft Corporation has one plan for nonrepresented salaried positions, including both supervisory and nonsupervisory positions,[13] and a distinct plan for technical and office hourly paid jobs. Lockheed also has another plan for engineering jobs. The S. C. Johnson Company of Racine, Wisconsin, has four plans besides its "Factory plan": office plan, specialized and technical plan, supervisory plan, and executive plan.[14] Most companies use a single plan for all salaried jobs but add one or more measures for supervisory jobs.

[12] F. Westbrook, Jr., "Company-Union Committee Works Out Job Evaluation Program," *Mill and Factory*, March, 1947.

[13] O. R. Winjum, "How to Evaluate Supervisory Jobs," *American Machinist*, August 26, 1948.

[14] H. S. Briggs, "Executive Position Evaluation," NICB *Management Record*, XII, No. 7,

The Procter & Gamble Company plan for clerical jobs is rather different from its plan for factory jobs. Eight characteristics are weighted percentagewise as follows: complexity 16, experience and training 16, contacts with others 10, dexterity 5, concentration 16, accuracy 16, working conditions 5, and responsibility 16. Each of these is scored from one to ten. These scores are then multiplied by the fixed weightings to derive a total job rating, which can be anywhere between 100 and 1,000. The characteristics are doubtless defined but the 1 to 10 scoring seems to be a matter of ranking without the aid of predetermined degree definitions. Thus some plans for the office have been set up independently without any intention of keeping unit worth identical with that of the shop. If the first purpose in any job evaluation is to achieve correct relative worth, why should a management build up two structures, each internally related but externally unrelated? We advocate one complete classification relationship, no matter how different the minor characteristics and their measuring scales may need to be. Failing to achieve equivalent unit worth between the shop and office evaluations, it is still possible to find job class equivalency by applying the comparison technique to certain comparable jobs and then ranking the rest accordingly. In fact, the jobs of similar classification should contribute much toward keeping the classes consistent throughout the higher levels where there is no shop-office equivalency.

The Weed plan for salary evaluation was set up separately from, but not inconsistently with, the plan for hourly jobs. It uses the same universal credit of 400 points and the whole layout is harmonious with that for hourly paid jobs. We think the 31 grades are excessive but perhaps unavoidable for such an extensive case.[15] A point range of approximately 5 per cent per grade is used, which means that the worth ranges increase in number of points from 460–485 for Grade 1 to 2,315–2,430 for Grade 30. Small or even medium-sized companies can conveniently group their salaried jobs into 10, 12, or 15 classes. We strongly advise the use of job descriptions and objective evaluations as the best means of classification. Select one or more key jobs to typify each class and build the classes around them. If the company is too large for any one committee to be familiar with all classes of work, the relationships can be built up by separate committees and harmonized in conferences between their representatives. A good organization chart may be of considerable help in classifying supervisory positions.

[15] E. N. Hay found 15 grades sufficient for all salaried jobs lying between $50 a month and $400 a month. See A.M.A. *Personnel Series*, XXII, No. 11; XXIII, No. 1, 2, 3, 4, 5; XXIV, No. 1; XXVI, No. 4.

Locality Surveys. If there are any differences in the matter of surveys, they are in respect to the confidential nature of higher salaries and to their greater variation, although much of the variation in rate is likely to be due to the difficulty of finding identical jobs. Certainly the number of individuals receiving each rate should be retained together with explanations as to job variation, and also as to certain man variations such as experience or length of service. We particularly recommend A. L. Kress' graphic analysis,[16] Chapter 10, Figure 93, together with the National Electrical Manufacturers Association summary, Chapter 10, Figure 92.

Measuring Scales. The scales are similar to those for hourly jobs except that the number of degrees are sometimes extended beyond five. We give a single example from the McKinsey plan.

I. *Characteristic:* Skill—600 points (within a total of 1000 points.) The characteristic Skill, considered in its broad sense, has as its components Complexity, Training, Routines, Judgment, Education, and Relationships required by proper job performance.

  1. *Component:* Complexity—100 points
    This component considers the extent and amount of details present in the job represented by the factors Procedures and Equipment.

    1) *Factor:* Procedures—75 points
      This factor is broken down into five *elements* descriptive of the extent of difficulty encountered.

	Points
1) A simple procedure, that is, an operation with only a few details	5
2) A combination of several simple procedures in which the details are readily understood	15
3) A wide variety of simple procedures in which some of the details are slightly involved	30
4) A complicated procedure, that is, one in which the steps are relatively few, but each requiring exactness	50
5) An involved procedure, that is, one in which there are many steps, each of which requires exactness	75

[16] Mr. Kress' whole paper entitled "Making a Salary Survey," published in the A.M.A. *Office Management Series* No. 84, should be read. In the case he cites, descriptions of 70 clerical positions, from office boy to draftsman-designer, were used and comparisons were made jointly by a representative of the inquiring company and a representative of the answering company at the plant of the latter.

FIELD		JOB ANALYSIS	AKRON PLANTS	
District.........................		**BFG**	Division...........................	
Sales Div........			Br. Plant...........................	
Store Location........................		**QUESTIONNAIRE**	Dept. No............................	

1. Job Title...

2. Immediate Superior: Name.. Title......................................

3. Describe the need or purpose for which this job is performed.

4. Describe the duties of this job in detail and sequence of importance. At the left, give your best estimate of the percentage of the working time consumed by each duty described.

Pct. of total working time	A. Daily duties (those performed every day or nearly every day):
	B. Periodic duties (those performed weekly or monthly):
	C. Occasional Duties (those performed less frequently than monthly):

(If more space is needed, attach separate sheet)

FIGURE 150. EXAMPLE OF FORM FOR GATHERING JOB DATA. (B F. Goodrich Company.)

COMPLEXITY

5. Describe the phases of this job that require the exercise of independent judgment, initiative and ingenuity.

SUPERVISION GIVEN

6. (a) What jobs, if any, come under the direct supervision of this job?

Job Title   No. of Employees

(b) Approximately what percentage of time is devoted to direct supervision.............. ....?

(c) Indicate by checking below, the nature and extent of this supervision.

☐ Assign work   ☐ Recommend hire.   ☐ Grievances
☐ Check work.   ☐ Recommend dismissal.   ☐ Discipline

Specify others:..

SUPERVISION RECEIVED

7. (a) What is the nature of the instructions, written or verbal, relative to the methods by which this job is performed?

(b) Describe the type (physical check by superior or mechanical controls) and frequency of supervision under which this work is performed.

(c) What *normally* would happen if an error were made on this job?

(d) When would such an error be detected?

FIGURE 150. (*Continued.*)

COMPANY ASSETS

8. What trust is imposed for the safeguarding of confidential information, money, materials, equipment, employee goodwill, customer goodwill, and/or other company assets?

EDUCATION

9. (a) Indicate below the *minimum* of formal education or mental equivalent required to perform this job. (Note: Do not enter the present incumbent's education unless it coincides with your opinion of the minimum requirement.)

☐ Grammar School   ☐ Business School (1 to 2 years)
☐ Partial High School (2 yrs.)   ☐ Partial College (2 yrs.)
☐ High School   ☐ Complete College
☐ Business School (up to 1 year)   ☐ College Post Graduate

(b) What course of study should this training include?

EXPERIENCE

10. Assuming the requisite educational qualifications specified in Question 9, indicate what additional experience is required to perform this job and check below the *minimum* time required to obtain said experience.

Experience required:

	Months		Years				
From	N O N E	1	6	1	2	4	6	10
To	6	12	2	4	6	10	15
Check Here							

JOB TRAINING PERIOD

11. Assuming the requisite education and experience specified in Questions 9 and 10, indicate the *minimum* length of time required to learn this job.

From .... to .... months.

MACHINES AND EQUIPMENT

12. Indicate below what machines or equipment are operated or require an operating knowledge to satisfactorily perform this job.

Machines or Equipment   **Experience Required**
Operated   Operating Knowledge

FIGURE 150. (*Continued.*)

INTERNAL CONTACTS

13. What personal or telephone contacts are required *within* the organization in the performance of this job and for what purpose must they be made?

Persons Contacted   Purpose of Contact

EXTERNAL CONTACTS

14. What personal contacts are required *outside* the organization in the performance of this job and for what purpose must they be made?

Persons Contacted   Purpose of Contact

WRITTEN EXPRESSION

15. What types of written reports, statistics, letters, etc. are prepared on this job and to whom are they directed?

PHYSICAL WORKING CONDITIONS AND ENVIRONMENT

16. (a) What phases, if any, of this job require an abnormal degree of physical effort or strain?

(b) What features of the place at which this job is performed are below normal when compared with normal office conditions?

(c) What body or health hazards are involved in the performance of this job?

17. List the names of the employees in this department who perform the work described herein.

1. ....   4. ....

2. ....   5. ....

3. ....   6. ....

18. Signatures:

Store Supervisor
C. & O. Manager
Dept. Manager.. Date............................

District Manager
Division Head.. Date............................

FORM NO. 04086   PRINTED IN U. S. A.

FIGURE 150. (*Concluded.*)

Job Description-Specification. S. L. H. Burk, in a short but masterly paper entitled "Bases for Sound Salary Determination," [17] lists five principles and four rules for collecting job data as follows:

Principles:

1. Follow organization lines in starting the work.
2. Go to the best possible sources of information, that is, the employee and the immediate supervisor, interviewing the employee on the job at his workplace.
3. Questionnaires [18] may be used if desired, but not as substitutes for the workplace interview (see Figure 150).
4. In addition to securing facts in connection with duties, responsibilities, working hours, working conditions, etc., the interviewer should seek to draw out employees' and supervisors' opinions as to minimum qualifications for the job.
5. It must be made perfectly clear at all times that the analyst is interested only in the job and not the qualifications or effectiveness of the man on the job.

Rules:

1. That some record must be made of the basis on which the grade or rate has been determined, and that this record should be in such form as to facilitate the grading process.
2. The jobs should be described as they are now actually being performed, not on the basis of what should be done, what used to be done, or what is expected to be done.
3. Qualified and understanding agreement about all the items entered on the job description or specification should be secured from the supervisors and department heads involved.
4. The employee should at least have the opportunity to agree or disagree with the description of job content and duties.

As might be expected, little attempt is made to get job data as exactly as for hourly paid jobs. Instead the proportionate time is stressed, i.e., are the duties continuous or intermittent? Are they frequent and routine or occasional? What percentage of time does each take, etc.? For a thorough and intelligently made example we turn again to the McKinsey case (Figure 151).

---

[17] A.M.A. *Office Management Series* No. 92.
[18] C. H. Lawshe's Form A, "Job Description Check-List of Office Operations," contains 139 items on 8 large pages.

JOB SPECIFICATION SHEET

DESCRIPTION

Daily Operations

1. Receive copy of invoice from Accounts Payable or Cost Department; check invoice against Purchase Order previously received and arrange for any necessary corrections.

2. Prepare certificate of payment and pass on, with supporting papers, to Department Secretary for distribution.

3. Watch discount on all D. P. C. invoices.

4. Prepare separate certificate on invoices where a partial payment has been made.

5. Itemize, by accounts charge, the total amount of each certificate and make entry at the bottom of each certificate prepared.

6. When invoices and certificates have been prepared in the field for D. P. C. jobs, check for accuracy and file; on all others prepare complete invoice from data received from Field office.

7. Receive, from Field offices, payrolls and summary sheet showing expense of labor and accounts chargeable; check for accuracy, arrange for any adjustments and also for any required journal entry.

8. Pass payroll records on to clerks for checking extensions and posting earnings.

9. When invoice or payroll certificates are complete, post according to job, by construction projects and accounts; at end of month check totals with those of the Bookkeeper of General Accounts.

10. Receive voucher checks with invoices covering job purchases.

11. Enter in disbursement register, according to account distribution for cash, inventory, and operating.

12. Record amount of cash deposits made by bookkeeper for each job, and balance register at close of each monthly period with the Bookkeeping Department.

Weekly Operations

1. Payroll expense is entered, weekly, on a Payroll Summary Sheet, showing taxable and nontaxable items, number of employees in each group, amount of Social Security or State taxes paid, the States designated where employees are located, and the earnings paid by such divisions; at close of each accounting period sheets are totaled and summary of account distribution made on the reverse side and then passed on to Assistant Treasurer's Executive Assistant.

Miscellaneous Operations

1. Watch freight charges on all invoices to make sure charges have been handled and invoiced accordingly.

2. Handle charge-back entries received from the Field offices, to make sure the necessary invoices and/or credits are issued to adjust.

3. All voucher and payroll expense must be watched for items not properly reimbursable; these items are furnished the Construction Department.

4. Carry on all necessary correspondence between Field men, client or vendor representatives, and interdepartment employees, in an effort to coordinate and keep all work in agreement as to records and amounts.

FIGURE 151. JOB SPECIFICATION SHEET.

Monthly Operations

   A. Bank Reconciliations

   1. Receive monthly statement and canceled checks from banks handling job expense and payroll accounts.

   2. Pass checks on to be checked against bank tapes and arranged numerically.

   3. Check off checks against payrolls and voucher listings; list those outstanding to prove balance shown by bank.

   4. Give list of unpaid checks, and bank statements to General Accounts Bookkeeper for use in combined reconciliation.

SPECIFIC

DIRECTION AND INSTRUCTION Standard routine, verbal on some and general sometimes

PROCEDURES Calculate, post, and invoice

DIVERSITY Considerable   TIME SPEC. Promptness essential

LIMITS Work must be accurate   PRECISION IMPORT. Little-moderate on some

EQUIP. USED Adding machine   TIME USED About 1 hr. day

RELATIONSHIPS Interdepartmental, gov.   FREQ. Frequently
               auditors, vendors, and representatives

SUPERVISION GIVEN 1 clerk—general   NO. PEOPLE 1

PHYSICAL EFFORT Mostly desk work, some walking SUSTAINED % 90—10 and standing

AREA COVERED Various floors   MENTAL EFFORT Constant concentration

WORKING CONDITIONS Too warm most of the time

GENERAL

EQUIV. EDUCATION High School SPECIAL Accounting and business procedure

PREV. EXPERIENCE 1–2 years   TRAINING PERIOD 3 months–6 months

SUPERVISION REQ. Daily

COMMENT

EMPLOYEE John S. Mason (Interviewed)
         Edward Bowman, Henry Haverty, James P. Durkin

INTERVIEWER Laurie F. Dobb   APPROVED Joseph P. Green

JOB TITLE Job Unit Cost   NO. EMPLOYEES 4 DATE Mar. 11, 1943
        Accountant

DEPARTMENT Accounting SECTION Construction Cost Unit JOB GRADE VIII

FIGURE 151. (*Concluded.*)

A Simple Plan for Clerical Positions. The Revere Copper & Brass Company uses the weighted-in-points method, with separate treatment of universal requirements but with a smaller scale of weights (Figure 152).

Characteristics	Points
Skills:	
Educational requirements............................	0 to 16
Practical experience required	0 to 15
Analytical requirement and complexity of work...........	0 to 15
Accuracy	1 to 8
Memory	0 to 8
Manual dexterity	0 to 5
Responsibility:	
Supervisional requirements	0 to 15
Relations or contacts	0 to 8
Effort:	
Continuity of work	0 to 5
Physical strain on senses	0 to 5
Working conditions:	
Conditions of work.................................	0 to 5
Elemental credit (for all jobs)........................	– 45
Potential maximum	150

FIGURE 152. ADAPTATION OF MINOR CHARACTERISTICS. (Revere Copper & Brass Company.)

Weighted-in-Points Plan for Clerical Jobs. The Consolidated Water Power & Paper Company of Wisconsin Rapids installed a plan in 1952 that allows comparisons with nonclerical jobs. Twelve characteristics are used, five degrees each. The theoretical maximum number of points is 1500. Weighting in percentages was made on the first degree, and three times those weights were multiplied by the degree numbers to derive the points for all other degrees. We question the need or desirability of using threefold values or even twofold values, since the original weightings would total 500 in the fifth degree. The 1500 points are distributed as follows: Skill 972 points, 66 per cent; Responsibility 255 points, 17 per cent; Effort 150 points, 10 per cent; and Working Conditions 105 points, 7 per cent. The clerical employees to whom the plan applies are members of the Office Employees International Union, AF of L. The definitions are given in full (see Figure 153).

Weighted-in-Points Plan for Technical and Office Hourly Jobs. The Lockheed Aircraft Corporation uses a single plan for both office and technical hourly jobs. In fact the ten characteristics are

SKILL

EDUCATION

The attribute which measures the mental development or technical knowledge required by the job.

First degree (42 points)

The ability to do the following: Clerical duties of a minor nature, simple arithmetic, simple postings of weights, counts, etc., to forms, and understand simple instructions.

Second degree (84 points)

The ability to do the following: Clerical duties of a detailed nature, ordinary arithmetic, simple inventories, typing, filling out simple report forms, and basic bookkeeping.

Third degree (126 points)

The ability to do the following: Clerical duties of an extraordinary nature, advanced arithmetic, fill out difficult report forms, difficult inventories, lay out simple report forms, transcribing and typing, and write simple letters.

Fourth degree (168 points)

The ability to do the following: Clerical duties of a complex nature, elementary mathematics, lay out difficult report forms, compile, analyze, and prepare statistical data in the form of schedules, reports, graphs, or charts, write detailed procedures, elementary accounting, and write good business letters.

Fifth degree (210 points)

The ability to understand and perform work of a technical nature requiring a comprehensive knowledge of the applicable technical theory.

EXPERIENCE

The measure of time on related work plus job training usually required by an individual to learn to perform satisfactorily the particular work being evaluated. The measure of time should include only the time on related work and the actual job training required on the work to be performed. Satisfactory performance involves the doing of work of satisfactory quality in a quantity sufficient to justify continued employment on the job.

First degree (54 points)

Up to one year of experience gained through job training or on related work in addition to job training.

Second degree (108 points)

Between one and two years of experience gained through job training or on related work in addition to job training.

Third degree (162 points)

Between two and three years of experience gained through job training or on related work in addition to job training.

FIGURE 153. EXAMPLE OF DEGREE DEFINITIONS. (Consolidated Water Power & Paper Company.)

Fourth degree (216 points)

Broad, practical knowledge obtained from previous experience and association with related work, in addition to job training, of between three and four years.

Fifth degree (270 points)

Expert knowledge in a skilled occupation obtained from practical experience gained over a period of four years or more.

JUDGMENT

Judgment refers to the weighing of existing facts and conditions and then deciding upon the correct course of action. Consideration must be given to the variety of decisions and especially to the availability of existing rules, policies, and precedent that are available for guidance.

First degree (33 points)

Limited number of decisions, involving only a few courses of action, must be made within the immediate limits of a specific procedure or rule.

Second degree (66 points)

Decisions must be made where there are many problems but only a limited number of courses of action covered by a specific policy or rule. There may also be decisions covered only by general policies but the decisions are repetitive in character or there is ample precedent to follow.

Third degree (99 points)

Decisions must be made where the facts and circumstances are such as to make it necessary for the employee to choose between several alternatives. The problems fall within the limits of existing general policies but unforeseen circumstances not taken into consideration when developing policy make the use of discretion necessary. The employee interprets policy under such conditions but often secures the approval of a superior.

Fourth degree (132 points)

Numerous decisions involved where the choices of action are wide and where there are no applicable rules or policies but where there is some precedent.

Fifth degree (165 points)

Continuous decisions where there is little or no precedent and where the information available is of an extremely complex nature.

INITIATIVE AND INGENUITY

Relates to the job requirements for original conception, planning, and inventiveness. When evaluating this attribute, consideration should be given to the following factors:

1. Originality in the form of devising or developing methods of procedure.
2. Resourcefulness in the form of capacity for analyzing work and adapting methods, equipment, etc.
3. Initiative in the form of ability to see the need for and to take independent action.

First degree (33 points)

Requires the ability to understand and follow simple instructions such as are involved in simple clerical work where the employee is told exactly what to do.

FIGURE 153. (*Continued.*)

Second degree (66 points)

Requires the ability to perform standardized or routine operations from detailed instructions, using some judgment concerning the quality of work.

Third degree (99 points)

Requires the ability to understand, plan, and perform a sequence of diversified operations where standard or recognized methods are available, working from general instructions and layouts including some decisiveness as to quality, operation, and procedure.

Fourth degree (132 points)

Requires the ability to understand, plan course of action, perform unusual and difficult work where only general methods are available, and considerable originality and resourcefulness.

Fifth degree (165 points)

Requires outstanding ability to think clearly, accurately, and independently on involved and complex work requiring the devising of original methods or procedures, and an extremely high degree of originality and resourcefulness.

MACHINE OPERATIONAL SKILL

The measurement of the degree of skill required to operate various office machines and equipment in a manner to meet the accepted standard.

First degree (18 points)

Unskilled operators of any or all types of office equipment and machines.

Second degree (36 points)

Skilled operators of:

1. Adding machines.
    A. All makes and models, electric or manual.
2. Typewriting machines (copy work only).
    A. All makes and models, electric or manual, which print upper case characters (capital letters) only, including machines equipped with a numeric-symbolic keyboard used only for addition and subtraction.
    B. Teletypewriter machines (for transmitting and receiving messages).
3. Duplicating and printing machines (non-ink type).
    A. Standard duplicator.
    B. Ditto duplicator.
    C. Copyist.
    D. Bruning machine (white printing and developing).
    E. Dupligraph.

Third degree (54 points)

Skilled operators of:

1. Typewriting machines (copy work only).
    A. All makes and models, electric or manual, which print both upper case characters (capital letters) and lower case characters (small letters), including machines equipped with a numeric-symbolic keyboard used only for addition and subtraction.
2. Calculating machines.
    A. All makes and models, rotary or key-driven, electric or manual.

FIGURE 153. (*Continued.*)

3. Accounting machines (numeric).
   A. All makes and models, electric or manual, equipped only with a numeric-symbolic keyboard.
4. Addressing machines.
   A. Addressograph.
5. Telephone switchboard.
   A. Any make or model.
6. Duplicating and printing machines (ink type).
   A. Multilith.
   B. Multigraph.

Fourth degree (72 points)

Skilled operators of:

1. Typewriting machines (stenographic).
   A. All makes and models, electric or manual, which print both upper case characters (capital letters) and lower case characters (small letters) used in transcribing letters, memoranda, etc., from machines, shorthand notes, and rough drafts.
2. Transcribing machines (stenographic).
   A. All makes and models used in connection with #1 above.
3. Accounting machines (numeric-alphabetic).
   A. All makes and models, electric or manual, equipped with both numeric and alphabetic keyboards and which are used: to post books of accounts; to prepare checks, vouchers, and other accounting media; to prepare and record other accounting data and statistical reports.

CONTACTS

This attribute is the degree of personality, manners, and tact required in face to face business dealings.

First degree (18 points)

Contacts only with company employees in the same office.

Second degree (36 points)

Contacts with: company employees of other offices in other divisions; mill employees; mill departmental supervisors.

Third degree (54 points)

Contacts with: mill managers, mill superintendents; occasional contacts with outsiders.

Fourth degree (72 points)

Contacts with: company management personnel (not officers); frequent contacts with outsiders.

Fifth degree (90 points)

Contact with: company officers; consistent contacts with outsiders. (Applies to few.)

RESPONSIBILITY

ACCURACY

Pertains to the degree of accuracy required to avoid monetary loss or embarrassment. Errors may cause:

FIGURE 153. (*Continued.*)

1. Waste of product.
2. Waste of material.
3. Loss of time by employees locating or correcting errors.
4. Loss due to misinformation through erroneous reports.
5. Any other losses.

First degree (33 points)

Minor errors. No monetary loss involved. Work is rechecked or balanced to predetermined totals.

Second degree (66 points)

Errors of more serious nature. Could cause extended checking to locate. Possible monetary loss or embarrassment.

Third degree (99 points)

Errors in work of unchecked nature. May result in a more serious monetary loss or embarrassment.

Fourth degree (132 points)

Errors of a more serious nature resulting in very costly monetary loss or unusual embarrassment.

Fifth degree (165 points)

Errors of an extremely serious nature resulting in a major monetary loss or extraordinary embarrassment.

LEADERSHIP

This attribute relates to the nonsupervisory responsibility for instructing other employees, assigning work to them, coordinating their efforts, and maintaining the flow of work within a group.

First degree (18 points)

Responsible for own work only.

Second degree (36 points)

Responsible for instructing or directing the efforts of a maximum of three (3) employees.

Third degree (54 points)

Responsible for instructing or directing the efforts of a maximum of six (6) employees.

Fourth degree (72 points)

Responsible for instructing or directing the efforts of a maximum of nine (9) employees.

Fifth degree (90 points)

Responsible for instructing or directing the efforts of a maximum of twelve (12) employees.

EFFORT

PHYSICAL DEMAND

This attribute is measured by the amount of physical effort required. Consideration is given to the elements of the job which produce physical strain or fatigue

FIGURE 153. (*Continued.*)

and the extent to which they are present. Steady work other than machine operation such as pencil work, sorting, filing, etc., will be rated at 50 per cent of the values allotted below to steady machine operation.

First degree (12 points)

Exertion is of a varied nature. Little exertion of a consistent nature.

Second degree (24 points)

At least 20 per cent of time is spent on *steady* machine operation, or standing, or walking, or handling parcels, supplies, etc.

Third degree (36 points)

At least 40 per cent of time is spent on *steady* machine operation, or standing, or walking, or handling parcels, supplies, etc.

Fourth degree (48 points)

At least 60 per cent of time is spent on *steady* machine operation, or standing, or walking, or handling parcels, supplies, etc.

Fifth degree (60 points)

At least 80 per cent of time is spent on *steady* machine operation, or standing, or walking, or handling parcels, supplies, etc.

MENTAL DEMAND

Mental demand relates to the amount or degree of mental application required in performing the work. It does not relate to the degree of intelligence applied, but rather to the time and intensity of the mental application. From the two rate tables shown below is developed the product of the "net" sensings for each of the two elements, time and intensity, and this product determines the degree rating.

	Percentage of Time	Percentage of Intensity (Degree of Concentration)
Extreme	100	100
High	90	90
Medium	80	80
Low	70	70

Example: The degree of time rates on an average basis on one job as medium (80%) but the degree of intensity rates as high (90%). The product of the two sensings is 72% (80% × 90%) and therefore rates a combined degree of "Third degree—54 points" as indicated in the rate table following.

First degree (18 points)

The product of the time and intensity sensings is 49% to 58%.

Second degree (36 points)

The product of the time and intensity sensings is 59% to 69%.

Third degree (54 points)

The product of the time and intensity sensings is 70% to 79%.

Fourth degree (72 points)

The product of the time and intensity sensings is 80% to 89%.

Fifth degree (90 points)

The product of the time and intensity sensings is 90% to 100%.

FIGURE 153. (*Continued.*)

WORKING CONDITIONS

JOB CONDITIONS

This factor relates to the surrounding or physical conditions under which the job must be done over which the employee has no control and which affect his mental or physical well-being.

The following Schedule "A" shows elements to be considered and the degree of intensity with a numerical rating for each degree. Each job is to be rated for each element and the points totaled. The total number decides the degree rating according to the schedule of degrees and points shown following Schedule "A."

Schedule "A"

Elements	*Degree of Intensity*	
Eye strain	Extreme	5
Weather exposure	High	4
Noise	Medium	3
Vibration	Little	2
Dirt	None	1
Monotony		
Clothing maintenance		

First degree (12 points)
Total number is 7. (Minimum)

Second degree (24 points)
Total number is 8 to 10 inclusive.

Third degree (36 points)
Total number is 11 to 14 inclusive.

Fourth degree (48 points)
Total number is 15 to 19 inclusive.

Fifth degree (60 points)
Total number is 20 to 35 inclusive.

PHYSICAL HAZARDS

This attribute relates to the accident and health hazards to the employee in accomplishing the job being evaluated.

First degree (9 points)
Accident possibilities or hazards to health are negligible.

Second degree (18 points)
Office in which job is located is attached to or in the immediate vicinity of a production plant area that constitutes a hazard.

Third degree (27 points)
Job requires occasional exposure to production plant operations, weather, or vehicular traffic that is hazardous.

Fourth degree (36 points)
Job requires frequent exposure to production plant operations, weather, or vehicular traffic that is hazardous.

Fifth degree (45 points)
Job requires constant exposure to production plant operations, weather, or vehicular traffic that is hazardous.

FIGURE 153. (*Concluded.*)

little different from those used in some of the plans for factory jobs, but the definitions are broader and the scales are specially designed. For instance, while four of the scales have arithmetic progression, the rest have geometric progression—but not all the same. One scale, that for experience, reverses the progression much as the General Electric Company did for training (see Chapter 6, Figure 34). This should give truer measurement than the all-arithmetic scales commonly used without any validation. We submit the layout for this plan, Figure 154.

NEMA Plan for Accounting, Clerical, Supervisory, and Technical Jobs. This plan was developed from their hourly job rating plan and makes no pretense of tailor-fitting but it has been so widely used that it deserves ample treatment (see Figure 158). The NEMA Manual [19] lists the following nine basic policies which should underlie sound salary administration:

1. Comply fully with all federal and state legislation with respect to hours, overtime, and payment of salaries.
2. Assume that the company's salary level, considering of course other benefits, such as vacations, paid holidays, sick leaves, etc., compares favorably with that of other companies in the area on comparable jobs.
3. Establish and maintain fair salary differentials within and between jobs in all departments, based on differences in their relative job requirements, as reflected by a sound salaried job rating plan.
4. Fix differentials between jobs solely on differences in job requirements.
5. Inform each employee of his job title, grade, rate, or rate range.
6. Audit job descriptions and duties at least once a year in order to determine whether any significant changes in job content have occurred. Revise existing descriptions and grades where necessary.
7. Recognize and reward individual ability and merit.
8. Promote qualified employees from lower to higher grade jobs whenever opportunity permits.
9. Make promotions and award merit increases on the basis of performance.

NEMA wisely advises the analyst to start by making an informal organization chart to be approved by each department head con-

[19] *Manual of Procedure for use of NEMA Salaried Job Rating Plan.* Industrial Relations Department, National Electrical Manufacturers Association, 1949.

HOURLY JOBS

		Degree				
	1	**2**	**3**	**4**	**5**	**6**
Mentality Requirement	24	48	72	96	120	
Per cent of total plan	1.97	3.94	5.91	7.88	9.85	
Per cent degree difference		(1.97)	(1.97)	(1.97)	(1.97)	
Experience Requirement	1 mo. 13	1 yr. 111	2 yrs. 163	3 yrs. 196	4 yrs. 222	5 yrs. 242
Per cent of total plan	1.07	9.11	13.38	16.09	18.23	19.87
Per cent degree difference		(4.24)	(4.24)	(2.71)	(2.14)	(1.64)
Initiative Requirement	16	32	56	88	136	
Per cent of total plan	1.31	2.63	4.60	7.22	11.17	
Per cent degree difference		(1.32)	(1.97)	(2.62)	(3.95)	
Analytical Requirement	24	48	72	96	120	144
Per cent of total plan	1.97	3.94	5.91	7.88	9.85	11.82
Per cent degree difference		(1.97)	(1.97)	(1.97)	(1.97)	(1.97)
Judgment Requirement	24	48	72	96	120	
Per cent of total plan	1.97	3.94	5.91	7.88	9.85	
Per cent degree difference		(1.97)	(1.97)	(1.97)	(1.97)	
Mental Application	12	24	40	60		
Per cent of total plan	.99	1.97	3.44	4.93		
Per cent degree difference		(.98)	(1.48)	(1.48)		
Physical Application	10	30	60			
Per cent of total plan	.82	2.46	4.93			
Per cent degree difference		(1.64)	(2.47)			
Cost Responsibility	24	48	72	96	120	144
Per cent of total plan	1.97	3.94	5.91	7.88	9.85	11.82
Per cent degree difference		(1.97)	(1.97)	(1.97)	(1.97)	(1.97)
Cooperation and Contact Requirement	8	16	32	64	128	
Per cent of total plan	.66	1.31	2.63	5.25	10.51	
Per cent degree difference		(.65)	(1.32)	(2.62)	(5.26)	
Job Conditions	8	16	32	64		
Per cent of total plan	.66	1.31	2.63	5.25		
Per cent degree difference		(.65)	(1.32)	(2.62)		

Total minimum points (base points) 163   Maximum points (5 yrs. skill) 1218

FIGURE 154. TECHNICAL AND OFFICE PLAN—HOURLY JOBS. (Lockheed Aircraft Corporation.)

cerned and then used as a check on what the descriptions say regarding who reports to whom, scope of supervisory responsibility, and the like. NEMA leaves much of the procedure to the local user of the plan but it broadly suggests that department heads examine their descriptions to see that: (*a*) assignments are logical, (*b*) possible reassignment of duties would be helpful, and (*c*) a better organization arrangement could be made. In fact, the success of this plan is doubtless due in part to this model manual. It includes many precautions and even gets down to the styling and wording of the descriptions. For examples of NEMA practice see Figures 155 to 159.

Points Assigned to Factors and Key to Grades

Factors	1st	2nd	3rd	4th	5th	6th	7th	8th	Per Cent
				Degrees and Points					
1. Education	20	40	60	80	100	120			17.50
2. Experience	25	50	75	100	125	150	175	200	29.20
3. Complexity of Duties..	20	40	60	80	100				14.60
4. Monetary Responsibility	5	10	20	40	60				8.75
5. Contacts	5	10	20	40	60				8.75
6. Working Conditions...	5	10	15	20	25				3.70
Add for Supervisory Jobs Only									
7. Type of Supervision...	5	10	20	40	60				8.75
8. Extent of Supervision..	5	10	20	40	60				8.75
Total Points........								685	100.00

Point Range	Grade
Up to 120..............................	A
125 – 160..............................	B
165 – 200..............................	C
205 – 240..............................	D
245 – 280..............................	E
285 – 320..............................	F
325 – 360..............................	G
365 – 400..............................	H
405 – 440..............................	J
445 – 480..............................	K
485 – 520..............................	L
525 – 560..............................	M

FIGURE 155*a*. NEMA JOB RATING PLAN FOR SALARIED EMPLOYEES IN ACCOUNTING, CLERICAL, SUPERVISORY, AND TECHNICAL POSITIONS

GENERAL DEFINITIONS OF NEMA CHARACTERISTICS

1. *Education* This factor evaluates the *job requirements* in terms of the *basic education or knowledge* which an employee should have acquired to do the job satisfactorily. In applying the factor, consider only the requirements of the job. Disregard the individual's formal education or the specific way in which he may have acquired the basic knowledge. *Rate the requirements of the job and not the person's education.*

2. *Experience* This factor evaluates the time usually required for a person to acquire the necessary ability to do the job. In appraising Experience, it should be correlated with Education. Do not confuse length of service of an individual with experience required to qualify on the job. Experience may have been acquired elsewhere, in whole or in part, by the individual on the job.

3. *Complexity of Duties* This factor evaluates the complexity of the duties in terms of the scope of independent action, the extent to which the duties are standardized, the judgment and planning required, the type of decisions made and the area within which the individual on the job is required to exercise discretion.

4. *Monetary Responsibility* This factor evaluates the responsibility for profit or loss to the Company as a result of actions or decisions which involve items such as equipment, material, labor, cost estimates, prices, forecasts, purchase commitments, investments. Consider the extent to which the work is checked or verified, the effect of actions or decisions on operating costs or profits, monetary loss, production delays or effect on employees or customers.

5. *Responsibility for Contacts with Others* This factor evaluates the responsibility which goes with the job for working with or through other persons, to get results. In the lower degrees, it is largely a matter of giving or getting information or instructions. In the higher degrees, the factor involves dealing with or influencing other persons. In rating this factor, consider how the contacts are made and for what purpose.

6. *Working Conditions* This factor evaluates the conditions under which the job must be done and the extent to which the conditions make the job disagreeable or unpleasant. Consider the presence, relative amount and continuity of exposure to conditions such as noise, heat, dust, fumes. Since the plan includes no factor for physical effort, that phase of the job may be considered under this factor where physical effort is involved.

SUPERVISION ONLY

7. *Type of Supervision* This factor evaluates the degree of supervision exercised in terms of the level of the job in the organization and the character of the responsibility for directing or supervising other persons.

8. *Extent of Supervision* This factor evaluates the responsibility for supervision in terms of the number of persons supervised.

FIGURE 155*b*. GENERAL DEFINITIONS OF NEMA CHARACTERISTICS

Occ. No.   105–11   JOB RATING SPECIFICATION

Division   Accounting   Salaried Job Rating Plan

Dept. or   Class _____
  Plant   Tabulating

Grade   ___E___

Job Name: TABULATING MACHINE OPERATOR

Job Description

Under direct supervision of Supervisor—Tabulating, operate various types of electric tabulating machines to analyze, calculate, translate, summarize information, represented by punched holes on tabulating cards and print translated data on form sheets, reports, or accounting records. Operate machines such as interpreter, multiplier, collator, sorter, tabulator, reproducing summary punch. Compile and print payroll and earnings statements, payroll deductions, accounts payable, sales analyses, billings, miscellaneous reports as requested. Change plug boards; wire up boards. Repunch cards which fail to pass through machines. Keep machines clean and oiled.

Promote From_____ to _____

	Analyst			Dept. Head	Revised	Revised	Revised
Initials							
Date							

This job description is not a complete statement of all the duties and responsibilities which go with the job. It contains only the facts necessary to rate the job fairly.

FIGURE 156a. EXAMPLE OF NEMA DESCRIPTION

JOB RATING SPECIFICATION

Salaried Job Rating Plan

Class _____

Occ. No.	105–11
Division	Accounting
Dept. or Plant	Tabulating
Grade	E
Points	255

Job Name:
TABULATING MACHINE
OPERATOR

Factor	Specification	Rating	
		Deg.	Pts.
Education	Use arithmetic. Work with punched cards, statements and reports. Knowledge of operation of electrical tabulating machines equivalent to general academic education plus specialized training up to 1 year.	3	60
Experience	Over 1 up to 2 years.	4	100
Complexity of Duties	Plan and perform a sequence of semi-routine duties working from standard procedures. Make decisions which require some judgment to wire up boards, check form of data, assure all cards are sorted for run, determine action to be taken within limits prescribed.	3	60
Monetary Responsibility	Limited monetary responsibility since the work is usually checked or verified before it leaves the Section.	2	10
Responsibility for Contacts with Others	Routine contacts with Accounting, Payroll, Sales, to give or get information requiring only courtesy.	2	10
Working Conditions	Somewhat disagreeable due to noise from equipment.	3	15
	FACTORS TO BE ADDED FOR SUPERVISORY JOBS ONLY		
Type of Supervision			
Extent of Supervision			

FIGURE 156b. (Obverse.)

SALARY SCHEDULE, MONTHLY RATES
(20% × 12½%)

		Rate Range		
Grade	Minimum	Mid-point	Maximum	Range
A	$135	$148	$160	$25
B	150	165	180	30
C	165	185	205	40
D	190	210	230	40
E	215	240	265	50
F	245	270*	300	55
G	275	305	335	60
H	310	340**	375	65
J	350	385	420	70
K	390	430	470	80
L	440	485	530	90
M	500	550	600	100

* Mid-point actually $272.50.   ** Mid-point actually $342.50.

NOTE: This schedule is constructed to give a 20 per cent range within each
Grade (leveled to the nearest $5) with a 12½ per cent differential
between mid-points.

FIGURE 157. EXAMPLE OF RATE TABULATION UNDER THE NEMA SALARIED JOB
RATING PLAN

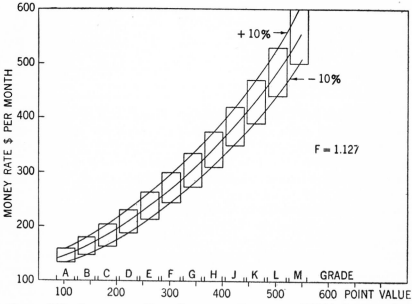

FIGURE 158. EXAMPLE OF RATE STRUCTURE UNDER THE NEMA SALARIED JOB
RATING PLAN

NEMA Plan for Learners. The Learner Progression Schedule (Figure 159) is to be applied to inexperienced employees. In the case of grades A to C, it would apply to persons with little or no previous work experience, such as high school graduates. Beyond those grades, the minimum hiring rate has been graduated on the basis that persons for such jobs would have had work experience though not necessarily in the field for which they were hired. Beyond grade F or G, the schedule is primarily for promotion purposes. The schedule should be regarded as a minimum progression schedule. Supervision should advance employees more rapidly if they make exceptional progress.

Grade	Hiring Min. Rate	3 mos.	6 mos.	9 mos.	12 mos.	15 mos.	18 mos.	24 mos.	30 mos.	Range
A	$125	$135								$10
B	130	140	$150							20
C	135	145	155	$165						30
D	155	165	175	190						35
E	175	185	195	205	$215					40
F	195	205	215	225	235	$245				50
G	215	225	235	245	255	265	$275			60
H	240	250	260	270	280	290	300	$310		70
J	270	280	290	300	310	320	330	340	$350	80
K	310	320	330	340	350	360	370	380	390	80
L	360	370	380	390	400	410	420	430	440	80
M	420	430	440	450	460	470	480	490	500	80

FIGURE 159. LEARNER PROGRESSION SCHEDULE

L. O. M. A. Job Element Evaluation Plan.[20] This novel plan was evolved several years ago as a means of classifying multiple jobs in the smaller insurance offices for which the Bills Classification Plan is unsuitable. It is based on the premise that all clerical work can be divided into three categories: (1) doing the work, (2) checking the work, and (3) supervising the work; and also that each of these can be subdivided into a limited number of distinct, not necessarily uniform, operations (see Figure 160). In other words, the real differences among jobs are found in how such distinct operations are combined rather than in the variations of the operations themselves. This is similar to the practice in factories where re-

[20] See Life Office Management Association, *Clerical Salary Study Committee Report* Nos. 3, 5, and 6; and also *Clerical Salary Administration*, edited by L. W. Ferguson, 1948.

corded data for standard elements are selectively synthetized to describe in advance any combination of elements that may arise. In the shop the conditions and operations are usually standardized so that the records represent standard elements and are much more accurate; 84 to 90 per cent of all large factories now depend on "standard data" for their task setting. Curiously few of them have adopted this practice to the more qualitative functions of job analysis and evaluation. The Edo and Lockheed Aircraft companies did a little experimenting but little application of the principle has been made as yet. Nevertheless it seems that L. O. M. A. has found a very happy means of evaluating not only clerical multiple duty jobs, but all multiple duty jobs. In fact, we think their "job element" plan is most promising for certain higher jobs such as those of staff and supervision, which are distinctly multiple in nature.

	Grades	Points
Messenger Work............	4	800 to 840
Sorting	8	800 to 990
Filing or Pulling from File....	7	850 to 1560
Counting	2	820 to 890
Posting (including calculating)	26	820 to 2900
Checking and Reviewing......	15	970 to 1470
Balancing	13	960 to 5000
Correspondence or Discussion	53	960 to 4710
Machine and Secretarial......	21	840 to 1730

FIGURE 160. L. O. M. A. JOB ELEMENT PLAN

NOTE: Each of these fundamental operations is expanded by means of predetermined "grade" definitions. See L. O. M. A. Report No. 3, *Clerical Salary Study Committee*, September 1, 1940, pages 40–45.

Procedure for L. O. M. A. Job Element Plan. The point values for the elements are derived by pooled ratings of each distinct operation just as each would be if it took 100 per cent of the operator's time. For the supervisional operations two dimensional tables are set up to combine the number of clerks supervised, the variety of the work supervised (on the vertical), the difficulty of the work supervised, and the completeness of the supervision (on the horizontal). See Report No. 3, pp. 46–47. The point values resulting from these studies are now recorded (see Figure 161 for sample of one). The tabular parts are coded and the two dimensional code numbers, such as 60–10 in Figure 161 are entered with the point values, such as 970 in Figure 162. From these established operations and their values it is now a matter of identifying those described in any job description which may come up for evaluation. As each operation is identified, its established point value is multiplied by the percentage of time it bears to the whole job and the modified value is entered on the job description (see Figures 162 and 163). When complete these modified operation values are added to give the point value for the multiple job. There are, however, two further corrections, one the use of a complexity multiplier where the number of distinct operations is high, and a second disregarding the values for a minority of the operations if the majority of time is taken by opera-

Evaluations of Fundamental Clerical Operations—Table of Values

Checking or Reviewing	Code No.	Operations Value (Points)
Checking for the presence or absence of a few items of information	60–10	970
Checking direct information with reference to authentic records when the information should be identical on two records.....................	60–20	1000
Checking direct informaion with reference to authentic records when the information on the two should correspond but may not be identical..		
involving a few items..................	60–30	1070
involving many items..................	60–31	1280
Checking for internal consistency on work sheet....		
involving a few items..................	60–40	1170
involving many items..................	60–41	1440

FIGURE 161. FUNDAMENTAL CLERICAL OPERATIONS

tions of relatively considerable difficulty. In such a case the average value of the more difficult operations is extended to cover the whole job. Eventually such a job should be changed in content on the principle of skill conservation.

Scatter Diagram. Where large numbers of jobs are involved it is common to reduce each scatter to a median figure. The several medians for a department are then plotted by job classes and the resulting curve for the main departments is superimposed on a single chart. The Westinghouse Electric Company did not attempt trend and limit lines for the whole series but treated each functional group separately, curves not shown. The York Ice Machinery Corporation followed the more traditional use of separate point scatters

Analysis of Job Description
Based on Fundamental Clerical Operations

JOB DESCRIPTION		Evaluation			
JOB NAME Loan Calculator (Cash Loans— Straight) **DEPT.** Policy Loan	**JOB NO.** **DIVISION**	Code No.	Value	Per Cent of Time	Weighted Value
Checks signature on loan note against signature on application. Notes type of payment requested on transmittal form		60–20	1000	5%	50
Checks for completeness of loan note and transmittal form. Checks all titles		60–10	970	5	49
Figures time from policy issued date on application to premium-paid-to-date on transmittal. Computes from table in application loan value for that time..................		50–40	980	20	196
Calculates annual interest on new loan at 6 per cent and initial interest figured from present date to anniversary of policy except when anniversary comes within two months using special interest tables. Copies amount of loan, initial interest, and annual interest on transmittals....		50–80	1260	70	882
Total				100%	1177

FIGURE 162. JOB DESCRIPTION, LOAN CALCULATOR

(Figure 164) on which a geometric trend line and ± 15 per cent limit lines were fitted. The General Electric Company (Figure 165) established a set of two straight trend lines and then fixed the limits at ± 15 per cent. Eastman Kodak Company calls its set of geometric lines "Master Curves," and uses them like a budget to control the granting of rate changes.

Choosing Trend and Limit Lines. Perhaps for clerical work alone one set of straight lines can be as well justified as for hourly paid jobs, but if the higher salaried positions are to be included then a single set of straight lines will not do. Two sets of straight lines,

Analysis of Job Description
Based on Fundamental Clerical Operations

JOB DESCRIPTION		Evaluation			
JOB NAME Mail Clerk	JOB NO.	Code No.	Value	Per Cent of Time	Weighted Value
DEPT. Life Accounts	DIVISION				
Receives and stamps incoming mail. Sorts and passes to units. Collects mail from the units and sends it out		10–20	840	20%	168
Receives checks returned for insufficient funds from Unit Head and sends to photostat unit..........		10–10	800	1	8
Gets from file any applications which are needed immediately..........		10–10	800	14	112
Assists File Clerk, filing surrendered policies, renewal receipts returned for credit and reinstatement records.		30–11	940	20	188
Receives from the units loan repayment memos. Lists on traveler in duplicate. Passes original with the loan repayment memo to the Loan Division and files the duplicate record		50–31	1020	35	357
Receives balance sheets from Units each month. Passes to Tax Department marking received on agency lists		50–21	970	5	49
Receives old and terminated premium record cards from Change Unit. Passes to File Clerk		10–10	800	5	40
Total				100%	922

FIGURE 163. JOB DESCRIPTION, MAIL CLERK

to allow for upturn in slope, may be tolerated but it takes three sets of them to get at all close to any geometric curve. In Figure 166 we have plotted a series of 31 rates running from $24 per week to $240 per week, $1,248 per year to $12,480 per year.[21] One

[21] At the time of writing, supervisors who were department heads were receiving take-home earnings from $275 a month to $650 a month. N.W.L.B. *Foreman Panel Report*, Jan. 31, 1945.

line was set according to the preferred numbers formula, another was taken from a semilog plotting of a straight line, and last we inserted two straight lines to show how much they overpay intermediate jobs. The semilog line falls considerably below the preferred numbers line through intermediate classes but is very close to the latter along both ends. Doubtless the semilog line is liked by employers, primarily because it undercuts the preferred numbers line but also because it is much easier to derive. After using a log-

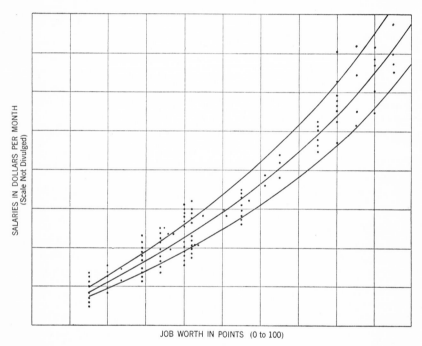

FIGURE 164. YORK ICE MACHINERY CORPORATION, TREND AND ±15% LIMIT LINES.
(*N.A.C.A. Bulletin*, XXIII, No. 20.)

log slide rule half a day to get this one curve we are inclined to recommend the use of three straight lines. In practice the lines must be set accurately, which means the use of logarithms, from tables or by means of a calculating machine, for both trend and limit lines if straight lines are not used. Worst of all, very few if any of the employees can check the correctness of geometric rates; nevertheless, we do insist that the geometric principle is the proper one to follow. This can, however, be done for guidance only, that is, as a means of locating a set of straight trend lines. Three straight lines can give very close approximations; two cannot.

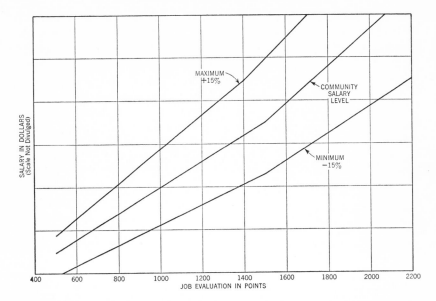

FIGURE 165. THE GENERAL ELECTRIC COMPANY TREND AND LIMIT LINES FOR
SALARIED POSITIONS

Ranges and Ingrades. The design of range boxes is the last and
most interesting act in fixing any rate structure. The principles and
techniques are, however, no different from what we have discussed
and illustrated in Chapter 11. In the case of high-salaried jobs
these ranges must be authorized by top management.

Details of a Rate Structure. Figures 167*a*, *b*, and *c* set up the
data for an eight-grade structure suitable for hourly paid jobs in an
office. In this example no trend line was used. The floors and ceilings were laid out as straight lines on a semilog grid (Figure 167*a*)
and the values transferred to a Cartesian grid, Figure 167*b*. This
gives geometric progression for the two essential limits and saves
the time of finding the line of mid-points. The latter can quickly
be approximated by marking half-way points in each box. That
will not be the true mid-line percentagewise, but if bargaining is on
the limits it is permissible and entirely practical; in fact it is easier
to explain because these points will be exactly half way. Notice in
Figure 167*b* that the ceiling of Class No. 1 gave no lapover so that
one had to be arbitrarily provided by lifting the derived ceiling
five cents. This structure is tabulated in Figure 167*c*. For structures
with more grades see Chapter 11.

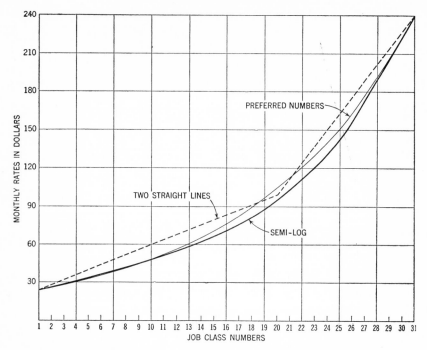

FIGURE 166. COMPARISON OF TREND LINES

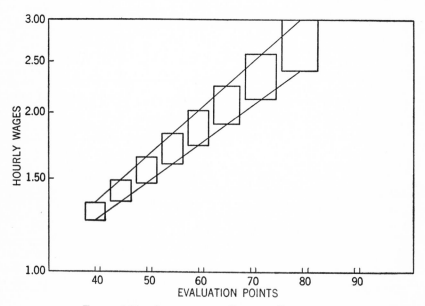

FIGURE 167a. STRUCTURE ON SEMILOG COORDINATES

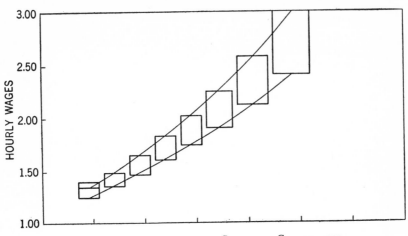

FIGURE 167b. STRUCTURE ON CARTESIAN COORDINATES

Classes			Dollar Rates					
No.	Points	Range	Floor Dif-feren-tial	Range Limits	Overlap Between Ranges	Ceiling Differ-ential	Difference Between Differen-tials	% Limits
1	38–41	4		1.25–1.35 (lifted to 1.40)				± 3.85
2	43–46	4	.11	1.36–1.49	.04	.09	2	± 4.56
3	48–51	4	.11	1.47–1.65	.02	.16	5	± 5.77
4	53–56	4	.13	1.60–1.83	.05	.18	5	± 6.70
5	58–61	4	.14	1.74–2.02	.09	.19	5	± 7.44
6	63–67	5	.16	1.90–2.25	.12	.23	7	± 8.43
7	69–74	6	.22	2.12–2.58	.13	.33	11	± 9.78
8	76–82	7	.28	2.40–3.00	.18	.42	14	±11.10

FIGURE 167c. TABULAR STRUCTURE FOR HOURLY CLERICAL JOBS. (Leon Gleimer.)

Salary Control. Budgetary control as a means of controlling salary costs may not be entirely satisfactory because a budget does not necessarily show the causes of salary variance. Confronted with this, E. N. Hay [22] has devised what he calls the Compa-Ratio. For any one department the ratio is the sum of all present salaries divided by the sum of the mid-points of ranges multiplied by 100. Any variation of the ratio from 100 will indicate how much the group is above or below the mid-point. In applying this, Mr. Hay

[22] *Control of Salary Expense*, A.M.A. Financial Series No. 79.

uses the geometric mid-points which run slightly below the arthmetic mid-points. For instance, if the allowed spread of the ranges is 33 per cent and the present total of a group is $572, he multiplies that by the square root of the allowable variation, $\sqrt{1.33}$, and gets a mid-point value of $660.08. This shows a Compa-Ratio of 102.1 per cent. For the spread of 33⅓ per cent the limits of the ratio are 86 and 115. Discovery that the ratio is above standard may restrain the department head from granting further salary increases until someone has quit and been replaced by a beginner at a lower rate. Personally, we would prefer to establish limit lines and use them directly, but where there is no merit rating system it is necessary to resist the pressure for increases and this method is effective. If merit rating is in operation the increases should be automatic until each individual reaches the top ingrade for his classification. In that case the correctness of classification is the thing to watch.

Some Conclusions. We have not attempted to thresh out many of the moot questions in this field but we like the "recapitulation" of one who has reported on some of these questions.[23]

1. Salary administration must have as its underlying motive a sincere desire to achieve equitable salary rates. Systematic methods cannot effectively be employed for purposes of payroll reduction.

2. The "consent of the governed" is essential. It may be possible to impose evaluation plans upon unwilling employees, but the act of forcing precludes any possibility of genuine acceptance, without which real success is impossible.

3. No single best system exists. The details, and indeed the broad general approach, are functions of the particular company. The best system for a given firm is the one which harmonizes best with the existing relationships.

4. The system is at most an expression of broad general policy, subject to alterations as indicated by its actual administration. It must be flexible and adaptable to ever changing human situations.

5. The system is not a substitute for sound judgment. It is valueless without intelligent interpretation and application. By itself, it solves no problems. Unintelligent administration may be a source of real grief.

We would add that with job evaluation the supervisors can be allowed complete freedom within the structure to award or withhold salary increases, and thereby regain the authority and prestige which under some managements has been all but lost in recent times.

[23] Frank H. Hall, Jr., *Controversial Issues in Salary Determination*, Report No. 4, Sponsored Fellowship Investigations in Industry, Department of Business and Engineering Administration, Massachusetts Institute of Technology.

15

APPLYING EVALUATION TO
EXECUTIVE AND PROFESSIONAL POSITIONS

> The benefits to be derived from clear statements of supervisory
> responsibilities and limits of authority are genuine and are
> realized particularly in better results in selection, more effective
> training programs, more accurate and reliable merit ratings, and
> more realistic approach to the problem of salary administration.
> —W. W. WAITE

Jobs Difficult to Fill Need Evaluation. Evaluation plans for
the jobs of supervisors and department heads sometimes include the
job of works manager, but they usually exclude top executive and
single-incumbent jobs such as those of controller, medical director,
general sales manager and, except NEMA, the professional-technical jobs in engineering, metallurgy, and chemistry. These fields
are now the frontiers and little regarding them has as yet reached
the printed stage. It is known, however, that applications of job
evaluation to these hitherto exempt jobs are increasing. For instance, the NICB survey of 1946 indicated that one third of the
companies had applied job evaluation to the managerial level. A
1951 survey made by NICB reported that 123 companies or 55 per
cent of the 244 firms covered had extended job evaluation to their
managerial positions. Some of this advance in the use of job evaluation can be accounted for by the time element; companies which
began to apply it to hourly jobs in the 1930's have long since completed those first applications and have found that they are of value.
With that in mind and with confidence gained from experience they
naturally are going on to include all other jobs. There is, however,
another cause for this last and most difficult extension. Government orders on the one hand and surtaxes on the other hand, plus
ramifications, have made it more of a problem to secure and retain
managers and professional technicians, the supply of which is by
no means abundant. Out of this situation comes an almost new
anxiety to plan ahead for replacements. One of the first corpora-

tions to undertake a formal plan for long-run promotion was the Standard Oil Company of California. It began in 1941 and took ten years to complete it, if this outstanding accomplishment can be called completion. Such a plan usually sets up five steps:

1. Analyze all operating functions and responsibilities, align and chart as an integrated organization.
2. Write descriptions and manpower specifications of all higher jobs, classify and harmonize with Step 1.
3. Assess performances of present incumbents and appraise against the standards.
4. Prepare a replacement schedule [1] theoretically in terms of men who have evinced promotability.
5. Rotate and train those selected for promotion and if all this does not provide understudies for all jobs recruit new persons at a level below the jobs needing understudies.

Notice that Step 2 is job evaluation, Step 3 is merit rating, and that the other steps hinge considerably on these two.

Descriptions of Managerial Jobs. In an earlier chapter we have stressed the organizational nature of job descriptions. This becomes particularly apparent when we get to the top, or rather as we start from the top as General Electric Company has done. In fact we are so impressed with the G. E. concept [2] of job descriptions that we cannot resist quoting their "steps" verbatim as follows:

First Step. The General Manager, working with his superior, and after general exploratory talks with all individuals reporting directly to him, prepares a draft of his position description and a preliminary functional organization chart showing his position and the positions of all such individuals who will continue to report directly to him.

If a new organization structure is being established, the General Manager will assign functions to positions in the way he believes will best permit him to accomplish his over-all management objectives, being sure that all needed work is covered, without gaps, overlaps, unnecessary jobs, or effort. If the organization structure is already in place, the General Manager will at this point further consider how he can eliminate either unnecessary levels or unduly short spans of control, and also how he can reassign functions or otherwise modify his organization pattern to provide an improved organization structure for the future.

Second Step. After the General Manager and his superior are in essential agreement with respect to organization structure and functions, he will

---

[1] See "Bring Up the Boss," *Fortune*, XLIII, No. 6, p. 120.
[2] H. F. Smiddy and B. A. Case, "Why Write a Description of Your Position?" *G. E. Review*, July, 1952.

call together the incumbents of the positions that are under his direct super-vision and discuss with them the draft of his position description and the pre-liminary functional organization chart. The important point here is that each shall understand clearly his own part of the job and also understand, accept, and respect the parts of all the others on the team.

Third Step. Each incumbent who reports directly to the General Man-ager analyzes his own position and prepares lists of the "objectives to be accomplished" and the "work to be done."

Fourth Step. The incumbents of this "team" will discuss their "lists" with each other and will endeavor to reach agreement as to how their posi-tions should mesh together without overlap or gaps.

Fifth Step. Each subordinate meets with the General Manager, reviews his "lists," the General Manager's position description, and the functional organization chart with him, and then prepares a draft of his position description.

Sixth Step. The General Manager's subordinates hold a series of meet-ings, preferably with him present only when his specific counsel is essential, and they work together to the end that complete, mutual understanding and agreement are reached with respect to organization structure, functional organization chart, and all position descriptions. This provides an oppor-tunity for teamwork participation and for the consideration of alternative solutions before agreeing on which is best for the business and its future, with the General Manager still having final responsibility to make decisions among alternative solutions or where differences of viewpoint may exist.

Seventh Step. Each of the individuals reporting directly to the General Manager then repeats this procedure with his subordinates, and so on, until all position descriptions have been prepared. In this respect, cross-checking between individuals in different functional sections and units, at each succeed-ing organizational level, needs to be worked out as carefully as between the members of the General Manager's staff in the first place.

As for lower jobs, it is well to develop an orderly outline of mat-ters that should go into the job description and eventually standard-ize a form or questionnaire. This should, however, be according to company conditions, that is, tailor-fitted. For any who wish to see how another company has done this we can refer only to one form from industry that has so far been published.[3] The United States Government does publish a "Guide for Writing Position Descrip-tions" (see *Federal Personnel Manual*).

At the top are the necessary identifying data; then follow three to five line spaces for *Objective, Scope,* and *Market* (in case of a sales manager). Next is a 2½″ space for *Volume* with column headings, *Type of Sales, Number of Accounts,* and *195– Sales.* Also in this space are described: *Institutional Sales, Premium Sales,*

[3] Edward N. Hay and Dale Purves, "The Analysis and Description of High-Level Jobs," *Personnel,* XXIX, No. 4.

Retail Sales, and *Summary.* Next is a line headed *Budget 195–,* showing total allotment. Next is a space headed *Personnel* which is subdivided and the number of direct subordinates recorded. Finally is space for *Evaluation Data* subdivided into *Know-How, Mental Activity,* and *Accountability,* each of which is evaluated in points and totaled. The reverse side is divided to describe *Organization, Policy Formation, Supervision,* and *Specialization,* each of which is again subdivided to suit.

The Basic Abilities Ranking Plan for High-Level Positions. Since 1948 the Allen-Bradley Company, of which Mr. R. W. Ells is Chief Economist, has been developing a concept of job rating that finds a common denominator in terms of abilities and knowledge that can dispense with characteristics having to do with performance and thereby get satisfactory results in much less time. Mr. Ells says:

> We now analyze, grade, and price jobs in five to ten minutes, where we formerly spent two to three hours. . . . the terms "abilities" and "knowledges" are merely another way of expressing duties, responsibilities, and working conditions. And the reason why the use of such terms is advocated is their practicability.[4]

The differences in ability requirements are considered constants while the differences in performance requirements are considered variables. As Mr. Ells sees it, if an employee has the necessary ability to do a job, it is immaterial to what extent that ability is due to his mental and physical traits, which he calls inherent, or to his education, skill, and experience which he has acquired. In short, Mr. Ells considers what is the net requirement regardless of what it is due to and would leave specific performance requirements for intragrade consideration which does not affect job grading and pricing. He claims that with this approach much confusion is obviated, but when he says, "Under our former plan if the abilities possessed by an individual didn't match the abilities required of the job, we had to do a lot of juggling. Now, all we do is change the duties and responsibilities of the job to whatever degree is necessary to suit the ability requirements," he is of course remaking a job to fit the man. While we disavow such an approach for ordinary jobs, we see some merit in it for executive and professional positions. Mr. E. N. Hay goes so far as to say, "high-level jobs are people," or "the man makes the job."

[4] R. W. Ells, "Simplified Job Evaluation," *A.M.A. Personnel Series* No. 140, and *Wisconsin Commerce Report* III, No. 2.

PARTIAL LIST OF ABILITIES AND KNOWLEDGES USED IN VERTICAL GRADING
OF A SALARY SCHEDULE

A. *SEMISKILLS* (or those which, if they can be acquired, take from 3 to 6
   months in the acquisition.)
   *1. Knowledge of company and departmental procedures.
   *2. Ability to get along with people.
   *3. Ability to meet the public.
   *4. Ability to handle confidential information.
   *5. Ability to work under unpleasant conditions.
    6. Ability to type.
    7. Knowledge of bookkeeping.
    8. Ability to take dictation.
    9. Ability to transcribe dictation.
   10. Knowledge of mechanical drawing.
   11. Ability to trace.
   12. Ability to operate a bookkeeping machine.
   13. Ability to operate a calculating machine.
   14. Ability to operate address-o-graph equipment.
   15. Ability to operate a key-punch.
   16. Ability to operate a PBX switchboard.
   17. Ability to operate multigraph machines.
   18. Ability to operate tabulating equipment.
   19. Ability to operate a billing machine.
   20. Etc.

B. *SKILLS* (or those abilities which, if they can be acquired, take at least
   12 months or more in the acquisition.)
   †1. Knowledge of company products.
   †2. Ability to organize and direct the work of others.
   †3. Ability to plan the work of others.
   †4. Ability to exercise independent judgment.
   †5. Ability to work under hazardous conditions.
   †6. Ability to create or design new products.
   †7. Ability to develop new procedures and methods.
    8. Knowledge of accounting.
    9. Knowledge of sales techniques.
   10. Knowledge of engineering.
   11. Knowledge of library techniques.
   12. Knowledge of nursing.
   13. Knowledge of law.
   14. Knowledge of chemistry.
   15. Knowledge of buying techniques.
   16. Knowledge of employment techniques.
   17. Knowledge of traffic rates and tariffs.
   18. Ability to make designs or layouts.
   19. Ability to wire tabulating equipment.
   20. Etc.
   * Upgrading skills.
   † Basic skills.

FIGURE 168. ELLS'S SUBSTITUTE FOR USUAL CHARACTERISTICS. (Society for Advancement of Management.)

Figure 168 illustrates Mr. Ells's concepts of abilities and knowledges which he calls vertical. Beyond the "upgrading skills" of A and the "basic skills" of B the items would vary for different divisions or professions. Perhaps the difficulty in using this plan is to identify these requirements as they are brought out in the job descriptions as duties, responsibilities, and the like, that is, when the duties, responsibilities, working conditions, and other items are determined, they must be analyzed to determine the abilities and knowledges required to carry out the job. The data are usually acquired by questionnaire and on-the-job inspection, but a supervisor or manager may fill out a preliminary form to set some of the requirements. These sheets are then sent to the job analyst, who determines the abilities and knowledges required for each job. This is probably the most important step in the entire process, since the abilities and knowledges determine the position of a job within the hierarchy.

Next the jobs are sorted according to the abilities and knowledges specified. Job classification titles are assigned to jobs; all jobs with the same abilities and knowledges have the same *classification title*. This step is entirely separate from job grading. Whereas job titles help management set up lines of authority, job classification titles help them to arrange jobs with different duties and responsibilities, but requiring the same abilities and knowledges. A good example of this is the typist (Grade 3), Figure 169. Here the classification title is "typist," whereas the job titles are Copy, Record, and Billing typists, which constitute subgrades. Mr. Ells calls them horizontal. This classification permits job pricing by indirection and simplifies grading. Mr. Ells suggests that a permanent classification unit be set up since job contents are changing constantly. Therefore, classification must be on a current basis. To avoid confusion he also suggests the following rules:

1. If duties, responsibility, and working conditions are the same, then the basic abilities and knowledges must be the same.
2. If the abilities and knowledges are the same, then the classification title must be the same, regardless of organizational classification titles.
3. A job classification title can be used for one set only of abilities.

The committee should issue quarterly rank-order lists so supervisors and managers can review and list those classifications they disagree with. This prevents any job from being out of classification for more than a few weeks. This list should be issued at a different

Level of Reponsibility	Salary Grade	Typical Job Classifications
Unskilled	1	Messenger
	2	File Clerk
Semiskilled	3	Typists
	4	Stenographers
Skilled	5	Steno-Secretary
	6	Nurses
Specialists	7	Student Engineers
	8	Cost Accountants
Dept. Head	9	Dept. Manager
	10	Dept. Head
Division Mgr.	11	Ass't. Div. Mgr.
	12	Division Mgr.
Executive	13	Vice President
	14	President

FIGURE 169. EXAMPLE OF ELLS'S JOB HIERARCHY. (Allen-Bradley Company.)

NOTE: The number of grades recommended is from six to eight for companies with less than 200 employees and from ten to fourteen for companies that are larger.

time from the salary or merit reviews. This keeps abilities and knowledge separate from performance in the supervisor's mind and helps insure consistency as to grade.

The grading is done by a permanent managerial committee on a periodic basis. It is primarily a matter of judgment, and management must see that the committee is fair and impartial. The grading is merely the combined opinions of the committee, but the grading determines the position of the job within the hierarchy. For example of Job Analysis see Figure 170.

The Profile Ranking Plan for High-Level Positions. This plan [5] switches directly from duties to functions in the original job descriptions. Only three characteristics are used: knowledge, mental application, and accountability. To aid in determining the relative importance of these characteristics as needed in each job, a "profile" or percentage breakdown for the characteristics is made for each job. Extreme precision for the percentage breakdown is not claimed but approximate proportions are judged by considering the functions. For instance, a typist's job is given the profile of 80 per cent K or knowledge, 9 per cent M or mental application, and 11

[5] E. N. Hay and Dale Purves, "The Profile Method of High-Level Job Evaluation," *Personnel*, XXVIII, No. 2.

JOB AND PERSONNEL SPECIFICATION FORM

JOB CLASSIFICATION: _____ Executive Secretary _____ SALARY GRADE: ___7___

SECTION A—JOB SPECIFICATION

DUTIES, RESPONSIBILITIES AND WORKING CONDITIONS	BASIC ABILITY AND KNOWLEDGE REQUIREMENTS
1. Take and transcribe important and confidential dictation.	1. Ability to take and transcribe dictation.
2. Maintain records and personal files.	2. Ability to type.
3. Make appointments, handle telephone calls and routine mail.	3. Knowledge of company and departmental procedures.
4. Prepare and type special reports.	4. Ability to exercise independent judgment.
5. Take care of personal mail, records and reports.	

SECTION B—PERSONNEL SPECIFICATION

PHYSICAL REQUIREMENTS	SKILL REQUIREMENTS	PERSONALITY REQUIREMENTS
1. SEX _____ Female	1. TYPING _____ 60 words a min.	1. EMOTIONAL STABILITY _____ Above Average
2. AGE _____ 25–40	2. STENOGRAPHIC 90 words a min.	2. FINANCIAL STABILITY _____ Average
3. HEALTH _____ Average		3. MATURITY _____ Average
4. APPEARANCE Neat		4. MOTIVATION ___ Above Average
		5. DRIVE _____ Average
MENTAL REQUIREMENTS	**CHARACTER REQUIREMENTS**	6. PERSEVERANCE Average
		7. JOB INTEREST Above Average
1. INTELLIGENCE Above Average	1. LOYALTY _____ Above Average	8. GET ALONG WITH OTHERS Average
2. JUDGMENT ____ Above Average	2. SELF-RELIANCE Above Average	
	3. ETHICS ____ Above Average	9. LEADERSHIP ___ Average

OTHER DESIRABLE CHARACTERISTICS

1. EDUCATION: ___ College or its equivalent. _____

2. EXPERIENCE: ___ Five years as a stenographer or secretary. ___

FIGURE 170. EXAMPLE OF ELLS'S JOB ANALYSIS. (Society for Advancement of Management.)

per cent A or accountability. When such profiles have been tentatively determined separately, they are harmonized in relation to each other. This approach is supposed to obviate the alleged danger that predetermined scales may not be equally appropriate for different kinds of jobs. It is assumed that all jobs of a given type should have profiles similar enough to prove their relationship. Thus the Office Supervisor type of job would have a characteristic profile of about 41 per cent K, 27 per cent M, and 32 per cent A, while an Operations Supervisor, Accounting job would be about 40 per cent K, 26 per cent M, and 34 per cent A; the Head Statistical Analysis job about 38 per cent K, 29 per cent M, and 33 per cent A, and the Supervisor Field Auditing job about 40 per cent K, 26 per cent M, and 34 per cent A. Out of these studies are evolved basic profiles for the various types of jobs. Individual job profiles are found to vary about 5 per cent either way from their bases. When all job profiles have been grouped and harmonized the jobs are ranked on the knowledge characteristic, that is, with respect to the requirements for knowledge (importance and extent). Next the analyst or committee must decide how many (if any) intervals or steps should be between the jobs. Mr. Hay uses 25 numerical steps 15 per cent apart, that is, starting with 12 and ending with 200. Notice that the values double every five steps.

The Hay procedure for stepping jobs is so unusual we do not trust ourselves to transmit it except in his own words.

a) If you can see no difference in the knowledge requirements of two jobs, they are the same.

b) If you think you see a difference after thorough study, the magnitude of the difference is probably one step (15 per cent).

c) If you are sure you see a difference after thorough study, the magnitude of the difference is probably two steps (33 per cent).

d) If you see a difference *clearly* without having to study the jobs carefully, the magnitude of the difference is probably three steps (50 per cent), or more. Differences greater than three steps can best be determined by comparing a chain of jobs where the differences between any two jobs are not more than three steps. It is difficult to "sense" accurately differences over 50 per cent.

Now if a sales manager's job, 33 per cent K, 27 per cent M, and 40 per cent A finds itself on step 175, and a sales specialist's job 42 per cent K, 31 per cent M, and 27 per cent A finds itself on step

57, the K percentages take the step values 175 and 57 respectively and the other percentages are prorated accordingly:

$$27/33 \times 175 = 143 \qquad 31/42 \times 57 = 43, \text{ etc.}$$

From which the metamorphosed profiles are

$$175\,K + 143\,M + 213\,A \qquad 57\,K + 42\,M + 37\,A$$

Of these all but the first items are out of step so they are adjusted to:

$$175\,K + 150\,M + 200\,A \qquad 57\,K + 43\,M + 38\,A$$

To this point the jobs have been ranked only on their K's so now they get ranked on their M's and A's. From which new sums appear as follows:

$$175\,K + 133\,M + 200\,A = 508 \qquad 57\,K + 43\,M + 43\,A = 143$$

These two totals, which must not be called points, are the job worths.

Straight-Point Plan for Executives Only. S. C. Johnson and Son has distinct plans for the several kinds of occupations,[6] one of which is exclusively for executive positions. It starts where the supervisory plan ends—with the jobs of department heads. Ten broad characteristics are used and for most of these the definitions are divided into two aspects, such as degree and scope, difficulty and complexity, level and breadth, level and frequency. Thus the table of point values provides for combinations of these two aspects. This makes a large table but determinations are no more difficult than with a smaller number of degrees, perhaps less difficult. We omit this table. The maximum of point values is 30 for each of the characteristics. Within each are weighted values for the combinations, which begin with 1 or 2 and rise to 30 in from 4 to 65 choices. Some of these within a single scale give different combinations the same values.

FACTOR DEFINITIONS

I. Policy

Appraise the position for its level of responsibility in the development, final determination, and interpretation of policies and for the importance of the policies as indicated by their breadth of application and effect on operations and net profits.

[6] H. S. Briggs, "Executive Position Evaluation—A Case Study," NICB *Management Record*, XII, No. 7.

A. Degree

1. Assist in formulation
2. Formulation and primary recommendation
3. Final recommendation
4. Decision as part of a group
5. Decision as an individual

B. Scope (Policies defined in Policy Manual)

1. Operating policies
2. Company policies
3. Corporate policies

II. PLANNING

Appraise the position for its level of responsibility in the original development, final determination, and interpretation of objectives and plans for the organization and conduct of the business, and the importance of the plans as indicated by the breadth of application and effect on operations and net profits.

A. Scope of Application of Plans

1. Section, area, or small staff unit
2. District or group of sections
3. Region
4. Department or a portion of company-wide activity
5. Division
6. Company-wide

B. Degree

1. Assist in development
2. Development and primary recommendation
3. Final recommendation
4. Decision as part of a group
5. Decision as an individual

III. METHODS

Appraise the position for its level of responsibility in the development, specification, and approval of methods, procedures, and physical facilities required for the performance and control of operations to accomplish the established objectives and for the complexity of the methods and the breadth of application. Consider only methods of doing, not methods of planning.

A. Scope or Complexity (Difficulty of Development)

1. Simple methods applying to operations under direct control
2. Simple methods applying to operations beyond direct control
3. Complex methods applying to operations under direct control
4. Complex methods applying to operations beyond direct control
5. Intricate methods applying to operations under direct control
6. Intricate methods applying to operations beyond direct control

B. Degree

1. Assist in development or detailing specifications
2. Development and primary recommendations
3. Final recommendation or establishment
4. Decision as an individual

IV. ADMINISTRATION

Appraise the position for the amount of management activity required in the coordination and direction of personnel, the use of equipment and the attainment of results, and for complexity of the operations administered.

A. Difficulty of Direction and Control

1. Direct supervision
2. One level of subordinate supervision within the community
3. One level of subordinate supervision beyond the community
4. Two levels of subordinate supervision within the community
5. Two levels of subordinate supervision beyond the community
6. Three levels of subordinate supervision within the community
7. Three levels of subordinate supervision beyond the community
8. Four levels of subordinate supervision within the community
9. Four levels of subordinate supervision beyond the community
10. Five levels of subordinate supervision beyond the community
11. Six levels of subordinate supervision beyond the community

B. Complexity of Function To Be Administered

1. Single function of a routine nature
2. Diversified functions of routine nature or a single function involving routine but varied work
3. Diversified functions, routine but varied work, or a single function involving nonroutine work
4. Diversified functions involving nonroutine work

V. PERSONNEL RELATIONS

Appraise the position for the importance of handling and development of personnel as indicated by the number of personnel involved, the nature of their responsibility, and the scope of influence.

A. *Opportunity to Influence Employees*

Grade	Frequent Collaboration	Functional Responsibility	Direct Responsibility
1	Under 11 employees	Under 6 employees	....
2	11–50 employees	6–10 employees	Under 6 employees
3	51–100 employees	11–50 employees	6–10 employees
4	101–200 employees	51–100 employees	11–50 employees
5	Over 200 employees not company-wide	101–200 employees	51–100 employees
6	Company-wide	Over 200 employees not company-wide	101–200 employees
7	.... Company-wide		Over 200 employees
8	....		not company-wide

B. Scope of Influence
1. Employees directly supervised only
2. Through one level of supervision
3. Through two levels of supervision
4. Through three levels of supervision or functional influence on a full department
5. Division
6. Company-wide

VI. EXECUTIVE CONTACTS

Appraise the position for its importance in influencing and obtaining cooperative action of nonsubordinate executives as indicated by the number of divisional and nondivisional contacts, number of nondepartmental contacts, and the level of executives contacted.

A. Level of Executives To Be Influenced
1. To department manager level within own division—frequently
2. To division vice-president level within own division—occasionally
3. To division vice-president level within own division—frequently
4. To department manager level outside own division—occasionally
5. To department manager level outside own division—frequently
6. To division vice-president level outside own division—occasionally
7. To division vice-president level outside own division—frequently
8. To executive vice-president level—occasionally
9. To executive vice-president level—frequently
10. To president—occasionally
11. To president—frequently
12. To board of directors—occasionally
13. To board of directors—frequently

B. Breadth of Contacts at Own Level or Company-wide
1. Few executives—occasionally
2. Few executives—frequently
3. Many executives—occasionally
4. Many executives—frequently
5. Continuous company-wide staff contacts

VII. OUTSIDE CONTACTS

Appraise the importance of outside contacts as measured by the frequency of opportunity to build company prestige through personal relation with the public and by the level of individuals seen.

A. Level
1. Routine business contacts
2. Important business contacts
3. Nonoperating contacts with influential persons

B. Frequency

   1. Infrequent
   2. Frequent
   3. Daily

VIII. ORIGINAL THINKING

Appraise the position for the importance of developing and applying of ideas for the improvement of the operations of the business and the degree of creativeness, originality, imagination, and ingenuity required.

A. Degree

   1. Ingenuity in revision or application of methods
   2. Imagination and originality on assigned problems
   3. Creative thinking from established practice
   4. Original thinking

IX. ANALYSIS

Appraise the position for the amount and complexity of analysis of factual information required for determination of courses of action or for control of operations.

A. Degree

   1. Repetitive or simple analysis
   2. Diversified analysis or decision on repetitive analysis
   3. Decision on diversified analysis

B. Scope

   1. Occasional
   2. Frequent
   3. Principal effort

A Weighted-in-Money Plan Applied to Top Management. In 1946 General Foods developed a simple plan for top management, that is, for positions paid $6000 or more per year.[7] This simplified plan replaced a straight point plan which gave skill 40 per cent of the worth (4 minor characteristics at 10 points each) and responsibility 60 per cent (6 minor characteristics at 10 points each). The plan is indeed simple. Three major characteristics are used. They are rated by the characteristic comparison technique and thirteen steps are used rather than the usual grade boxes.

In starting this plan the Evaluation Board selected bench mark jobs, which happened to be 13 in number, ranked them eventually

[7] B. B. Warren, "Evaluation of Managerial Positions," *Personnel Series* No. 107. Also E. F. Gill, "Management Positions Can Be Evaluated Successfully," *Personnel Journal*, XXVII, No. 11.

on total worths, and placed them in geometric progression, each step 15 per cent above the preceding one. The board then evaluated 100 positions and grouped them according to the six divisions in the whole company. This established the framework.

Each of the remaining positions (500) was described on an eight-page set of forms. It was done primarily by the incumbents but when desired the assistance of a staff man was available. It is reported that it took 10 to 12 hours to complete each description. Each description is then read and eventually approved by superiors on two levels, after which it goes to the "Area Board." There was excellent agreement in rating knowledge and there was fair agreement in rating decisions but they had considerable difficulty in agreeing on responsibility. Nevertheless, it was found that the executive positions were easier to rate than the staff and service positions and the scientific-professional positions were hardest to rate.

The three characteristics used in this new plan are:

I. Knowledge—what does the incumbent have to *know* in general, technical, and specialized fields or "areas."
   a) formal training
   b) specific job knowledge—including how to direct people skillfully
   c) special knowledge—of the particular company

Consider in judging this characteristic:

1. number of different fields of knowledge required
2. extent of details of each field required, i.e., thorough, working, or general acquaintance.
3. complexity of each field

The knowledge characteristic was highest for staff and scientific personnel.

II. Decisions—how *new* and complicated and how *difficult* are the situations to which the incumbent must apply his knowledge and on which he must form correct *decisions* and *judgments*.

Consider in judging this characteristic:

1. difficulty
2. complexity
3. novelty
4. limits imposed by higher supervision
5. extent to which decisions are controlled by precedent, etc.

Case No._____

MILWAUKEE PLAN JOB SPECIFICATION FORM

This is an outline of technical job requirements for a particular job and title. Indicate below the minimum requirements and supplement where and if necessary.

1. Job Title _____   3. Department _____

2. Company _____   4. No. Employees _____

5. General description of duties and products dealt with

_____

_____

_____

_____

_____

6. General fields of activity (indicate approximate time distribution by %)

   a. Research _____   e. Service _____
   b. Product development ____   f. Install _____
   c. Industrial engineering ____   g. Sales _____
   d. Production _____   h. Design _____
                                  Others _____

7. General nature of work done (indicate approximate time distribution by %)

   a. Administration _____   e. Clerical _____
   b. Negotiation _____   f. Mathematical _____
   c. Experimenting _____   g. Manual _____
   d. Testing _____   Others _____

8. Indicate minimum educational requirements or their equivalent:

   a. High school graduate_____
   b. Special vocational training_____Type and length_____
   c. Apprenticeship_____Type and length_____
   d. Technical Institute graduate_____Type and length_____
   e. College graduate—degree and field_____

FIGURE 171. FORM FOR GATHERING JOB DATA. (Engineers' Society of Milwaukee.)

Case No._____

9. Practical experience required in this or related fields_____years_____
   Describe _____
   _____
   _____

10. To what degree is this position supervised: (indicate)
    a. Closely _____
    b. Generally _____
    c. Minimum direction _____

11. Does position entail supervision of others_____
    If so, how many_____

12. Nature of work done by people supervised:
    a. Routine _____
    b. Diversified _____
    c. Highly complex _____

13. Diversity and judgment required:
    _____ a. Diverse and complex work requiring mature and highly technical judgment based on much experience_____
    _____ b. Complex problems requiring independent judgment and co-ordination of varied elements_____
    _____ c. Unusual problems requiring independent judgment_____
    _____ d. Some routine, requiring some judgment_____
    _____ e. Routine or semi-routine, minor decisions only_____

14. Responsibility:
    _____ a. For major expenditures, or major policy decisions and action _____
    _____ b. Involves recommending important expenditures or policy actions _____
    _____ c. Seldom extend beyond department limits_____
    _____ d. Involves little beyond own personal work_____

15. Contacts:
    _____ a. Frequent with customers, government agencies or organizations (including labor) with responsibility for conducting negotiations _____
    _____ b. Regular or frequent with others in equal or higher positions, or as a representative of management, or with outsiders on special assignments _____
    _____ c. Interdepartmental or routine outside contacts_____
    _____ d. Casual—within own department _____

FIGURE 171. (*Continued.*)

Case No._____

SUMMARY OF CHARACTERISTIC MINIMUM REQUIREMENTS

Indicate the amount (by A,B,C,D, or E) required of the characteristic shown below for this particular job. The Milwaukee Plan characteristics are listed on the attached sheets. Special notes can also be made below. If desirable, supplement the characteristic description on the back of this sheet and check here——.

PREPONDERANTLY TECHNICAL

_____T—1. Scientific and engineering knowledge
_____T—2. Mathematics
_____T—3. Plans, drawings, diagrams, and codes
_____T—4. Research
_____T—5. Organization of technical work
_____T—6. Clarity of expression in speech
_____T—7. Clarity of expression in writing

PREPONDERANTLY PSYCHOLOGICAL

_____S—8.   Self-reliance and drive
_____S—9.   Social intelligence and tact
_____S—10. Emotional stability
_____S—11. Dependability in scientific and engineering work
_____S—12. Leadership in work direction
_____S—13. Sales ability and interest
_____S—14. Professional aims and development

PHYSICAL AND MANUAL

_____M—15. Appearance and bearing
_____M—16. Manual abilities and skills

Describer of Job_____Date_____

FIGURE 171. (*Concluded.*)

This characteristic includes all duties and functions of a position, including those delegated to others. It is high for positions where information is complete or involves humans.

    III. Responsibility—what is *entrusted* to the incumbent that is valuable to the company and that may be affected by his decisions and judgments.

        a) men
        b) markets and products
        c) assets—money, materials, and equipment (including design)
        d) records
        e) methods
        f) outside contacts

Consider in judging this characteristic:

    1. frequency of exposure to loss
    2. probability of loss
    3. seriousness of loss

Weighted-in-Points Plan for Technical Positions. This plan, developed by the Engineers' Society of Milwaukee, is thorough in concept and should give excellent results. Nevertheless sixteen characteristics (see Summary at end of Figure 171), five degrees each, make it an expensive plan to install and operate. We think it is best suited to small professional groups. The degrees A to E, defined in one to two lines each, are omitted here, but we have seen few sets of definitions that are so brief and at the same time so truly definitive.

Weighted-in-Points Plan for Middle and Top Management Positions. Thanks to the liberality of W. J. Pedicord, Administrator —Salary and Wages, and that of his company, General Aniline and Film Corporation, we are able to describe completely a plan for all executive jobs above Assistant Foreman, that is, for middle and top management jobs including the president's job. Evaluation of these positions is called the "Exempt Salary Administration" because these positions do not come under the jurisdiction of the Fair Labor Standards Act. This company has three divisions and many professional-technical jobs so that this plan has been applied to all kinds of situations. Twenty-three grades are used. The descriptions-specifications are worked out jointly and tentatively evaluated by the Wage and Salary Administrator and the various department heads. These tentative evaluations are reviewed by the Division Salary Committees (one for each division), consisting of top management personnel who report direct to the Vice-president of Operations.

The Division committee submits a final evaluation to that Vice-president recommending approval. If he approves, or rather when the descriptions and evaluations are such that he can approve them, he in turn submits them to the Corporation Wage and Salary Administrator, who gives final approval for all evaluations through Grade No. 7. For Grade No. 8 and higher the descriptions and evaluations must be reviewed by the Corporation Salary Committee, consisting of the Vice-president and Controller, the Director of Administration, and the Director of Personnel Relations, who serves as Chairman of the committee.

Originally there were 17 characteristics but Accuracy (No. 4), which was assigned only 30 points, was later dropped out because in the case of high level line positions the details that involve accuracy are mostly delegated to assistants. What remains on the higher levels "will receive consideration under Judgment and Policy Interpretation factors." Hence the number of characteristics was reduced to 16 and we have closed up the numbers.

Policies are summarized as follows:

1. All position grades have salary ranges with spreads varying from 30 per cent in Grade 1 to about 50 per cent in Grade 23. These salary ranges are determined by analysis of comparative industry, area, and national salary data and, in the lower grades, are determined somewhat by the necessity for adequate differentials between supervisory employees and those supervised.

2. Employees are generally hired at the minimum of these ranges and progress through the range is based upon performance evaluation. Our average salary within range is at or about the mid-point and only employees exhibiting exceptional or outstanding performance may progress to the upper limits of the ranges.

3. Employees are generally performance rated annually on their anniversary dates, but performance ratings may be made more often if it is felt that unusual performance or progress has been demonstrated.

4. Merit increases are generally limited to 10 per cent of base salary but exception can be made with the approval of the President.

Details of the plan are as follows: Figure 172 shows the layout of 16 characteristics together with their maximum points, which total 1,970 (originally 2,000). Figure 173 shows definitions of 16 characteristics, degrees, and allotted weights.

POSITION MEASUREMENT

	Maximum Points
1. Knowledge	240
2. Judgment	240
3. Planning	60
4. Creative Work	150
5. Relationships Inside the Corporation	100
6. Relationships Outside the Corporation	120
7. Line Control	220
8. Functional Control	120
9. Policy Formulation	200
10. Policy Interpretation	100
11. Investment of Capital in Fixed Assets	160
12. Care of Corporation Assets	120
13. Confidential Information	70
14. Physical Demand	20
15. Personal Hazards	30
16. Surroundings	20
Total	1970

FIGURE 172. LAYOUT OF SIXTEEN CHARACTERISTICS AND POINTS FOR THE GAF "EXEMPT SALARY POSITIONS." (General Aniline and Film Corporation.)

FACTOR 1—KNOWLEDGE

This factor measures the amount of knowledge required by the position holder to understand and solve the problems that arise in the discharge of the assigned duties and responsibilities. This knowledge represents accumulated mental development acquired both through academic means (basic education) and practical experience. In applying this factor, care must be taken to measure the actual knowledge required and not the knowledge held by persons now holding the position.

Consider first the education required and second the experience.

Education	Degree	Experience (the horizontal dimension)							
		A	B	C	D	E	F	G	H
Requires knowledge and ability to use ordinary business mathematics; understand and issue verbal or written instructions; understand blueprints, systems, methods or paper work procedures, or a mechanical trade; write or dictate ordinary correspondence. Perform or supervise activities within a section or part of a departmental function, for example, shipping, inspection, testing, construction and repairs, production, clerical and/or accounting.	1	21	26	32	39	48	59	72	88
Requires additional training on-the-job, or outside, in technical phases of work to qualify for performance or supervision of somewhat complex activities of a section or part of a departmental function. For example, drafting, accounting, laboratory work, production, inspection, testing, etc.	2	28	34	41	50	61	76	92	113
Requires general academic training equivalent to a B.S. or knowledge of basic principles in a particular field to perform or supervise activities of importance. For example, accounting, engineering, chemistry, production, sales, industrial relations, etc.	3	35	43	53	65	79	98	119	145
Requires additional academic or on-the-job training in basic principles in a technical field to perform or supervise activities of considerable importance. For example, accounting, finance, engineering, chemistry, physics, marketing, manufacturing, industrial relations, budgetary techniques, etc.	4	48	57	69	84	102	125	152	187

FIGURE 173. DEFINITIONS OF CHARACTERISTICS, DEGREES, AND WEIGHTS. (General Aniline & Film Corporation.)

Education	Degree	Experience (the horizontal dimension)							
		A	B	C	D	E	F	G	H
Requires highly specialized knowledge of basic principles and fundamental concepts in a science or profession and experience in the application of this knowledge in solving new or highly complex problems in such fields as research and development, corporate law, etc.; or advanced knowledge in more than one specialized field, and a good working knowledge of most major business functions as usually required successfully to discharge general management responsibilities.	5	60	73	89	108	132	161	197	240

FIGURE 173. (*Continued.*)

FACTOR 2— JUDGMENT

This factor measures the degree of judgment required by the position. Judgment may be defined as the operation of the mind, involving comparison and discrimination by which knowledge of values and relations is mentally formulated.

Consider first the character of judgment required and second the importance of decisions.

Character of Judgment Required

Importance of Decisions	Degree	A — Occasional independent decisions made within framework of well-organized systems, methods, procedures, and schedules. Most problems usually considered by higher supervisory authority.	B — Decisions required when the problem is not clearly covered by standard instructions or established techniques, systems, or procedures. Subject to review before serious consequence.	C — Decisions frequently require revisions in organization and systems, use of new techniques, methods, and procedures, or a new and different use of precedent. However, facts bearing on decision usually still relate to conditions within a specific function. Adverse effects accrue before ordinarily reviewed by supervision.	D — Decisions require complete understanding of requirements for a specific major divisional or important corporate function, with sufficient understanding of other division and/or corporate objectives to maintain effective operations within a function. Some decisions have important horizontal effect on other important functions.	E — Decisions require complete understanding of divisional and/or corporate objectives to permit application of judgment to major policies, affecting plant-wide activities or one major corporation-wide activity.	F — Affecting most or all major divisional policies and objectives; or several corporate functions	G — Final decisions on all corporation-wide policies and objectives.
							Decisions have a major influence on a variety of major functions and objectives.	
Of some significance	1	24	30	37	45	56	69	85
Of significance to a division, or a part of corporate activities	2	30	37	45	56	69	85	105
Of importance to a division or the Corporation	3	37	45	56	69	85	105	129
Of considerable importance to a division and/or the Corporation ..	4	45	56	69	85	105	129	158
Of major importance to a division and/or the Corporation	5	56	69	85	105	129	158	195
Total Corporation activities involved	6	69	85	105	129	158	195	240

FIGURE 173. (*Continued.*)

444

FACTOR 3—PLANNING

This factor measures the position requirement for developing plans within the framework of approved policies for present and future operations; for example, scheduling production to satisfy market requirements; planning organization changes to meet changing conditions, coordination of different lines of endeavor, etc. . . .

Consider first the scope of application and second the conditions under which planning must be done.

		Relative Complexity and Frequency of Situations Requiring Planning		
		Only *occasional changes* in systems, volume of work, and conditions	*Frequent changes* in systems, volume of work, and conditions	Sudden *or continuous changes* requiring continuous follow-up in systems, work volume, programs, objectives, operations, etc.
		Most situations routine	Many situations complex	Many situations highly complex
Scope of Application	Degree	A	B	C
Some planning of a few activities and procedures for a section of a department. Basic activities and objectives usually governed by established departmental systems, methods and procedures.	1	13	17	22
Planning of activities for a department of a division.	2	17	22	28
Planning activities for a large department of a division.	3	22	28	36
Planning activities for a whole operating division or department of a corporate-wide staff.	4	28	36	47
Planning total corporate activities.	5	36	47	60

FIGURE 173. (*Continued.*)

FACTOR 3—PLANNING

Interpretive Bulletin

There are four conditions under which credit may be given in the Planning Factor:

1. Planning of the activities of others as involved in all line supervisory positions.

2. Planning of the activities of a single position by its incumbent if the variety and complexity are such that prescheduling is impossible. The following two examples may help to clarify this interpretation:

   a) in the position of Sales Engineer or Sales Representative, considerable planning is involved in order for the sales program to be carried out successfully since a variety of problems involving technical service, ordering samples, a definite program of call-backs, and a definite plan of any account contacts is involved.

   b) in the position of Engineering Equipment Inspector, considerable planning must be done in order to coordinate the inspection program with production and production control functions. For example, if a certain type of equipment requires inspection twice a month and cannot be inspected unless shut down, the inspection program must be planned to allow for the continuance of the production program.

3. Planning in a service function to relieve line supervisors of certain planning responsibilities. Examples of this type of planning are found in Production Control, Industrial Engineering.

4. Planning as required:

   a) in a staff position in situations wherein a major executive has delegated a part of his planning responsibility to a Staff Assistant, or

   b) in a functional position that is required to provide a portion of the planning for those operating departments over which the functional control is exercised.

No credit for planning should be given in the following instances:

1. To laboratory chemists who are working alone on experiments or projects without responsibility for supervising other chemists or supervising a project in which others may participate.

2. To salesmen whose itinerary is clearly defined and whose responsibilities such as initial contacts, call-backs, issuance of samples, etc., are established by procedure or policy.

3. Cashier, Editor, Draftsman, Junior Engineer, Chemist II—PD.

FIGURE 173. (*Continued.*)

FACTOR 4—CREATIVE WORK

This factor measures the position responsibility for performing creative work, i.e., conceiving, developing, and perfecting products, processes, design, equipment, methods, programs, etc.

Consider first the type of creative work and second the complexity and variety of the work.

Type of Creative Work

Complexity and Variety of Creative Work	Degree	Required to devise improvements or shortcuts within established systems.	Required to visualize the need for, devise, and install new systems, methods, and procedures.	Required to apply imaginative and creative effort to major problems in sales, marketing, engineering, human relations, etc. . . .	Required to organize and direct creative effort.	Regular performance of important creative work is the principal position requirement.
		A	B	C	D	E
Somewhat complex	1	7	10	15	22	32
Complex	2	10	15	22	32	47
Complex and somewhat varied	3	15	22	32	47	69
Considerably complex and varied	4	22	32	47	69	102
Highly complex and varied	5	32	47	69	102	150

FIGURE 173. (*Continued.*)

FACTOR 5—RELATIONSHIPS INSIDE THE CORPORATION

Interpretive Bulletin

This factor measures the responsibility required by the position holder frequently or regularly to persuade or influence others inside the Corporation to undertake a course of action which furthers the Corporation's interests and thereby either directly or intangibly affects corporation profits. No credit is given here for contacts with straight "line" subordinates or superiors.

Consider first the importance and type of corporation required, second the frequency and difficulty of contacts, and third the number of persons contacted.

Frequency and Difficulty of Contacts

Degree	Importance and Type of Cooperation Required	A Contacts on routine matters	B Contacts on important but non-controversial matters	C Contacts on important matters; where differences of opinion are normal expectancy. *Infrequent* position requirement	D Contacts on important matters; where differences of opinion are normal expectancy. *Frequent* position requirement	E Contacts on important matters; where differences of opinion are normal expectancy. *Constant* position requirement
1	Maintain good working relations with others on own position level or with higher levels on relatively important matters.	10	13	17	23	31
2	Secure cooperation on matters of *importance*. Maintain good working relations with associated section heads, functional heads, etc.	13	17	23	31	42
3	Secure cooperation and concurrence of others in matters of *considerable importance*; convince others to accept and cooperate with a course of action for single or collective benefit, e.g., important revisions in methods and procedures, policies and long-range objectives, etc. Generally consulting with important executives.	17	23	31	42	56
4	Persuade others to adopt new or alternate course of action where *major programs* are involved, e.g., major revisions or departures in the plan of organization, major changes in product lines or processes, radical departures from current manufacturing, sales, or financial methods, etc. Generally consulting with major executives.	23	31	42	56	75
5	Reconcile divergent viewpoints of top-management personnel on major policy or operating problems. Generally consulting with major executives.	31	42	56	75	100

FIGURE 173. (*Continued.*)

FACTOR 6—RELATIONSHIPS OUTSIDE THE CORPORATION

This factor measures the ability required by the position holder to make favorable impressions; to use tact and diplomacy in sales, public relations, etc. . . . ; to exchange ideas and discuss problems objectively; to secure from others (customers, contractors, etc. . . .) *outside* the Corporation the proper degree of respect, attention, cooperation, and concurrence which will promote the interests of the Corporation.

Consider first the benefit to the Corporation, second the frequency and difficulty of contacts, and third the number of persons contacted.

Frequency and Difficulty of Contacts

Benefit to the Corporation	Degree	Contacts on routine trade or professional matters	Difficult contacts an *occasional* requirement	Difficult contacts a *frequent* requirement		Difficult contacts a *constant* business requirement		Contacts on levels above ordinary trade channels
				Complex	Varied & Complex	Complex	Varied & Complex	
		A	B	C	D	E	F	G
Has a *minor* effect on Corporation profit.	1	10	13	17	22	29	39	52
Has a *moderate* effect on Corporation profit.	2	13	17	22	29	39	52	69
Has a *substantial* effect on Corporation profit.	3	17	22	29	39	52	69	91
Has a *major* effect on Corporation profit.	4	22	29	39	52	69	91	120

Interpretive Bulletin

This factor measures the responsibility required by the position holder frequently or regularly to persuade or influence others outside the corporation to undertake a a course of action which furthers the corporation's interests and thereby either directly or indirectly affects corporation profits.

Credit should be given positions held by technical consultants and staff specialists whose outside contacts are regular, expected, and necessary to the continuing favorable operation of the corporation. Such assignments, inherent in the job, must obviously appear in the position's job description and must, therefore, be recognized as an important element in assessing the position holder's performance.

In assigning points on the difficulty of contacts, high credit should be given where a high order of persuasive powers, ingenuity, tact, and follow-up are necessary. Routine dealings with vendors of material or equipment or dealings on noncontroversial matters are not of this order.

FIGURE 173. (*Continued.*)

FACTOR 7—LINE CONTROL

This factor measures the responsibility for the selection and training of personnel properly to understand and perform their work; the assignment of the work load and the maintenance of follow-up to assure adequate performance.

Consider only the number of persons supervised.

Degree	NUMBER OF PERSONS SUPERVISED		Points
	From	To	
1	2 —— 7		10
2	8 —— 15		15
3	16 —— 30		25
4	31 —— 64		35
5	65 —— 125		45
6	126 —— 216		55
7	217 —— 343		65
8	344 —— 512		75
9	513 —— 728		85
10	729 —— 1000		95
11	1001 —— 1331		105
12	1332 —— 1728		115
13	1729 —— 2197		125
14	2198 —— 2744		135
15	2745 —— 3375		145
16	3376 —— 4096		155
17	4097 —— 4913		165
18	4914 —— 5832		175
19	5833 —— 6870		185
20	6871 —— 8000		195
21	8001 —— 9260		205
22	9261 —— up		220

Note: Where line control is shared (as in the case of some assistant department heads or revolving assignment of work forces) examine actual delegation of authority and modify credit on Factor 7 to reflect said delegation.

FIGURE 173. (*Continued.*)

FACTOR 8—FUNCTIONAL CONTROL

This factor measures the position responsibility for exercising "Functional Control." This may be defined as the responsibility for determining the adequacy of approved policy, method, procedure, or program for either present or future use and/or appraising the effectiveness of performance in areas not under the line control of the position holder.

Consider first importance of responsibility and second the nature of follow-up required.

Nature of Follow Up Required

Importance of Responsibility	Degree	Simple to follow up, or responsibility can be discharged through infrequent checks.	Difficult to follow up, or discharge of responsibility requires frequent checks.	Difficult to follow up and necessary to give function almost constant attention in discharge of the position responsibility.
		A	B	C
Some Responsibility Check performance, methods, and systems of *some significance* to departments within a division.	1	7	12	19
Moderate Responsibility Check application of policy and performance pertaining to *portions* of divisional programs.	2	12	19	30
Important Responsibility Check application of policy and performance pertaining to *important divisional* or *parts of corporate programs.*	3	19	30	47
Responsibility of Considerable Importance Check application of policy and performance pertaining to *major divisional programs* or *major parts* of *major corporate programs.*	4	30	47	75
Major Responsibility Final recommendations concerning corporation-wide programs, policies, and systems of *major importance,* with full responsibility for execution through executives in positions of line authority.	5	47	75	120

FIGURE 173. (*Continued.*)

FACTOR 8—FUNCTIONAL CONTROL

Interpretive Bulletin

Functional responsibility is a staff function and can be defined as the responsibility for determining the adequacy of approved policy, method, procedure, or program for either present or future use; or for appraising the effectiveness of performance in areas not under the line control of the position holder.

To receive credit on this factor, the functional responsibility:

a) must be a continuing responsibility for formulating policy, method, procedure, or program at its inception or at least having played an important part in its formulation.

b) must be active. It is not enough that an employee observe that a procedure is inadequate or substandard. He must also have the responsibility for remedying such a condition. This may be done either by recommending action to a higher functional position or by making contact with the proper level of line authority.

This functional responsibility is inherent in staff positions set up to guide and implement line operations by furnishing technical advice and guidance.

FIGURE 173. (*Continued.*)

FACTOR 9—POLICY FORMULATION

This factor measures the responsibility for formulation of policies. These may be defined as "Plans of Action" or "Rules" formulated for the purpose of obtaining consistency in thinking, planning, and execution by personnel throughout the Corporation in their attainment of desired objectives.

Consider first the importance of policies and second the area of application.

Importance of Policies

Area of Application	Degree	Of *minor* importance	Of *some* significance	Of *importance*	Of *considerable* importance	Of *major* importance	Total corporation activities
		A	B	C	D	E	F
Policy formulation for small parts of a function.	1	7	10	14	20	27	
Policy formulation for parts of important functions.	2	10	14	20	27	38	
Policy formulation for parts of major functions or one important function.	3	14	20	27	38	53	
Policy formulation for one major function or several important functions.	4	20	27	38	53	73	
Policy formulation for several major functions.	5	27	38	53	73	101	
Final policy decisions for all major functions.	6						200

Interpretive Bulletins

This factor measures the administrative or organizational responsibility for the development (or contributing to the development) of policies for the administration of a given Division, Plant, or function. No credit is given here for the preparation of job instructions, procedures, or chemical processes.

Only those position holders whose jobs require that they have sufficient background or administrative experience or knowledge of operations are considered eligible to make a contribution to the establishment or revision of policies.

FIGURE 173. (*Continued.*)

FACTOR 10—POLICY INTERPRETATION

This factor measures the responsibility for understanding Corporation policies and for correct interpretation of them to associates and subordinates inside the Corporation and to suppliers, customers, agencies, and others outside the Corporation. Laws, acts, or directives issued by governmental agencies having jurisdiction become, perforce, Corporation policy.

Consider first the importance of policies and second the area of application.

Area of Application

Importance of Policies	Degree	A small group or section	A department or a small section of the public	Several departments; large section of the public	Many departments or wide area of public interest	Total Corporation or diverse public bodies
		A	B	C	D	E
Policies of *minor importance* or of little complexity or variety.	1	7	10	14	19	26
Policies of *some importance* and some complexity but generally within a function.	2	10	14	19	26	37
One important policy; or a variety of policies of some importance; or a major policy with little variety.	3	14	19	26	37	51
One major policy or several important, diverse policies.	4	19	26	37	51	72
Many policies of *major importance*.	5	26	37	51	72	100

Interpretive Bulletin

Measures the responsibility for understanding broad policies and for the use of judgment and decision in the application of such general policies to specific day-to-day problems encountered by associates and subordinates inside the corporation and to suppliers, customers, agencies, and others outside the corporation. Laws, acts, or directives issued by governmental agencies having jurisdiction become perforce corporation policy.

Staff or training positions having only the responsibility for disseminating interpretations of policies for others will not receive credit on this factor.

FIGURE 173. (*Continued.*)

FACTOR 11—INVESTMENT OF CAPITAL IN FIXED ASSETS

This factor measures the responsibility for the effective use of the Corporation's money to invest in buildings, machinery, equipment, furniture, etc. . . . Credit is given only to those positions charged with the responsibility for determining requirements and approving, or recommending to the appropriate executive for approval, the investment of capital in fixed assets. The major responsibility for use of capital is found in top-executive positions because normally such positions are held responsible for investments affecting quantity, quality, standards, and unit cost of production or performance. The top-executive position customarily delegates to the supervisors of important areas the responsibility to determine and recommend for approval necessary investments in fixed assets for expansion, modernization or replacement of buildings, facilities, etc. . . .

Consider only the scope of application.

Scope of Application	Degree	Points
Required to make recommendations for substantial replacement or additions to facilities in a section of a divisional function, e.g., a laboratory, production center, accounting, etc.	1	10
Required to make recommendations for replacement and/ or modernization of facilities for an important operating function; or an important section of a major divisional operation.	2	22
Required to make recommendations for expansion, replacement, or modernization programs for a substantial portion of a major divisional operation.	3	33
Required to make recommendations for expansion, replacement, or modernization programs for an important divisional operation; or a relatively large divisional plant operation.	4	49
Required to make recommendations for expansion, replacement, or modernization programs for a large divisional plant operation.	5	73
Required to recommend expansion, replacement, or modernization programs for a large division; or approval from the standpoint of corporation-wide financial and operating control of major corporation-wide expansion or modernization programs.	6	108
Final approval of recommendations to Board of Directors for action on major investments in fixed assets.	7	160

With few exceptions, positions lower than those "line" positions that report directly to a Division or a Works Manager will receive no credit on this factor.

FIGURE 173. (*Continued.*)

FACTOR 12—CARE OF CORPORATION ASSETS

This factor measures the position of responsibility for protecting the Corporation's assets. For instance, safe storage of finished products, raw materials, and supplies; maintenance of buildings, machinery, and equipment to prevent loss or damage beyond normal wear or obsolescence; safekeeping of funds, negotiable documents and papers, etc. . . .

Consider first the importance of assets and second difficulty of protecting assets.

Difficulty of Protecting Assets

Importance of Assets	Degree	Operations where assets are easy to protect	Operations where normal safety measures, care, and maintenance result in adequate protection to assets	Operations where fire, explosion, corrosion, etc., hazards require extraordinary care to protect assets	Operation including conditions in A, B, and C, where assets are dispersed geographically or not a tight unit
		A	B	C	D
Little or *no* responsibility for care of corporation assets—or assets of *very small value*.	1	5	7	10	15
Responsibility for care of corporation assets of *minor value*.	2	7	10	15	23
Responsibility for care of corporation assets of *significant value*.	3	10	15	23	35
Responsibility for care of corporation assets of *considerable value*.	4	15	23	35	53
Responsibility for care of corporation assets of *major value*.	5	23	35	53	80
Responsibility for care of all corporate assets.	6	35	53	80	120

Interpretive Bulletin

Measures the direct and immediate responsibility usually vested in a line supervision for the protection, proper utilization, and maintenance of existing physical assets of the corporation, i.e., the safe storage of finished products, the handling of raw materials, the maintenance of building, machinery, and equipment to prevent loss or damage, the safekeeping of funds, negotiable documents, and papers.

Staff positions having a functional and, therefore, indirect responsibility for the utilization of materials and equipment do not receive credit here.

Process Development Chemists and Field Engineers receive credit on this factor for a limited responsibility for "care of assets."

FIGURE 173. (*Continued.*)

FACTOR 13—CONFIDENTIAL INFORMATION

This factor measures the position responsibility for guarding against the disclosure of confidential information to others. "Confidential information" as used here means the knowledge of or authorized access to the knowledge of processes, formulas, products, and technical plans, the disclosure of which could result in financial loss to the Corporation.

Consider first the importance of confidential information held and second the possible damage due to disclosure.

Possible Damage Due to Disclosure

Importance of Confidential Information Held	Degree	Of significance	Of importance	Of considerable importance	Of major importance
		A	B	C	D
Technical knowledge of small phases of research and/or development projects; or administrative performance of membership duties on research committees.	1	8	13	18	25
Technical knowledge of an entire but restricted research or process development project, or several phases of a large project; or knowledge of production processes in a section of a manufacturing department.	2	13	18	25	35
Technical knowledge gained by supervising one or more sections of technical personnel associated with a wide range of research and/or process development projects in a related field; or knowledge of production processes in one or more integrated production departments.	3	18	25	35	50
Technical knowledge of processes in a large production and/or process development area; or intimate knowledge of corporation-wide research projects.	4	25	35	50	70

FIGURE 173. (*Continued.*)

FACTOR 14—PHYSICAL DEMAND

This factor measures physical effort required in performing the assigned work such as climbing stairs, standing for long periods, frequent traveling, etc. . . .

Consider only the nature of physical effort.

Degree	Nature of Physical Effort	Points
1	**Light Physical Effort:** Requires *some* physical exertion, walking or climbing stairs, or standing for long periods, in such positions as: Supervisors of small production areas Laboratory positions requiring considerable movement or standing most of the day	5
2	**Medium Physical Effort:** Requires *considerable* physical exertion (more than one half of the work day), walking or climbing stairs, or frequent traveling in such positions as: Supervisors of fairly large production areas Supervisors of construction, maintenance, etc. Supervisors of sales	10
3	**Heavy Physical Effort:** Requires *almost constant* physical exertion (most or all of the work day), walking, climbing stairs, or traveling in such positions as: Supervisors of construction, heavy maintenance work, etc. Supervisors of large production areas, viz: one or more buildings, etc. Sales positions requiring constant traveling and change of location and conditions	20

FIGURE 173. (*Continued.*)

FACTOR 15—PERSONAL HAZARDS

This factor measures the personal hazards that may be involved in the performance of the work.

Consider the possibility of accidents or impairment of health, and the degree of attention to established safety measures to protect workers during performance of the assigned work.

Degree   Points

Degree		Points
1	Work having little accident or health hazard.	3
2	Possible minor injury, unless simple safety regulations observed.	5
3	Possible lost time accident, unless normal safety regulations observed.	9
4	Possible lost time accident, unless strict safety measures observed.	17
5	Hazards, such as fire, explosion, etc. . . . unless rigid safety measures and operating instructions observed.	30

Credit on this factor is given in proportion to the probable frequency and the seriousness of the effects of accidents.

Highest credit should be given to positions where probability of accident may be high in spite of all precaution. Involved in such positions is the element of chance against which little or no precautions can be taken.

Positions in relatively hazardous areas may receive little or no credit here for the reason that accident frequency is under rigid control.

FIGURE 173. (*Continued.*)

FACTOR 16—SURROUNDINGS

This factor measures the degree of discomfort to which the position occupant is exposed, for example, heat, cold, weather conditions, dust, fumes, noise, etc. . . .

Consider only the nature of surroundings.

Degree	Nature of Surroundings	Points
1	*Occasional* exposure to unpleasant conditions such as odors, fumes, etc., but generally protected from excessive exposure to dirt or bad weather conditions, etc. . . .	3
2	*Frequent* exposure to unpleasant conditions such as odors, fumes, wetness, dirt, or weather conditions.	6
3	*Almost constant* exposure to disagreeable conditions such as bad odors, fumes, dust, wetness, dirt, or bad weather conditions.	11
4	*Constant* exposure to highly disagreeable conditions such as corrosive fumes, excessive wetness, dirt, weather conditions, etc.	20

FIGURE 173. (*Concluded.*)

The position specifications and position measurements shown in Figures 174, 175, and 176 illustrate the weighted-in-points plan for middle and top management positions shown in detail in Figure 173. In each instance the original fourth characteristic, Accuracy, has been retained, making the total number of characteristics seventeen rather than sixteen, as they are shown in Figure 173.

Note that the position specification shown in Figure 176 carries an additional signature. This is necessary, as was pointed out earlier (pp. 439–40), because of the additional review required for all positions above Grade 7. The descriptions and evaluations of the several specifications, as tentatively worked out and subsequently approved or amended by the required officials or committees, portray so clearly the qualifications to be possessed by the successful applicant for each position as to make the selection of the proper person relatively free from guesswork.

It is well to recall also that all grades have salary ranges varying from 30 per cent in Grade 1 to 50 per cent in Grade 23. Employees are generally hired at the minimum rate, and increases in salary are based upon performance evaluations.

POSITION SPECIFICATION

POSITION TITLE 11/22/50	POSITION NO.

WORKS OR OFFICE LOCATION	DIVISION	PRODUCTION FOREMAN	GRADE
Grasselli	GAW	Intermediates Area	5

DEPARTMENT		Vat Colors Area	
Production		Sulphur Color	POINTS
SECTION		& Textile Auxiliaries	210
Various			

GENERAL RESPONSIBILITIES

Under the direction of the Production Supervisor, supervise, assign, and coordinate the activities of the Assistant Production Foreman, Shift Foremen, and operating personnel to produce the requirements scheduled in a section of a production area. Train and instruct employees in the performance of their assigned tasks, and in company policies and procedures.

SPECIFIC DUTIES

1. Supervise, assign, and coordinate the activities of the Assistant Production Foreman, Shift Foremen, and operating personnel in the production of an Area Section. Assign and schedule necessary personnel to carry out the production program. Assist the Production Supervisor in determining personnel requirements. Inspect or supervise inspections by subordinates of operating equipment to assure proper condition for the next operation. Check and report to the Production Supervisor on the status of production operations. Inform Production Supervisor of any irregularities in production, correct such irregularities within the scope of ability and jurisdiction, and collaborate with Production Supervisor in determining the cause of the irregularity. If irregularity occurs at a time during other than normal working hours, give instructions to subordinates by telephone or, in cases of necessity, make trip to plant and personally supervise the correction of the irregularity.

2. Recommend to the Production Supervisor improvements and revisions in policies and procedures within the scope of jurisdiction. Cooperate with Production Foremen of other production sections to achieve coordination of activities. Coordinate work of day employees with that of shift employees. Train and instruct Assistant Production Foreman, Shift Foremen, and operating personnel in the performance of their assigned tasks. Follow up the efficient use of operating equipment, supplies, energies and labor; and maintenance of building. Order repair and maintenance work on equipment and building, cooperating and working directly with C&R Trades Foremen in the execution of such work. Supervise personally the handling of sensitive or easily contaminated products. Assign storage space for materials within building.

3. Handle Section grievances; recommend to the Production Supervisor disciplinary action, promotions, demotions, transfers, separations, etc.; interpret company policies to subordinates; enforce safety and good housekeeping practices; prepare records and reports. Maintain frequent contacts with Warehousing supervisors, Chemists, Field Engineers, and C&R Trades Foremen.

POSITION ANALYZED AND MEASURED BY	DATE 4/20/47		DATE 6/32
APPROVED BY	DATE 4/30/51	APPROVED BY	DATE 5/24/51
APPROVED BY	DATE 5-21-51	APPROVED BY	DATE 6/7/51

FIGURE 174. POSITION SPECIFICATION, PRODUCTION FOREMAN. (General Aniline and Film Corporation.)

POSITION MEASUREMENT

POSITION REQUIREMENTS	POSITION TITLE PRODUCTION FOREMAN—Intermediates Area, Vat Colors, Sulphur Colors & Tex. Aux.		
	BASIS OF MEASUREMENT	DEGREE	POINTS
1. KNOWLEDGE	Thorough experience in the safe operation of chemical process equipment, such as kettles, dryers, stills, filters, etc. Detailed knowledge of the process requirements of intermediates, chemicals and auxiliaries. Experience in supervision of chemical production, in training and instructing personnel, and in following up results of subordinates.	1D	39
2. JUDGMENT	In the selection of personnel and assignment of work to carry out the production schedule; in decisions necessitated by mechanical failure of equipment; in correcting irregularities in production; in handling or preventing grievances.	1B	30
3. PLANNING	Assist Production Supervisor in scheduling production. Coordinate work of day employees with that of shift employees. Maintain proper operating conditions to assure standard quality and economy.	1B	17
4. ACCURACY	In preparing daily production reports, checking daily time and equipment occupancy reports, temperature control charts, etc.	1A	7
5. CREATIVE WORK	In organization of efficient working force and improvements in operating techniques. Make emergency repairs in order to permit uninterrupted operation.	1A	7
6. RELATIONSHIPS— INSIDE	Maintain frequent contacts with Warehouse supervisors, Chemists and Field Engineers, and C & R foremen. Cooperate with Production Foremen of other sections to achieve coordination of activities.	1B	13
7. RELATIONSHIPS— OUTSIDE	None.	..	..

FIGURE 174. (*Continued.*)

POSITION MEASUREMENT	POSITION TITLE PRODUCTION FOREMAN—Intermediates Area, Vat Colors, Sulphur Colors & Tex. Aux.		
POSITION REQUIREMENTS	BASIS OF MEASUREMENT	DEGREE	POINTS
8. LINE CONTROL	Supervise the activities of approximately 51 to 73 employees.	4	35
9. FUNCTIONAL CONTROL	None.	..	..
10. POLICY FORMULATION	Recommend to Production Supervisor improvements and revisions in policies and procedures within area of jurisdiction.	1A	7
11. POLICY INTERPRETATION	Interpret company policies to subordinates.	1B	10
12. INVESTMENT OF CAPITAL IN FIXED ASSETS	None.	..	..
13. CARE OF CORPORATION ASSETS	Responsible for losses of material in process, or damage to equipment through carelessness. Responsible for the proper identification of products.	1B	7
14. CONFIDENTIAL INFORMATION	Access to processes, production methods and development of new products in assigned area.	1A	8
15. PHYSICAL DEMAND	Walking, standing; some desk work.	2	10
16. PERSONAL HAZARDS	Operations involve utilization of corrosive chemicals. Many processes are carried out at high temperatures, under pressure, and under vacuum.	3	9
17. SURROUNDINGS	Exposure to dyestuff factory conditions, fumes, steam, wetness, etc.	3	11
GRADE 5		TOTAL POINTS	210

FIGURE 174. (Concluded.)

POSITION SPECIFICATION

WORKS OR OFFICE LOCATION	DIVISION	POSITION TITLE	POSITION NO.
Grasselli	GAW	GENERAL ACCOUNTING SUPERVISOR	GRADE
DEPARTMENT			5
Accounting			
SECTION			POINTS
General Accounting		7/26/50	204

GENERAL RESPONSIBILITIES

Lay out and supervise, under the direction of the Assistant Plant Accountant, the compilation, maintenance, and coordination of accounting records and reports. Recommend and set up changes in general accounting procedures and personnel.

SPECIFIC DUTIES

1. Supervise, lay out and schedule the activities of the General Accounting Section personnel. Supervise the preparation and assembly of monthly journal vouchers for accounting operations from the following sources: daily cash receipts and disbursements, weekly and semi-monthly payrolls, invoices forwarded daily to Hudson Street Office, Home Office, and Rensselaer. Other journal vouchers provide for accrual of expenses, distribution of repair and maintenance expense, auto truck operations, etc. Supervise the posting of these vouchers to the plant general and operating expense ledgers, from which monthly financial statements are prepared for Hudson Street Office.

2. Supervise the distribution of monthly operating expenses; the preparation of operating expense statements, and monthly, semi-annual and annual reports on Research and Development expense. Determine the basis for distribution of expense. Verify cash receipts and disbursements; maintain and reconcile Works and Payroll Bank Accounts. Personally reconcile the Supervisory Payroll. Make daily requests to the National City Bank, New York, for transfer of funds to the Linden Trust Company to cover payroll checks.

3. Supervise the Accounts Payable section and approve invoices for payment. Prepare a daily transmittal listing of approved invoices and forward to Hudson Street Office for payment. Issue and receive General Office Settlements to and from Hudson Street Office to effect transfers of items between the plant and general office.

4. Recommend to the Assistant Plant Accountant changes in General Accounting Section organization and procedures which are designed to facilitate or improve the work of the section, or to meet new situations. Interpret and enforce company policy. Train new employees in general accounting procedure. Recommend to the Assistant Plant Accountant disciplinary action, promotions, demotions, transfers, terminations, and salary treatment. Coordinate activities of section with those of other sections of the Accounting Department.

POSITION ANALYZED AND MEASURED BY	*Paul L. Davis* DATE 4/9/51	*signature*	DATE 4/30
APPROVED BY	*signature* DATE 4/11/51	APPROVED BY *C. White* DATE 5/1	
APPROVED BY	*Baker* DATE 4-26-51	APPROVED BY *signature* DATE 6/1/51	

FIGURE 175. POSITION SPECIFICATION, GENERAL ACCOUNTING SUPERVISOR. (General Aniline and Film Corporation.)

POSITION MEASUREMENT

POSITION REQUIREMENTS	POSITION TITLE GENERAL ACCOUNTING SUPERVISOR		
	BASIS OF MEASUREMENT	DEGREE	POINTS
1. KNOWLEDGE	High school education plus at least four years of higher accountancy. Several years of actual accounting experience.	3C	53
2. JUDGMENT	Advise Assistant Plant Accountant on personnel requirements. Interview, recommend for hiring, train new personnel. Decide within framework of company policy, personnel problems such as grievances, disciplinary action, etc. Recommend action on personnel changes such as layoff, promotions, demotions, wage and salary changes. Recommend solutions of operational and clerical difficulties.	2B	37
3. PLANNING	Schedule burden distribution, accounts payable operations, journal entries, and manpower utilization, with a view toward meeting schedules for the preparation of financial statements.	1B	17
4. ACCURACY	Responsible for the processing of invoices for payment and the preparation of a variety of detailed accounting reports submitted to the Plant, Hudson Street and the Home Office.	3C	19
5. CREATIVE WORK	Use ingenuity and resourcefulness in fully utilizing existing office equipment. Keep informed on newly available equipment and latest methods of accounting operations.	2A	10
6. RELATIONSHIPS— INSIDE	Contact supervisors of Cost, Property and Payroll Sections of the Accounting Department on data supplied by each for balancing purposes. Contact supervisors in Accounting Department, Hudson Street Office.	2B	17
7. RELATIONSHIPS— OUTSIDE	Contact Treasurer's Office, National City Bank, New York, for transfer of funds to Linden Trust Company to cover payroll checks.	..	..

FIGURE 175. (*Continued.*)

POSITION MEASUREMENT

POSITION REQUIREMENTS	POSITION TITLE GENERAL ACCOUNTING SUPERVISOR		
	BASIS OF MEASUREMENT	DEGREE	POINTS
8. LINE CONTROL	Supervise 9 employees. Constantly check on their performance, institute training and instruct in operations. Select new personnel.	2	15
9. FUNCTIONAL CONTROL	Responsible for reporting on the adequacy of data forwarded regularly from all departments and which is necessary in the preparation of General Accounting reports.	1A	7
10. POLICY FORMULATION	On basis of knowledge, recommend changes in accounting policies (operational and personnel) to the Assistant Plant Accountant.	1B	10
11. POLICY INTERPRETATION	Responsible for interpretation of company policies to all employees in the General Accounting Section.	2C	19
12. INVESTMENT OF CAPITAL IN FIXED ASSETS	None.	..	..
13. CARE OF CORPORATION ASSETS	None.	..	..
14. CONFIDENTIAL INFORMATION	Minor.	..	..
15. PHYSICAL DEMAND	Very light.	..	..
16. PERSONAL HAZARDS	None.	..	..
17. SURROUNDINGS	General office.	..	..
GRADE　　5		TOTAL POINTS	204

FIGURE 175. (*Concluded.*)

POSITION SPECIFICATION		POSITION TITLE		POSITION NO.
WORKS OR OFFICE LOCATION Grasselli	DIVISION GAW	FIELD ENGINEER	GRADE	8
DEPARTMENT Engineering			POINTS	
SECTION		10/10/51		289

GENERAL RESPONSIBILITIES

Under the direction of the Chief Field Engineer, organize, plan, schedule, and functionally supervise, through Master Mechanic—Areas, Assistant Master Mechanics, and finally through Trade Foremen, all maintenance, repairs, and construction work in the plant, preparing the necessary estimates, sketches and other engineering and cost data. (Each Field Engineer is assigned to a specific area and therefore the duties described herein apply only to the area assigned to the engineer involved.)

SPECIFIC DUTIES

1. Consult with Department Managers, Area Superintendents, Plant Chemists, and Supervisors so as to organize and plan all construction, repair and maintenance work in the respective area. Schedule such work economically and consistent with production requirements and orderly plant operations, collaborating closely with the Master Mechanic—Areas, Assistant Master Mechanics, and Trade Foremen in scheduling and in reviewing the work performed.

2. Prepare cost estimates on new construction, equipment replacement or rebuilding. Determine which expenditures are to be charged against capital assets in accordance with established accounting procedures.

3. Determine most effective, efficient and economical methods of effecting maintenance, repair and construction work consistent with sound engineering principles and practices.

4. Recommend to Department Managers or Area Superintendents, equipment suitable for specific production requirements, incorporating in such recommendations materials of construction best suited for chemical handling.

5. Investigate existing equipment and method of mechanical handling to determine if such equipment and methods are efficient and economical or whether they warrant improvement.

6. Consult and cooperate with Chief Project and Design Engineers in design and layout of proposed new processes, and on proposed alterations in existing facilities.

7. Determine, through periodic building and facilities inspections and after consultation with Department Manager or Area Superintendent, Master Mechanic—Areas, and Assistant Master Mechanic, the need for preventive maintenance work. Schedule such work in a manner that will not interfere with orderly operation of the area involved.

8. Prepare sketches and drawings of maintenance work for the guidance of Assistant Master Mechanics and the Trade Foremen.

POSITION ANALYZED AND MEASURED BY	(emp) 10-18-51	W. W.	DATE 11/5/51
APPROVED BY	DATE 10/22/51	APPROVED BY C. I. White	DATE 11/7/51
APPROVED BY P. I. Baker	DATE 10-29-51	APPROVED BY	DATE 1-23-52
		W. S. Pedrick	2-13-52

FIGURE 176. POSITION SPECIFICATION, FIELD ENGINEER. (General Aniline and Film Corporation.)

POSITION MEASUREMENT

POSITION REQUIREMENTS	POSITION TITLE FIELD ENGINEER		
	BASIS OF MEASUREMENT	DEGREE	POINTS
1. KNOWLEDGE	Engineering degree plus practical on-the-job experience in chemical and mechanical engineering. Understanding of basic accounting procedures, knowledge of the various trades. Knowledge of safety regulations and governmental codes. Knowledge of materials of construction.	3D	65
2. JUDGMENT	Must use judgment with respect to extent, methods and materials used in construction and repair to effect maximum savings. Judgment in determining capital expenditures. Determine sequence of work in accordance with plant requirements and plant operations.	2C	45
3. PLANNING	Schedule and plan all C & R work in a specific area of the Plant in accordance with requirements for preventive maintenance work, construction and repairs, economically and with a minimum of inconvenience to normal plant operations.	1C	22
4. ACCURACY	Accuracy required in estimating costs, preparing engineering data, bids and estimates. Accuracy required in checking work performed under his functional jurisdiction.	3B	15
5. CREATIVE WORK	Required in improvising, improving and inventing new procedures, methods and apparatus for existing or new facilities and equipment.	2C	22
6. RELATIONSHIPS— INSIDE	Coordinates activities with Production Department and C & R Trade Foremen, Assistant Master Mechanics, Production Area Supervisors, Department Heads, and other Plant supervisory personnel.	2C	23
7. RELATIONSHIPS— OUTSIDE	Occasional contact with outside contractors and suppliers.	..	..

FIGURE 176. (*Continued.*)

POSITION MEASUREMENT	POSITION TITLE		
POSITION REQUIREMENTS	FIELD ENGINEER		
	BASIS OF MEASUREMENT	DEGREE	POINTS
8. LINE CONTROL	None.	..	..
9. FUNCTIONAL CONTROL	Exercise strong functional control over Assistant Master Mechanics and Trade Foremen doing construction, repair and maintenance work in the area.	2C	30
10. POLICY FORMULATION	Recommend to the Chief Field Engineer, policies and procedures concerning methods and general handling of all construction, repair and maintenance activities, cost estimating, preventive maintenance, etc.	2B	14
11. POLICY INTERPRETATION	Interpret engineering standards and safety regulations to Assistant Master Mechanics and C&R personnel.	2B	14
12. INVESTMENT OF CAPITAL IN FIXED ASSETS	None.	..	..
13. CARE OF CORPORATION ASSETS	Responsible for care and maintenance of all Engineering equipment and facilities in assigned area, and for the care of Plant buildings and equipment while under construction.	3A	10
14. CONFIDENTIAL INFORMATION	Has technical knowledge of some phases of research and development in a specified area, the divulging of which may cause damage of some importance.	1A	8
15. PHYSICAL DEMAND	Requires considerable physical exertion, such as frequent walking, climbing stairs, and standing during long periods of time.	2	10
16. PERSONAL HAZARDS	Possible injury unless normal safety precautions are taken.	2	5
17. SURROUNDINGS	Frequent exposure to unpleasant conditions such as odors, fumes, dirt, mud and weather conditions of dust and heat.	2	6
	GRADE 8	TOTAL POINTS	289

FIGURE 176. (Concluded.)

16

INCENTIVES VITAL TO MAN-JOB
UNIT CONTROL

Human incentives are simple, and relatively few in number. Most of us derive personal satisfaction from a knowledge that we have done our best, and some would consider this inner satisfaction as adequate reward. Some strive for the prestige success will bring, for the admiration and respect of their fellowmen. Some work for power and the influence so obtained over the lives and activities of others. But for most of us, I think we will agree that the strongest and most desirable incentive of all is financial gain—not, of course, in money itself, but because of what one can do with it. Much has been said about the vulgarity of the money motive, but I doubt one could find a cleaner or more honest basis for rewarding high performance. A desire for power is surely less worthy, and I cannot believe that efforts simply to win the admiration of the crowd are ethically more desirable.

—CRAWFORD GREENEWALT

Incentives in General. As may be seen in Figure 1 a wage incentive plan belongs to the quantitative side of job control, is operational in character, i.e., it can be effective in keeping operation at the optimum level, and with the tasks set for it, allows real control. Either subfunction, Job Evaluation or a Wage Incentive, can be applied without the other and no one can say in general where either may expediently be omitted. Certainly Job Evaluation provides the base rates which need to be justly derived for all jobs, but, as a prime force in production, "payment by results," as the English call the extra financial incentive, may be equally vital. That some incentive is basic to good performance no one would deny, but a few otherwise smart managers seem to forget how much extra performance can be obtained by using extra incentives.

For all animate life nature has related results to foregoing actions, so that in natural relationships there is always appropriate incentive to do or not to do things. "Self-interest is the first law of life." For social beings this needs judicious self and governmental restraint but without strong positive and negative incentives our early ancestors would soon have damaged themselves, perhaps starved, and probably ceased to have offspring. Certainly progress would never have arisen. We leave such preposterous considerations to the imagination—but it would be well to pause and do the imagining, because taking for granted the tie-in of incentives leads, in artificial relationships, to neglect of the prime mover which must function properly to activate the most carefully planned operations. In other words, the pains and expenses of acquiring the best machines and methods may be half wasted if the operational incentive is deficient.

Incentive Management. Undoubtedly the outstanding large-scale achievement in applying incentives to employees has been made by the Lincoln Electric Company of Cleveland, Ohio. In December of 1952 its 1208 employees received in total a year-end bonus of $5,131,810 and had $498,000 added to their retirement annuities. Nearly all these employees had also been receiving piece-rate payments at high efficiency. Their productivity per man measured in dollar sales was $35,600. Lesser but steadily increasing results have been regularly achieved at Lincoln's for nineteen years. All that time productivity has been increasing, selling prices have been declining, markets have been expanding, and company profits have been gaining. This case has been much publicized and there are two little books which tell the story [1] officially.

We cannot do justice to the Lincoln achievement in the space allowed but we wish to explain that "incentive management" means more than any one device, such as the piece-rate plan, the annual bonus, the retirement plan, or all these monetary benefits. Mr. Lincoln's management develops the latent abilities of all the employees. "All men would be geniuses if they should develop to the extent they can." He believes that "The feeling that we are outstanding and are so recognized by our fellows . . . is the primary drive on which all successful effort to increase man's efficiency in any human effort must be based." To that end he creates dynamic leadership and develops every employee to think in terms of improving everything. In effect it is an all-plant league comprising many teams through which contributions come voluntarily from all individuals. This is vastly different from a plant-wide group task on which a single efficiency is credited. In fact a merit rating system is used to

[1] J. F. Lincoln, *Lincoln's Incentive System* (New York: McGraw-Hill Book Co., Inc.); J. F. Lincoln, *Incentive Management* (Cleveland: The Lincoln Electric Co.).

see that each individual is rewarded proportionately to his self-made credits.

The Scanlon Plan. The plant-wide group task as a base for bonus payment, tried in desperation during World War II, was not very successful because the task was always crude and attention to part-nership possibilities was rarely or incompetently undertaken, but both of those matters can be improved and such improvement is intended in the Scanlon plan. In fact the plan at best seems to approach the goals of Lincoln Electric's "incentive management" and in one respect the Scanlon plan is superior, in that it officially draws the union into constructive cooperation. Lincoln has no unions.

In 1936 Joseph Scanlon, temporarily an open-hearth worker, but previously an accountant, was elected president of his local in the newly organized Steel Workers' Organizing Committee. His em-ployer was a marginal producer of steel and losing money by 1938. Scanlon and other union officers persuaded this employer to visit Clinton S. Golden, the union vice president in Pittsburgh. Golden, long an advocate of cooperation, advised them to devise a plan of joint action and try to save the enterprise. The resulting plan did save that enterprise and in no uncertain terms, so Golden got the late Philip Murray to put Scanlon in S.W.O.C. National head-quarters where he could spread the new "union-management pro-ductivity" plan. The largest of the plants which promptly followed this "principle of participation" was one of the basic steel units employing 4,000, the smallest one a water-heater company employ-ing 150. All gained extraordinary success.[2] Soon the Adamson Company of East Palestine, Ohio, installed the plan and it was written up in *Life*.[3] The spectacular results at the Adamson plant attracted the attention of Douglas McGregor, then head of the industrial relations section of M.I.T. (now president of Antioch College). McGregor succeeded in bringing Scanlon to M.I.T., where he became professor of industrial relations.

The plan itself is based on the observation that for any one kind of manufacturing business, or at least for a particular plant, the total labor cost will over the years bear a constant ratio to the total production value. Thus a normal labor cost is established for a particular plant and labor saving can be measured against that "norm." When the products are too diverse to allow the establish-ment of this labor cost, an equivalent norm may be a calculated

[2] See *The Dynamics of Industrial Democracy* by C. S. Golden and H. J. Ruttenberg.

[3] "Every Man a Capitalist," by John Chamberlain, December 23, 1946.

percentage of operating profits. Good accounting is, of course, necessary. For instance, the monthly value of product should be corrected for inventory changes, namely, monthly sales plus or minus changes in inventory. Changes in prices of products or in the prevailing wage level also require changes in the norm percentage. If management makes an investment that will raise labor productivity without increase in labor hours, that too justifies a change in the norm.

Assume that the norm is 38 per cent, total shipments for a given month $70,000, and inventory change a plus $30,000, then the total production value would be $100,000 and the normal labor cost would be $38,000. If the actual payroll is $35,000, the difference of $3,000 is made available for employee bonus. Usually none of this direct saving goes to company profit. The sole profit gain is derived from increased sales which are achieved without increase in total burden (overhead and labor costs). All employees share in the bonus, and in some applications members of the management are included. Scanlon prefers that, but often no one is included above immediate supervision. For instance, at the Lapointe Machine Tool Company of Hudson, Massachusetts, fourteen top executives are not included because they have a separate bonus plan based on sales. Whoever is eligible for the Scanlon bonus draws the calculated percentage multiplied by his basic rate per week or month. This percentage sometimes goes as high as 39 per cent and averaged 18 per cent at Lapointe in 1949.

The norm is set with great care by a joint committee which studies cost and sales records for several years back. Abnormal years are excluded to make sure that the norm will be a fair figure. The plan should be incorporated in the collective bargaining agreement, but one of the claims for the plan is that both parties are usually willing to concede more than the letter of the contract whenever an emergency arises. In short, the employees and employer should take on a partnership spirit. Base wages, grievances, and the like are kept scrupulously separate from the work of the "productivity committee." [4]

Because the productivity curve may dip lower than expected (labor costs going above the norm), it is necessary to hold some of the bonus in a reserve fund and distribute what is left of it at year's end only.

With no task expressed in quantity per hour, it is obvious that the rise in efficiency must be brought about chiefly through good will

[4] "Enterprise for Everyman," by R. W. Davenport, and "The New Kind of Collective Bargaining," *Fortune*, XLI, No. 1, January, 1950.

in applying constructive suggestions as to how time and effort can be saved. These suggestions are handled by productivity committees whose members, from both sides of the partnership, are always on the job and easily accessible. Thus operation of this plan depends wholly on participation, and cannot be expected to succeed unless the leaderships of both parties are intelligent and cooperative in attitude. Similarly management must not think in terms of its traditional prerogatives. From president on down all must be willing to give ample time to the committees and withhold no facts, must listen to all views, and accept impartially any criticism.

Usual Group Applications. It is well established that employees who are both skilled and ambitious will produce most when put on individual task-incentive arrangements. In fact, it is generally predictable that they will average around 114 per cent of the Taylor-Gantt *high task* or around 143 per cent of an *intermediate task,* where 100 per cent = Normal Performance. Of course, this kind of application makes them independent in attitude, that is, they feel that they are working for themselves, and dislike being interrupted by calls to help any one else, such as a beginner. Hence, individual applications are recommended for all conditions where there is no need for employees to "lend a hand." Conversely, group applications are recommended for employees who are likely to be called upon to lend a hand. This likelihood exists in any team where several or many employees are needed to operate a big machine, assembly line, or other process type of operation. Such situations are further characterized by close proximity of adjacent workers, interdependence of sequential suboperations, that is, on foregoing portions of a whole operation, and relatively greater importance of esprit de corps. Hence, although the "star type" of individual operator is sure to drop back at least 10 per cent from what he or she would do on his own, the group application has its place in most factories, a growing place in many. The principle may be summed up by saying that a group application is better wherever cooperation is more desired than maximum individual performance and vice versa.

A group task allows a single reckoning of efficiency for all members of the group but the members may be of different skill levels with different pay rates. Sometimes the less competent members are upgraded in efficiency because of the team psychology. The number in a group should be kept as low as practicable to facilitate intimate leadership and the demarcations between groups should be put at natural separation points to make sure of a unified community of interest within each group. Best results come where the number of members is less than twenty, although there are successful groups where the numbers are much larger.

Efficiency Without Extra Financial Incentive. No one seems to claim that the average efficiency of time-paid employees ever exceeds 75 per cent of the Taylor-Gantt high task or about 92 per cent of the intermediate task, and that limit presupposes good conditions plus good supervision. Where either of these matters is deficient the average efficiency is more likely to be around 62 per cent of the Taylor-Gantt high task or 78 per cent of the intermediate task. In badly managed spots we have found some individuals as low as 30 per cent and 37 per cent respectively. Even in the best of these no-extra-incentive situations the overhead costs must be distributed over small volumes of production so that total costs per unit are shockingly high. At the other extreme the distribution of overhead is on such large volumes of production that it is possible to increase the labor costs per unit and still keep a low total cost per unit or even decrease the latter—a fundamental principle in the strategy of designing strong incentive earning curves.

Efficiency With Extra Financial Incentive. A properly located piece rate or standard hour rate earning curve, individually applied, can be expected to effect percentage gains in efficiency over the low levels described of about 130 per cent, where it has been around 62 per cent of high task, or of 52 per cent where it has been 75 per cent of high task; in either case to around 114 per cent of high task or 143 per cent of intermediate task. All percentage figures in these two paragraphs are averages taken from varied experience.

Task Scales for Earning Curves. A quantity standard per period of time or *task* can be set for any kind of work; however, for some nonrepetitive work the task setting is costly and if the number of like jobs is small it may be inexpedient to attempt it. Thus time rates survive almost everywhere for such jobs. For most large volume, repetitive jobs it is expedient to standardize methods in every respect, and with that accomplished it is only one further step to set tasks for them. This step is not at all simple for indirect production jobs but must be done if an extra financial incentive is to be applied. The next question is what scale to use, or where should the 100 per cent task be fixed. Frederick W. Taylor, Henry L. Gantt, and others of their school of thought found that when methods had been improved and standardized it was safe and advantageous to place the task well above normal performance so that when a step bonus was located there the operators would be sure to do "a fair day's work" in order to get the "fair day's pay."

Relative to this Taylor-Gantt *high task* it has been found that *machine perfection is at 150 per cent* (see Figure 177). By machine perfection we mean the rate of work done by an operator who keeps up with a constant mechanical repetition as typified in a buttonhole machine. It means that the operator must work with the machine all the time so that it never misses a cycle of work, not merely tending a hopper-fed automatic machine. Actually the "superworker" who approaches this machine perfection will usually miss a few cycles, so that he or she can hardly expect to exceed 145 per cent. Of course, no management asks any worker to become such an adjunct to a tireless machine, but occasionally we do find a 145 per cent champion.

At the other extreme Frederick A. Halsey and his followers avoided methods improvement through motion-time study, depended on records of performance under time-payment, and were content to locate their 100 per cent task at about ⅝ (62½ per cent) of the Taylor-Gantt high task. This *low task* is entirely workable and also preferable if refined improvements are not expedient, but the earning curve selected to accompany it must be less in slope than that of a proper piece rate. Such a low-task scale is always the safest one where task quantities come from estimates or are for any other reason not completely reliable.

In between the high and low tasks is the *intermediate task* where the 100 per cent is located to fit *normal performance*. This developed from the fact that any successful earning curve needed to pay 120 to 135 per cent of the prevailing time rate at high task and thereby brought a piece rate earning line through, to, or toward the time guarantee within the limits of 74 to 83 per cent of high task (see Figure 128). More lately the Porter-Lynch studies found that about 80 per cent of high task seemed to represent normal performance and so they located the 100 per cent intermediate task at four fifths of the Taylor-Gantt high task.

The Payment Scale for Earning Curves. On the vertical or earning scale, a horizontal line represents time payment. Such lines range from the mandatory government minimum up to a 125 per cent guarantee for cases of accommodation, but the 100 per cent time line represents the "going base rate" or trend line in job evaluation. This latter time payment line is the one generally used as part of any earning plan that includes a time guarantee below task efficiency or below the effective portion of a piece rate line. Piece

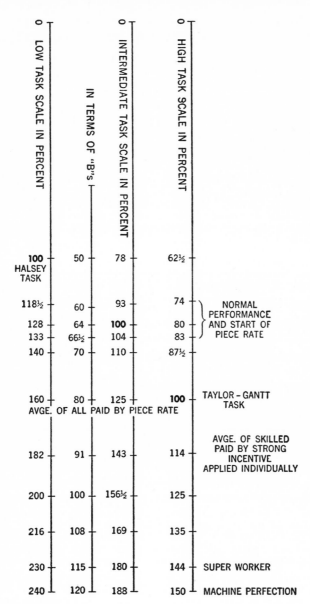

FIGURE 177. CONVERSION TABLE FOR THE THREE ABSCISSA SCALES USED IN MEASURING EFFICIENCY. (Under Intermediate scale is shown the equivalent Bedauxs or Bs.)

rate earning lines are always straight and directed toward the origin. Since they are designed to pay 120 per cent to 135 per cent base earnings at 100 per cent efficiency they should intersect the 100 per cent time guarantee at from 74 per cent to 83 per cent efficiency. If no step bonus is to be incorporated it is natural to make this point of inflection the 100 per cent task (intermediate scale). If a step is to be incorporated it should be located at 100 per cent (high scale.) Sharing of labor savings may be either constant or variable. If the sharings are constant, the earning lines are straight, and if extended, will *intercept* the vertical scale between 0 per cent and 100 per cent earning. The amount of intercept above the origin *will always be the employer's share;* 100 per cent minus that will be the employee's share. If the sharings are variable, they are represented by curved lines according to the formulas used and the vertical intercepts of their tangents will show the variable sharings. All sharing curves should start from the low-task point, which is (62½, 100) on the high-task scale or (100, 100) on the low-task scale: If so started they will lie above the piece rate lines through intermediate efficiencies and below piece rate lines after intersection. Hence they have theoretical incentive value from 62½ per cent to about 100 per cent efficiency, high-task scale, but because they provide decreasing rates per piece, average response to them will usually be weak after 85 per cent efficiency. Step bonuses are vertical jumps in earning and have strong incentive value. They must not be put much below 100 per cent efficiency (high-task scale) or they will tempt proficient operatives to fall back. Otherwise, they tend to raise production and assure average response to whatever point they are located. This result is important in cases of high machine charge.

Bonus, Premium, Intercept, and Slope. A *bonus* means pay above some time rate and is expressed in percentage of that time rate. It may take the form of a single 15 per cent to 25 per cent abrupt step, or there may be a series of small steps, as in the empiric efficiency-bonus plans. A *premium* means gradual increase in pay above some time rate and is expressed in percentage of time saved. This percentage is less than 100 per cent in all sharing plans, so that a so-called "100 per cent premium plan" means a piece rate. Curiously, when a piece rate line is cut away (74–100 per cent high task) to provide a step bonus from the time guarantee, the reward thereafter becomes part bonus and part premium, which add up to the original premium under piece rate. Thus the distinction between such bonus and premium need not be separately stated and is of interest only to the wage-plan designer. Also of interest only to the designer is the matter of earning line slope. By slope is meant the ratio of altitude to base of any right angle triangle the hypotenuse of which is the earning curve. This ratio is simplified to the amount of altitude if the base is 100 per cent efficiency (high-task scale). Steeper slopes, of course, give more premium for the same starting point but if a negative vertical intercept should be used the stronger effect may be lost by a too late inflection point, namely, the intersection with the time-guarantee line.

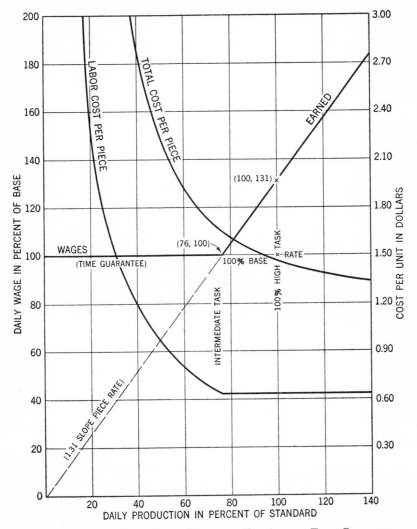

FIGURE 178a. HIGH PIECE RATE (STANDARD HOUR) WITH TIME GUARANTEE

HIGH PIECE RATE WITH TIME GUARANTEE DATA

Per Cent of Production H_s/H_a Task Scales High	Per Cent of Production H_s/H_a Task Scales Intermediate	Per Cent of Total to Base Wage for Full Day E/H_aR_h	Total Daily Wage in Dollars E	Number Pieces per Day	Time Saved per 8-Hr. Task in Hours H_s-H_a Relative to Tasks High	Time Saved per 8-Hr. Task in Hours H_s-H_a Relative to Tasks Intermediate	Labor Cost per Piece in Dollars	Total Cost per Piece in Dollars
0	0	100	11.52	0	....	....	....	....
10	12.5	100	11.52	2.4	−72.0	−56.3	4.80	9.96
20	25.0	100	11.52	4.8	−32.0	−24.0	2.40	5.16
30	37.5	100	11.52	7.2	−18.6	−13.2	1.60	3.56
40	50.0	100	11.52	9.6	−12.0	−8.0	1.20	2.76
50	62.5	100	11.52	12.0	−8.0	−4.8	.96	2.28
57	71.4	100	11.52	13.7	−6.0	−3.3	.84	2.04
62½	78.0	100	11.52	15.0	−4.8	−2.3	.77	1.90
66	82.5	100	11.52	16.0	−4.0	−1.5	.72	1.80
73	96.4	100	11.52	17.5	−3.0	−.8	.66	1.68
80	100.0	105	12.12	19.2	−2.0	0	.66	1.59
89	111.0	117	13.47	21.4	−1.0	.8	.63	1.53
100	125.0	131	15.12	24.0	0	1.7	.63	1.47
114	143.0	150	17.58	27.4	1.0	2.4	.63	1.41
133	156.5	176	20.16	32.0	2.0	3.3	.63	1.35
145	181.6	190	21.93	34.8	2.5	3.6	.63	1.32

To convert to Bs see Figure 180.

Altering to the Gantt Task and Bonus plan, two rows change as follows:

80	100.0	100	11.52	19.2	−2.0		.60	1.56
89	111.0	100	11.52	21.4	−1.0		.54	1.44

FIGURE 178b. HIGH PIECE RATE (STANDARD HOUR) WITH TIME GUARANTEE DATA

High Piece Rate (Standard Hour) Plan. Space does not allow adequate treatment of the various wage incentive plans.[5] A single earning line, namely, that of piece rate with time guarantee, Figure 178a, is, however, more used than all other earning lines. This is so partly because it is just to both parties, is simple to calculate or explain, and when properly used it is effective for many situations. On the data sheet, Figure 178b, the intermediate-task scale is the one to use with the plan as charted but the high-task scale is also given to use with the Gantt plan, which merely deletes the piece rate line (76, 100) to (100, 131) and extends the time guarantee line from (76, 100), to (100, 100). There are five different *formulas for setting up earning tables* for performance under piece rate–standard hour rate as follows (inflection point at 100, 100):

Rate per piece form $E = N_p R_p$

Rate per standard hour form $E = H_s R_h$

Efficiency form $E = \dfrac{H_s}{H_a} H_a R_h$

Premium form $E = H_a R_h + (H_s - H_a)\ R_h$

Bonus form $E = H_a R_h + \left(\dfrac{H_s}{H_a} - 1\right) H_a R_h$

Key: E = any earning in per cent of base wages.

  N_p = number of pieces accepted for payment.

  R_p = rate of pay per piece (*all individuals alike*).

  H_s = number of hours-standard performed.

  R_h = rate of pay per hour *per individual*.

  H_a = number of hours actual (*elapsed time*).

Thus:

Time payment = $H_a R_h$ and $\dfrac{E}{H_a R_h}$ is the ordinate; see **Figure 178a**

Efficiency = $\dfrac{H_s}{H_a}$ and is the abscissa; see **Figure 178a**

Unity $\dfrac{H_s}{H_a}$ is task so that $\dfrac{H_s}{H_a} - 1$ is excess over task,

Time saved = $H_s - H_a$ and wages saved = $(H_s - H_a)R_h$;

see Figure 178b

Standard hours $H_s = \dfrac{N_p R_p}{R_h}, \therefore N_p R_p = H_s R_h$

Note that the point (100, 100), where rates and high task are 100 per cent, is the bench mark for locating earning curves.

[5] For full analyses of twenty-five plans, their modifications, and applications to various factory and office situations, see C. W. Lytle's *Wage Incentive Methods* (New York: The Ronald Press Co., 1942).

Selection of a Wage Plan. After making preparation in matters of job standardization and job evaluation, there are at least seven basic considerations which should be canvassed before selecting a wage incentive plan. They are as follows:

1. The history of the case, type of employees, and union attitude.
2. Prevailing incentive earnings in the locality.
3. Characteristics of the jobs to be covered, capacities aimed at.
4. The proportion of overhead to labor cost involved.
5. The kind of tasks that have been or can be set.
6. Facilities for training and follow-up.
7. Readiness of top management and supervision to support further preparations and procedures.

History of the Case, Type of Employees, and Union Attitude. Even a new company will do well to consider what has gone on in the neighborhood of its new plant, and certainly an old company can never ignore its own record of trials, errors, and successes. In the first place there is the matter of employee confidence in the company. Such confidence cannot be built overnight and if it is weak in any aspect it may make a difference in what can be done in a matter so vital as extra compensation. It is not enough for an executive or supervisor to believe that he is right in management; the overwhelming majority of employees must also believe he is usually right and that he will never be far wrong. If there has been any rate reducing, or task lifting, that has been looked upon as unfair, some old-timers will teach the new employees to beware of exceeding some safe point of efficiency. If the union leaders are worrying about union strength, or their own re-elections, they will also be anxious to make a showing in their favor, even at the disfavor of management. But not infrequently the tough attitude of a union may be the direct result of management's having been tough at some unforgotten time. These underlying antagonisms are a menace to any innovation, particularly when the latter offers a way for the members to lessen their dependence on the union. On the other hand, a long enlightened management and a mature union can usually work out a constructive measure. The leaders of such unions have learned to appreciate good company management and know that the ultimate source of more wages is in higher productivity. When this stage has been developed it should be safe to put in both job evaluation and wage incentives, but the most constructive union leaders are the ones who may want to have a voice in new arrangements that affect work habits and pay. Hence it is advisable to take them into partnership in such arrangements, if that is wanted. If the majority of employees involved are not of the particularly ambitious type it may be expedient to use low tasks and sharing plans until the latent hopes for high productivity and corresponding earning have been awakened. The attitude of the most respected individuals is important because they can exercise considerable influence as to whether their companions will accept or condemn a new device. In fact, it is with such employees that many managements have cooperated in regard to any change of policy.

Prevailing Incentive Earnings in the Locality. No one company can disregard what other companies in the same community have been, and are, paying. A prosperous company may be able and willing to make higher wage earnings possible but it must know what are the prevailing earnings and what are the mores of those constituting the labor supply. Upgrading in these matters can be fostered but such efforts take time. A goodly number of already ambitious workers must be available, otherwise a strong high-task incentive plan will be like good seed on infertile ground. Even in a foreign location, where there has been no appreciation of advancing standards of living, incentives have been made successful. In any normal American industrial location free from antagonistic influences, the actual feel of extra pay is often enough to stir up ambitions; perhaps that is the most practical course in basic economics. Another asset that helps sound economic thinking is for a company to gain the reputation of giving ever-increasing values in its products. In short, the quality of the labor supply may not be all that might be desired, and that may make a difference in the kind of plan which will be most expedient, but a good company need not give up the thought of incentives; it merely means more careful ground work.

Characteristics of the Job; Capacities Aimed At. No one incentive plan will be suitable to all situations. Some companies have used as many as a dozen plans in one plant. At the least, the management should find out which jobs will be best served by group applications and which ones by individual applications. It is not necessary to put all jobs on incentive at the same time; it is usually better not to do so. Sometimes it is wise to modify the plans to suit women, particularly if there are many of the nervous type. Certainly some attempt should be made to classify job conditions as to quality difficulties, length of cycle, and kind of skill involved, because any one of these matters may call for some difference in the plan or in its administration. Where there are machine capacities that might be utilized in full, the company can afford to offer very strong incentives, so that matter is worth analysis. The standard time plan, two time lines broken by a step bonus, can be the means of steadying response at a definite point of capacity. The question of skill conservation may also come up if it has not been adjusted previously. In other words, when machine charge is high it may pay to have two levels of skill for an operation, even if one or more of the lower-level operators will be idle at times. If so, the team should be rewarded according to capacity utilization with no penalty for man-idleness. In general all man movements should be improved and standardized prior to making the job evaluation and setting the task, but both of these procedures introduce new views which may show up new problems.

Proportion of Overhead to Labor Cost Involved. Where overhead is high in proportion to labor cost, management can well afford to take all pains in methods improvement, and can make the piece rates or bonuses generous because the machine charges go right on when the machines are not producing. The behavior of total cost per piece should be studied in relation to operator efficiency. Standard illustrations will not fit all cases. More care must be taken to estimate *the average response point,* that is, the efficiency the department or the subdivision concerned will maintain on the average. It is this response to the incentive that is all-important, not the question of keeping the labor cost per piece low. This need for response holds true in principle for any situation, but it is particularly important where overhead is high, because the big objective is to get more volume per machine hour. If an increase in output per hour is accomplished then the high overhead will be distributed over enough units of production to keep the unit cost of overhead low. The strategy is to *pay a higher labor cost per piece if by doing so the total cost per piece can be held down,* and that has been done in many cases.

Kind of Tasks That Have Been or Can Be Set. The more competently the methods improvement work is done, the safer it is to use the higher tasks. Even for a piece rate, where task is not usually self-evident unless the change from time guarantee to piece rate is considered task, it is important to know that the 120 per cent to 135 per cent pay has been related to 100 per cent efficiency (high-task scale). Companies that have no formal methods improvement, or only a rough attempt at it, however, have no choice. Their estimates can be based only on past performances that are generally in the 50's or 60's. Thus they dare not use any strong incentive such as piece rate. Where they have ventured to do so, the earnings have soared without adequate gains in performance, rates have then been cut, and a vicious circle has been started instead of a constructive one. It is not too bad, however, to accept the combination of low tasks and some low slope, constant sharing line of earning if the equipment is not expensive. What happens is that an average response is secured, in the 80's, or at most in the low 90's, until some operative makes his own methods improvement. That enables him to go higher. He cannot for long keep the accomplishment secret from the management, and the disclosure raises some perplexing questions as to fair treatment all around.

He does sometimes manage to keep the way of improvement secret for a time so he can be the sole beneficiary, but concealment makes him unpopular with his fellow operators. Therefore, if improvement is not well done by the management, and the incentive acts on an ingenious operator so that he effects his own improvements, then his voluntary and amateurish industrial engineering should be recognized, rewarded as such, the improvement taught to the others, and the task tightened. All this is common experience and can be worked out satisfactorily, but at the time of selecting an incentive the management must be ready for such events if it will not take the more thorough course. In short, management has the choice between formal methods improvement and hit-or-miss improvement, between an average response of 114 per cent and say 85 per cent, between reliable, long-lived high tasks and unreliable, loose tasks constantly requiring adjustment. Historically, many plans have taken the latter course and in time have changed to the former course. Certainly the high-efficiency, high-earning course, when nothing hinders it, gives the lower total costs per piece. Of course, there are some situations even in the best managed plants where it is not expedient to make a thorough standardization. Thus it is possible to have both kinds of task in a single department. This situation causes no trouble if the cleavage is clean cut as between direct and indirect production, or between skilled and unskilled jobs, but no one incentive plan can serve more than one kind of task.

Facilities for Training and Follow-Up. When higher work tempos are in prospect the management should be ready to help those not already proficient to acquire ability to do the higher tasks. This training is profitable to both parties and particularly to management when time guarantees are applicable. Gantt found that the breaking down of existing work habits was a main prerequisite to building new ones. He also stressed the necessity of staying with a trainee on new repetitive motions until these motions become automatic, so that the operator will not revert to his former mehods as soon as he is left alone. New motions, although simpler, may take longer than old ones until automaticity is acquired. It is for this reason that management often asks a union not to make any protest on a new method until after two or three weeks. Most job training today is done at the workplace. If older operatives are able and willing to undertake such training, that is the simplest answer. Of course they must be given time rates commensurate with their accustomed earnings. It is not satisfactory to expect a supervisor to take full responsibility for training; he has too many other duties which are bound to interrupt. Because of limits on his time, and because training may be done better by one who has been selected for it, a special trainer is often employed. The urgency of two world wars brought out a veritable science of training. Hence training has become too important to be left to anyone who has not been drilled in the correct steps. Follow-up of each trainee is also wise because it builds morale at a time when discouragement is most likely to be faced. This follow-up should be assigned to the staff of the Personnel Department. If management does not see fit to do training properly, it may be necessary to use lower tasks and lower earning line slopes, thereby forgoing the higher responses which can come only from high skill.

Readiness of Top Management and Supervision to Support the Plan. It should be self-evident that anything as vital to all concerned as an efficiency-earning plan should have the full and competent support of top management, as well as of those close to operations, but the importance of such plans has not always been appreciated. All levels of management are involved. Incentives have revolutionary effects and these can boomerang on the company if any of the preparations, or any of the supporting measures, should be poorly effected. Related policy questions cannot all be treated here but they should be reviewed in connection with this subject. For instance, the so-called *nonfinancial incentives* may have considerable bearing on this development. They appeal to pride, peace of mind, and the like, which are elicited through many influences ranging from good supervision to the right kind of music! At least it is practical to ascertain what functionaries may be indirectly involved. The safety department should prepare for higher tempos. The maintenance department should really maintain, not wait for breakdowns. The inspection function should be stiffened and, if it is centralized, perhaps there should be a degree of decentralization to the effect that high-earning operatives will not have to wait in line for approval of a first piece. Setup should be separated from operation so that it will be expertly done and always ready. In war time all these services tended to break down, hence the turn to group applications whereby the older members of each group were willing to lend a hand. In brief, an individually rated incentive worker feels, and should be encouraged to feel, that he is in business for himself and should not be delayed. He also needs to have the facilitating kind of supervision.[6] Every function in shop management is affected by a strong incentive plan and supervision must make all of them coordinate on a service objective.

Selling the Proposed Plan. There are two stages in the "selling" of an incentive plan after primary preparations have been made. First, all employee leaders must be brought to the point of wanting the new plan, and, second, they and a substantial following must be satisfied that the plan is all or nearly all that they had hoped for. The first may or may not come easily but it must be more than a superficial impulse, and, if possible, it should be a genuine hope, not merely a permissive acquiescence. Desire for incentive rarely emanates from the union officers because they are predisposed in favor of getting any extra money for all employees through higher base rates. They will, however, respond to the wishes of influential members and when the latter are in favor of an incentive plan the officers will often do much to facilitate the management's efforts in getting it going. Thus the real selling begins with the influential employees. If their wish for the plan does not result in official union cooperation there may be difficulties, particularly where no such plan has been used before. Where an incentive plan has already been in successful operation an improved plan will not usually arouse opposition. In fact, there will already be a clause in the union agreement giving management the right to continue, alter, and extend such application. Whether or not the agreement does already provide for this situation, it remains important for the management to discuss any proposed change in this field so that the union officials will not be taken by surprise, and so that the management will learn union views before details of the plan become set. A union leadership that is sincerely cooperative can, and sometimes does, take over the major part of the selling problem, once the leaders are themselves sold. Often union acceptance is contingent on management's assurance that all piece-workers' earnings

[6] For author's analysis of supervisory bonus problems, see A.M.A. *Production Series*, No. 166, or *Personnel Handbook* (New York: The Ronald Press Co., 1951).

will average a certain amount, usually the earning at some specified percentage efficiency. In fact, some unions take disciplinary action on laggards who fall short of making it.

As soon as the general idea becomes accepted by the union officers, management should ascertain the efficiency-earning points which will be acceptable for the various classes of occupations to be put on incentive. With that information in hand, and not until then, the management can determine what earning curves it should adopt. For instance, a management may be anxious to upgrade present employees to an average efficiency of, say, 100 per cent, the high-task point, while the union officers may be anxious to raise wages 20 per cent above the existing level. The point of present efficiency-earning, say (60, 100), is a natural takeoff for the new plan, so that means that one point on the chart is already established. If the wage increase can be afforded at the proposed higher response, then a second point on the chart is established (100, 120). Two points determine the slope of a straight line, in this case a 30/70 sharing line. Thus a practical plan which meets both desires is indicated by bringing together the two sets of facts. If these two points happened to be (74, 100) and (100, 135) then the natural solution would be a very generous piece rate. To carry the leaders on from there, management should work out double column tables of efficiency-earning for all classes of work involved. These, with or without graphs, should be discussed with the leaders, and modifications made if necessary, to assure official union indorsement. From there on, selling the plan enters its second stage and should be mostly a matter of employee training and fair treatment. The whole matter can be expressed negatively by saying, Don't assume that acquiesence in the general idea is sufficient and don't fix all details in advance of bulletin board commitments. This precaution also applies in the case of supervision. The members of this responsible group must be spared any sudden fiat and brought over to full cooperation gradually.

Installation of an Incentive Plan. The best theoretical plan will fail if conditions and operations have not been standardized, or if mutual confidence has not already been achieved. When all these matters are in shape then installation can proceed without trouble. It should not, however, be pushed fast. Workers may need to get rid of old habits of work, may need time to practice the improved methods, etc. Thus, the use of training and the use of minimum guarantees are necessary to make a happy transition. Furthermore, a few of the more ambitious workers should be carried over to the new way of working, and get the feel of higher earning, before the less promising ones are brought over. A nucleus of workers who have prestige can do much to set the style in the right direction and, similarly, a minority of the other kind can give the whole plan a bad name if they are thrown hastily into the changed procedures. How fast installation should proceed will depend on several matters, such as the length of training required to meet the tasks, the attitude of those selected to start, and the tact of the supervision in meeting small troubles as they arise. The intangibles of human reaction, of course, are most difficult to foresee. For this reason alone management should choose slow progress and consultation with enlightened employees.

INDEX

Acme Steel Co., chart system of merit rating, 330, 339-40

Adjustment
automatic, 82, 301
by bargaining, 81-82, 311-27, 331, 473-74
by grievance machinery, 19, 82, 85-86, 319-26
by merit rating, 329, 356-72
by permissive renegotiation, 82
by reviewing committee, 300-1, 308-11, 429
change notice, 301
cost of living, 316-17
downgrading jobs, 17, 79-80, 294-95, 300-3, 306-11
keeping up with job changes, 17, 306-11, 485
needs for, 294-95
of incentive rates, 20, 84-85, 272, 303-6
of out-of-line jobs, 252, 294-95, 311
of salaries, 375-76, 413-20
of whole structure, 295-99
payroll variance a check on, 294-95
periodic checks on, 305-7
policies for, 18-20, 79-80
present jobholders exempt from downgrading, 80, 294-95
processing of rate changes, 306-7
seniority and, 311-12
tests for rate change, 300
transfer and, 312

Administrative and executive positions
exempt salary plan, 439-69
grouped, 379-81, 421-24

Air Associates, Inc., full cooperation, 268

Allen-Bradley Co., 424

Aluminum Co. of Canada, 385

American Engineering Standards Committee, report on preferred numbers, 283-84

American Federation of Labor and sound basis of wage adjustment, 76, 271, 396

American Machine & Foundry Co., 10 labor grades, 207-8

American Management Association
contribution to merit rating, 330, 347
credit to, v
handbooks of, 88, 132; see also footnotes

American Optical Co., pioneers in job analysis, 129

American Rolling Mill Co.
instructions to analysts, 39
interplant trend line, 263-65
pioneer in job analysis, 129
published policy, 16
too many grades, 207

American Seating Co.
manual on wages, 86-88
rate structure, 272-73

American Type Founders survey plan, 245-48

Analyst's job, 34

Anchor jobs; see Key jobs

Anderson, H. W., 325

Arbitrary Scales for Merit Rating, a numerical method, 333, 338-39

Arbitration, boards for, 19

Armstrong Cork Co., pamphlet for employees, 88

Army Air Force, 70, 331, 345

Army Civilian Personnel Division; see Services of Supply

Association of Pulp and Paper Manufacturers, plan of, 66-67

Atlantic Refining Co.
contribution to merit rating, 330
job evaluation plan, 207, 229
merit rating plan, 335
wage control committee, 376

Automatic time progressions, from hiring to qualifying, 267, 270, 285, 288, 301

Average production of skilled operators, 303-4, 475-77

Backgrounds
of job analysis, 11, 127-33
of job evaluation, 10-13, 56-59, 66
of merit rating, 327-33
of position classification, 374-75, 421-23

491